Stanley Gibbons
COLLECT
Channel Islands
and Isle of Man
STAMPS

A STANLEY GIBBONS CHECKLIST

2000 Edition

STANLEY GIBBONS LTD
London and Ringwood

By Appointment to
Her Majesty The Queen,
Stanley Gibbons Ltd., London,
Philatelists

Published by **Stanley Gibbons Publications**
Editorial, Sales Offices and Distribution Centre:
5 Parkside, Christchurch Road, Ringwood,
Hants BH24 3SH

SIXTEENTH COMBINED EDITION (2000)

© Stanley Gibbons Ltd 2000

Copyright Notice

The contents of this catalogue, including the numbering system and illustrations, are fully protected by copyright. No part of this publication may be reproduced, stored in a retrieval system, or transmitted in any form or by any means, electronic, mechanical, photocopying, recording or otherwise, without the prior permission of Stanley Gibbons Limited. Requests for such permission should be addressed to the Catalogue Editor at Ringwood.
This catalogue is sold on condition that it is not, by way of trade or otherwise, lent, re-sold, hired out, circulated or otherwise disposed of other than in its complete, original and unaltered form and without a similar condition, including this condition, being imposed on the subsequent purchaser.

Item No. 2855 (00)

Text assembled by Black Bear Press Limited, Cambridge
Printed in Great Britain by The Alden Press Ltd., Oxford

Introductory Notes

Scope. The listing of **stamps** for Guernsey and Jersey comprises German Occupation issues, the 1958–69 Regionals and the issues of the Independent Postal Administrations from their inception in 1969. Isle of Man sections cover the 1958–71 Regionals and the issues of the Independent Postal Administration from 1973 onwards.

Information is given on:

- Designers and printers
- The different printings for definitives and postage dues
- Distinctive papers
- Such varieties as imperforates and missing colours
- Phosphors
- Cylinder and plate numbers
- Sheet sizes and imprints
- Quantities sold
- Withdrawal and invalidation dates

The 'Notes' on page 1 may be found helpful in further explanation.
The checklist also covers:

- Miniature sheets
- First-day covers
- Presentation packs and Yearbooks
- Gutter pairs
- Stamp booklets
- Stamp sachets (listed, but unpriced)
- Postal stationery commemorative cards and covers

Items outside the scope and therefore *omitted* are: cylinder and plate varieties; non-postage stamps, such as revenues; and other classes of postal stationery.

Layout. Stamps are set out chronologically by date of issue. In the catalogue lists the first numeral is the Stanley Gibbons catalogue number; the black (boldface) numeral alongside is the type number referring to the respective illustration. The denomination and colour of the stamp are then shown. Before February 1971 British currency was:

£1=20s One Pound = twenty shillings *and*
1s=12d One shilling = twelve pence.

Upon decimalisation this became:

£1=100p One pound = one hundred (new) pence.

The catalogue list then shows two price columns. The left-hand is for unused stamps and the right-hand for used.

Our method of indicating prices is:

Numerals for pence, e.g. 5 denotes 5p (5 pence). Numerals for pounds and pence, e.g. 4.25 denotes £4.25 (4 pounds and 25 pence). For £100 and above, prices are in whole pounds and so include the £ sign and omit the zeros for pence.

Size of illustrations. To comply with Post Office regulations illustrations of stamps and booklets are three-quarters linear size. Illustrations of watermarks are actual size.

Prices. Prices quoted in this catalogue are our selling prices at the time the book went to press. They are for stamps in fine average condition; in issues where condition varies we may ask more for the superb and less for the sub-standard. With unused stamps prices are for unmounted mint (though where not available unmounted, stamps are often supplied at a lower price). Used prices are normally for stamps postally used but may be for stamps cancelled-to-order where this practice exists. All prices are subject to change without prior notice and we give no guarantee to supply all stamps priced, since it is not possible to keep every catalogue item perpetually in stock. Commemoratives may, at times, only be available in complete sets. Individual low value stamps sold at 399, Strand are liable to an additional handling charge.

Perforations. The 'perforation' is the number of holes in a length of 2 cm, as measured by the Gibbons *Instanta* gauge. The stamp is viewed against a dark background with the transparent gauge put on top of it. Perforations are quoted to the nearest half. Stamps without perforation are termed 'imperforate'.

Se-tenant combinations. *Se-tenant* means 'joined together'. Some sets include stamps of different design arranged *se-tenant* as blocks or strips and, in mint condition, these are usually collected unsevered as issued. Where such combinations exist, the individual stamps are priced normally as mint and used singles. The set price for mint refers to the unsevered combination plus singles of any other values in the set. The used set price is for single stamps of all values.

First day covers. Prices for first day covers are for complete sets used on special covers, the stamps of which bear an official postmark for first day of issue. Where the stamps in a set were issued on different days, prices are for a cover from each day.

Catalogue numbers used. The checklist uses the same catalogue numbers as the Stanley Gibbons *British Commonwealth* catalogue, 2000 edition.

Latest stamps recorded in this edition appeared in November 1999.

CONTENTS

Stanley Gibbons Holdings Plc Addresses

STANLEY GIBBONS LIMITED, STANLEY GIBBONS AUCTIONS

399 Strand, London WC2R 0LX

Auction Room and Specialist Stamp Departments. Open Monday–Friday 9.30 a.m. to 5 p.m.

Shop. Open Monday–Friday 8.30 a.m. to 6 p.m. and Saturday 9.30 a.m. to 5.30 p.m.

Telephone 020 7836 8444 and **Fax** 020 7836 7342 for all departments.

STANLEY GIBBONS PUBLICATIONS

5 Parkside, Christchurch Road, Ringwood, Hants BH24 3SH.

Telephone 01425 472363 (24-hour answer phone service), **Fax** 01425 470247

E-mail sales@stanleygibbons.co.uk

Publications Showroom (at above address). Open Monday–Friday 9 a.m. to 3 p.m.

Publications Mail Order. FREEPHONE 0800 611622 Monday–Friday 8.30 a.m. to 5 p.m.

Special Collections Available From Stanley Gibbons Mail Order

The Stanley Gibbons London Mail Order Department are pleased to offer the following special collections. They would make an ideal gift to a friend or relative who may be interested in stamp collecting, or just starting, or you could expand your current field of interest

Collection	Recommended Retail Price	Special Offer Price
Guernsey	£350	£280
Alderney (complete to 1998)	£230	£185
Jersey	£350	£280
Isle of Man	£550	£440

To take advantage of these special offers,
please contact Mark Leonard on 0800 731 8052 (UK Only)
or +44(0)207 836 8444 during office hours

The World's oldest and most famous name in stamps

Stanley Gibbons Limited
399 Strand, London WC2R 0LX
Tel: +44 (0)207 836 8444 Fax: +44 (0)207 836 7342
e-mail: mailorder@stangiblondon.demon.co.uk
http://www.stanleygibbons.com/

Printings
For definitives and postage due stamps released by the independent Postal Administrations we give the dates of the printings as announced, and relate them in the listings to the actual stamps involved. Users will therefore be able to see at a glance how many printings have been made of any particular item.

Cylinder and Plate Numbers
Following the listing of each issue we give the printers' cylinder or plate numbers known to us.

Sheet Size
In describing the sheet arrangement we always give the number of stamps across the sheet first. For example, '50 (5×10)' indicates a sheet of fifty stamps in ten horizontal rows of five stamps each.

Paper
Only distinctive types are mentioned. Granite paper can be easily distinguished by the coloured lines in its texture. *Chalky* or *chalk-surfaced* applies to paper which shows a black line when touched with silver.

Perforations
Perforations are normally given to the nearest half and the *Instanta* gauge is our standard. In this checklist we state if a perforation is by a line (L) or a comb (C) machine. A line machine only perforates one line at a time and consequently it requires two operations to do the horizontal and vertical perforations and where these intersect an irregular-shaped hole often results. A comb machine perforates three sides at a time and therefore produces a single hole at all corner inter-sections. The differences are easily seen in blocks of four.

The various perforations in this checklist are expressed as follows:

Perf 14: Perforated alike on all sides.
Perf 14×15: Compound perforation. The first figure refers to top and bottom, the second to left and right sides.

Abbreviations
des=designer, designed
eng=engraver, engraved
litho=lithographed
mm=millimetres
MS=miniature sheet
No.=number
perf=perforated
photo=photogravure
recess=recess-printed
typo=typographed
wmk(d)=watermark(ed)

Channel Islands

C **1** Gathering Vraic   C **2** Islanders gathering Vraic

Third Anniversary of Liberation

(Des J. R. R. Stobie (1d), or from drawing by E. Blampied
(2½d). Photo Harrison and Sons)

1948 (10 MAY). *Wmk Mult* G VI R. *Perf* 15×14 (C)

C1	C **1**	1d scarlet	30	30
C2	C **2**	2½d ultramarine	30	30
		First Day Cover		35·00

These stamps were primarily intended for use in the Channel Islands although they were also available at eight head post offices in Great Britain.

Cylinder Nos.: 1d 2; 2½d 4

Sheets: 120 (6×20)

Quantities sold: 1d 5,934,000; 2½d 5,398,000

Guernsey

THE GERMAN OCCUPATION 1940—1945

The first German soldiers to arrive in Guernsey set foot on the island on 30 June, 1940 and an official notice appeared in the local newspaper the following day announcing the occupation.

The first evidence of the occupation, philatelically, came towards the end of the year when supplies of Great Britain 1d stamps then in use began to dry up. It was decided that the bisecting of 2d stamps for use as 1d's be allowed and this commenced on 27 December. The decision to print 1d stamps locally had been taken in October, but these were not ready and were eventually issued on 18 February, 1941. In the meantime the two currently available 2d stamps, the 1937 definitive and the 1940 Postal Centenary, were bisected and used, as were 2d stamps of the reign of George V which were in collectors' hands. Other values are also known to have been bisected and used, and were allowed to pass through the post in most instances without a postage due charge being made.

When the decision to bisect the 2d stamps was taken the German Commandant in Guernsey decided on adding a swastika to each half of the stamp. This overprint was applied to the Postal Centenary stamp and these were submitted to Berlin for approval, but this proposal was turned down. Another proposal, the overprinting of the 1937 1d with a number of small swastikas, would appear to have been dealt with in a similar way. Examples of both items exist though these are very rare.

As previously mentioned, the locally printed 1d stamps were issued on 18 February, 1941. The ½d stamp was released on 7 April, 1941 and the 2½d on 12 April, 1944. This last stamp was issued in an effort to economise on the use of paper as it was found that sealed letters were franked with two 1d stamps and one ½d or a larger number of ½d's, a gross waste in times of shortage. Many printings of these stamps were made, the most notable being on the French bank-note paper in 1942.

Shades of these issues abound, the more outstanding ones being the bluish green (4th) and olive-green (8th) printings of the ½d., and the pale vermilion (11th) printing of the 1d. These stamps continued to be used after the liberation in 1945 until 13 April, 1946.

The Swastika Overprints

1940. *Prepared for use but not issued. Stamps of Great Britain overprinted*

(a) 1937 *definitive overprinted with a number of small swastikas*

Cat. No.		Unused
SW1	1d scarlet	£800

(b) 1940 *Postal Centenary issue overprinted with a swastika on each half of the stamp*

SW2	2d orange	£800

Example of bisected 2d Postal Centenary stamp

The Bisects

1940 (27 DEC)–**1941** (24 FEB).

(a) *Stamps of King George V*

Cat. No.			Price on cover
BS1	1912–22	2d orange	£200
BS2	1924–26	2d orange	£200
BS3	1934–36	2d orange	£225

(b) *Stamps of King George VI*

BS4	1937	1d scarlet	£450
BS5	1938	2d orange	22·00
BS6	1940	Stamp Centenary 1d scarlet	£450
BS7	1940	Stamp Centenary 2d orange	16·00
BS8	1940	Stamp Centenary 2½d ultramarine	£700
BS9	1940	Stamp Centenary 3d violet	

1 Arms of Guernsey

1a Loops

(Des E. W. Vaudin. Typo Guernsey Press Co Ltd)

1941–44. *Rouletted*

(*a*) *White paper. No wmk*

Cat. No.	Type No.		Unused	Used
1	**1**	½d light green (7.4.41)	3·25	2·50
		a. Emerald-green (6.41)	4·25	2·50
		b. Bluish green (11.41)	45·00	20·00
		c. Bright green (2.42)	28·00	11·00
		d. Dull green (9.42)	4·25	3·25
		e. Olive-green (2.43)	32·00	20·00
		f. Pale yellowish green (7.43 and later) (shades)	3·25	2·75
		g. Imperf (pair)	£200	
		h. Imperf between (horizontal pair)	£700	
		i. Imperf between (vertical pair) . .	£800	
2		1d scarlet (18.2.41)	2·75	1·50
		a. Pale vermilion (7.43) (etc.)	2·75	1·50
		b. Carmine (1943)	3·00	3·00
		c. Imperf (pair)	£150	75·00
		d. Imperf between (horizontal pair)	£700	
		da. Imperf vert (centre stamp of horizontal strip of 3)		
		e. Imperf between (vertical pair) . .	£800	
		f. Ptd double (scarlet shade)	£100	
3		2½d ultramarine (12.4.44)	4·50	4·50
		a. Pale ultramarine (7.44)	4·50	4·50
		b. Imperf (pair)	£500	
		c. Imperf between (horizontal pair)	£1000	
1		First Day Cover		6·00
2		First Day Cover		12·00
3		First Day Cover		8·00

(*b*) *Bluish French bank-note paper. Wmk loops* (*sideways*)

4	**1**	½d bright green (11.3.42)	21·00	22·00
5		1d scarlet (9.4.42)	12·00	24·00
4		First Day Cover		80·00
5		First Day Cover		45·00

The dates for the shades of Nos. 1/3 are the months in which they were printed as indicated on the printer's imprints (see below). Others are issue dates.

Printings and imprint: The various printings can be identified from the sheet imprints as follows:

½d 1st Printing 240M/3/41
    2nd Printing 2×120M/6/41
    3rd Printing 3×120M/6/41
    4th Printing 4×120M/11/41
    5th Printing 5×120M/2/42
    6th Printing 6×240M/2/42
    7th Printing 7×120M/9/42
    8th Printing 8×120M/2/43
    9th Printing 9×120M/7/43
    10th Printing 10×120M/10/43
    11th Printing Guernsey Press Co., (*stop and comma*)
    12th Printing Guernsey Press Co. (*stop only, margin at bottom 23 to 27 mm*)
    13th Printing Guernsey Press Co. (*stop only, margin at bottom 15 mm*)

1d 1st Printing 120M/2/41
    2nd Printing 2×120M/2/41
    3rd Printing 3×120M/6/41
    4th Printing 4×120M/6/41
    5th Printing 5×120M/9/41
    6th Printing 6×240M/11/41
    7th Printing 7×120M/2/42
    8th Printing 8×240M/4/42
    9th Printing 9×240M/9/42
    10th Printing 10×240M/1/43
    11th Printing 11×240M/7/43
    12th Printing Guernsey Press Co.
    13th Printing PRESS TYP.
    14th Printing "PRESS" (*inverted commas unlevel*)
    15th Printing "PRESS" (*inverted commas level, margin at bottom 28 mm*)
    16th Printing "PRESS" (*inverted commas level, margin at bottom 12 mm*)

2½d 1st Printing Guernsey Press Co.,
    2nd Printing "PRESS" (*inverted commas unlevel*)
    3rd Printing "PRESS" (*inverted commas level, margin at bottom 22 mm*)
    4th Printing "PRESS" (*inverted commas level, margin at bottom 15 mm*)

The numbered imprints occur in the left-hand corner, bottom margin on the 1st printing of the 1d, and central, bottom margin on all other printings of all three values.

In the numbered imprints, for example, 2×120M/6/41, the '2' indicates the number of the printing; '120M' denotes the number of stamps printed in thousands, in this case 120,000; and '6/41' denotes the date of the printing, June, 1941.

In the first ten printings of the ½d and the first eleven printings of the 1d the printing details are prefixed by the name of the printer, "Guernsey Press Co."

Sheets: 60 (6×10)

Quantities printed: ½d 1,772,160; 1d 2,478,000; 2½d 416,640

Withdrawn and invalidated: 13.4.46

REGIONAL ISSUES

Although specifically issued for regional use, these issues were initially valid for use throughout Great Britain. However, they ceased to be valid in Guernsey and Jersey from 1 October, 1969 when these islands each established their own independent postal administration and introduced their own stamps.

DATES OF ISSUE. Conflicting dates of issue have been announced for some of the regional issues, partly explained by the stamps being released on different dates by the Philatelic Bureau in Edinburgh or the Philatelic Counter in London and in the regions. We have adopted the practice of giving the earliest known dates, since once released the stamps could have been used anywhere in the U.K.

INVALIDATION. The regional issues of Guernsey were invalidated for use in Guernsey and Jersey on 1 November, 1969 (although Guernsey granted a further extension for British and regional stamps till the end of March 1970). The stamps continued to be valid for use in the rest of the United Kingdom until 29 February, 1972. Those still current remained on sale at philatelic sales counters until 30 September, 1970.

1b Multiple Crowns

2

3

4 Castle Cornet and Edward the Confessor

5 Map and William I

6 Martello Tower and Henry II

7 Arms of Sark and King John

8 Arms of Alderney and Edward III

9 Guernsey Lily and Henry V

10 Arms of Guernsey and Elizabeth I

(Des E. A. Piprell. Portrait by Dorothy Wilding Ltd. Photo Harrison and Sons)

1958–67. Wmk Type 1b. Perf 15×14 (C)

6	2	2½d rose-red (8.6.64)	35	40
7	3	3d deep lilac (18.8.58)	35	30
		p. One centre phosphor band (24.5.67)	25	25
8		4d ultramarine (7.2.66)	30	30
		p. Two phosphor bands (24.10.67)...............	25	25
6/8p		Set of 3	70	75
6		First Day Cover		25·00
7		First Day Cover		17·00
8		First Day Cover		7·50

Cylinder Nos.: 2½d 1, 3; 3d (ord) 4, 5; 3d (phos) 5; 4d (ord) 1; 4d (phos) 1

Sheets: 240 (12×20)

Quantities sold (ordinary only): 2½d 3,485,760; 3d 25,812,360; 4d 4,415,040

Withdrawn: 31.8.66 2½d

Sold out: 6.3.68 3d and 4d (ordinary); 10.68 4d (phosphor); 11.68 3d (phosphor)

1968–69. No wmk. Chalk-surfaced paper. One centre phosphor band (Nos. 10/11) or two phosphor bands (others). Perf 15×14 (C)

9	3	4d pale ultramarine (16.4.68)	10	30
10		4d olive-sepia (4.9.68)	15	20
11		4d bright vermilion (26.2.69)	15	30
12		5d royal blue (4.9.68)..........	15	30
9/12		Set of 4	40	95
10, 12		First Day Cover		2·00

No. 9 was not issued in Guernsey until 22 April.

Cylinder Nos.: 4d (pale ultramarine) 1; 4d (olive-sepia) 1; 4d (bright vermilion) 1; 5d 1

Sold out: 3.69 4d ultramarine

Withdrawn: 30.9.69 (locally), 30.9.70 (British Philatelic Counters) 4d olive-sepia, 4d bright vermilion and 5d

INDEPENDENT POSTAL ADMINISTRATION

Guernsey established their own independent postal administration on 1 October, 1969 and introduced their own stamps.

NO WATERMARK. All the following issues are on unwatermarked paper.

4

11 Arms of Alderney and Charles II

12 Arms of Sark and George III

13 Arms of Guernsey and Queen Victoria

14 Guernsey Lily and Elizabeth I

15 Martello Tower and King John

16 View of Sark

17 View of Alderney

18 View of Guernsey

Two types of 1d and 1s 6d

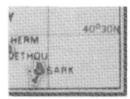

I Latitude inscr '40° 30' N'

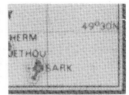

II Corrected to '49° 30' N'

(Des R. Granger Barrett. Photo Harrison (½d to 2s 6d), Delrieu (others))

1969 (1 OCT)–**70.** *Perf* 14 (½d to 2s 6d) *or* 12½ (others), all comb

13	**4**	½d deep magenta and black (a) . .	10	10
		a. Thin paper	40	50
14	**5**	1d bright blue and black (I) (a) . .	10	10
		a. Thin paper (b)	50	50
14b		1d bright blue and black (thin paper) (II) (eg)	30	30
		c. Booklet stamp with margins (thick paper) (c).	40	40
15	**6**	1½d yellow-brown and black (a) . .	10	10
16	**7**	2d gold, brt red, dp blue & blk (a)	10	10
		a. Thin paper (g)	40	40
17	**8**	3d gold, pale greenish yellow, orange-red and black (a)	15	15
		a. Error. Wmk Block CA	£1200	
		ai. Wmk inverted	£900	
		b. Thin paper (g)	40	40
18	**9**	4d multicoloured (a)	25	25
		a. Booklet stamp with margins (c)	40	45
		ab. Yellow omitted.	£250	
		ac. Emerald (stem) omitted	£110	
19	**10**	5d gold, bright vermilion, bluish violet and black (a)	25	15
		a. Booklet stamp with margins (c)	50	50
		b. Gold (inscription etc.) omitted (booklets).	£500	
20	**11**	6d gold, pale greenish yellow, light bronze-green & black (a)	30	30
		a. Thin paper (g)	30	40
21	**12**	9d gold, brt red, crimson & blk (a)	40	30
		a. Thin paper (g)	3·50	3·50
22	**13**	1s gold, brt verm, bistre & blk (a)	30	30
		a. Thin paper (g)	1·00	1·00
23	**5**	1s 6d turquoise-grn & blk (I) (a) . .	30	30
		a. Thin paper (d)	1·75	3·25
23b		1s 6d turquoise-green and black (thin paper) (II) (eg)	2·25	1·75

24	**14**	1s 9d multicoloured (a)	1·25	1·50
		a. Emerald (stem) omitted	£325	
		b. Thin paper (g)	2·50	2·50
25	**15**	2s 6d brt reddish violet & black (a)	5·00	4·25
		a. Thin paper (g)	6·00	6·00
26	**16**	5s multicoloured (a)	3·25	3·25
27	**17**	10s multicoloured (a)	26·00	22·00
		a. Perf 13½×13 (f)............	48·00	40·00
28	**18**	£1 multicoloured (a)	2·00	1·75
		a. Perf 13½×13 (fh)..........	2·00	2·00
13/28a		Set of 16	35·00	30·00
13/28		First Day Cover		32·00
13/28		Presentation Packs (incl. both 1d and 1s. 6d) (3) (9.70)	38·00	
13/25		Set of 13 Gutter Pairs	30·00	

Thinner paper – see note after Jersey No. 29.

There was no postal need for the ½d and 1½d values as the ½d coin had been withdrawn prior to their issue in anticipation of decimalisation. These values were only on sale at the Philatelic Bureau and at the Crown Agents as well as in the U.S.A.

Printings: (a) 1.10.69; (b) 24.11.69; (c) 12.12.69; (d) 1.70; (e) 4.2.70; (f) 4.3.70; (g) 18.5.70; (h) 7.71

Cylinder Nos.: ½d, 1½d, 2s 6d. 1A–1A, 1B–1B; 1d. (I) 1A–1A, 1B–1B, 2A–2A (b), 2B–2B; 1d. (II) 2A–2A, 2B–2B, 3A–3A (g), 3B–3B; 2d, 3d, 5d, 6d, 9d, 1s. 1A, 1B (each ×4); 4d, 1s 9d. 1A, 1B (each ×5); 1s 6d. (I) 1A–1A, 1B–1B, 1A–2A (d), 1B–2B; 1s 6d. (II) 1B–1B, 1A–2A, 1B–2B, 2A–3A (g), 2B–3B; 5s to £1 None

Sheets: 60 (2 panes 5×6) most sheets of the 5s, 10s and £1 were divided into two panes before issue

Imprint: Central, bottom margin (½d to 2s 6d)

Quantities sold: ½d 2,480,000; 1d (Nos. 14/14b) 1,560,971; 1½d 980,000; 2d 574,610; 3d 487,199; 4d 2,782,490; 6d 456,275; 9d 374,975; 1s 435,773; 1s 6d (Nos. 23/23b) 627,003; 1s 9d 255,111; 2s 6d 225,732; 5s 165,047; 10s (No. 27) 114,000; 10s (No. 27a) 55,200; £1 (No. 28) 120,000; £1 (No. 28a) 141,802

Sold out: 8.71 10 s (No. 27a)

Withdrawn: 6.10.69, ½d, 1½d; 4.2.70, 1d (No. 14), 1s 6d (No. 23); others 14.2.72 (except for No. 28a which remained on sale with decimal definitives until 31.3.76)
Although officially withdrawn the ½d, 1d (No. 14), 1½d and 1s 6d (No. 23) were subsequently included in Presentation Packs, whilst the ½d and 1½d remained on sale at the Philatelic Bureau until 14 February, 1972.

Invalidated: 14.2.72 (except £1)

21 Isaac Brock as Ensign

22 Arms and Flags

Birth Bicentenary of Sir Isaac Brock

(Litho Format)

1969 (1 DEC). Perf 13½×14 (2s 6d) or 14×13½ (others), all comb

29	**19**	4d multicoloured	20	20
30	**20**	5d multicoloured	20	20
31	**21**	1s 9d multicoloured	1·40	1·25
32	**22**	2s 6d multicoloured	1·40	1·25
29/32		Set of 4	2·75	2·50
		First Day Cover		4·00
		Presentation Pack.........	4·00	
		Set of 4 Gutter Pairs.......	£110	

Plate Nos.: 4d, 2s 6d 1A, 1B, 1C, 1D (each ×6); 5d 1A, 1B, 1C, 1D (each ×7); 1s 9d 1A, 1B, 1C, 1D (each ×5)

Sheets: 60 (2 panes 5×6) 2s 6d; (2 panes 6×5) others

Imprint: Right-hand corner, bottom margin

Quantities sold: 4d 940,956; 5d 732,658; 1s 9d 224,157; 2s 6d 218,955

Withdrawn: 30.11.70

Invalidated: 14.2.72

23 H.M.S. L103 (landing craft) entering St. Peter's Harbour

19 Isaac Brock as Colonel

20 Sir Isaac Brock as Major-General

24 British Warships entering St. Peter Port

25 Brigadier Snow reading the Proclamation

25th Anniversary of Liberation

(Des and photo Courvoisier)

1970 (9 MAY). *Granite paper. Perf* 11½ (C)

33	**23**	4d blue and pale blue	. . . .	40	40
34	**24**	5d brown-lake and pale grey	. . . .	40	40
35	**25**	1s 6d bistre-brown and buff	. . . .	2·50	2·50
33/5		*Set of 3*	. . . .	3·00	3·00
		First Day Cover	. . . .		3·50
		Presentation Pack.	. . . .	4·75	

Cylinder Nos.: A1–1, B1–1 (all values)

Sheets: 25 (5×5)

Imprint: Left-hand corner, top margin (4d, 5d); bottom corner, left-hand margin (1s 6d)

Quantities sold: 4d 968,873; 5d 817,958; 1s 6d 248,532

Withdrawn: 8.5.71

Invalidated: 14.2.72

26 Guernsey 'Toms'

27 Guernsey Cow

28 Guernsey Bull

29 Freesias

Agriculture and Horticulture

(Des and photo Courvoisier)

1970 (12 AUG). *Granite paper. Perf* 11½ (C)

36	**26**	4d multicoloured	. . . .	80	20
37	**27**	5d multicoloured	. . . .	90	20
38	**28**	9d multicoloured	. . . .	4·50	2·75
39	**29**	1s 6d multicoloured	. . . .	5·50	3·00
36/9		*Set of 4*	. . . .	10·00	5·50
		First Day Cover	. . . .		5·50
		Presentation Pack.	. . . .	23·00	

Cylinder Nos.: A1–1–1–1, B1–1–1–1, C1–1–1–1, D1–1–1–1 (all values)

Sheets: 25 (5×5)

Imprint: Central, bottom margin

Quantities sold: 4d 1,082,608; 5d 1,000,000; 9d 237,685; 1s 6d 241,816

Withdrawn: 11.8.71

Invalidated: 14.2.72

30 St. Anne's Church, Alderney

31 St. Peter's Church, Guernsey

32 St. Peter's Church, Sark

33 St. Tugual Chapel, Herm

Christmas. Guernsey Churches (1st series)

(Des and photo Courvoisier)

1970 (11 NOV). *Granite paper. Perf* 11½ (C)

40	**30**	4d multicoloured	. . . .	35	20
41	**31**	5d multicoloured	. . . .	45	25
42	**32**	9d multicoloured	. . . .	1·75	1·10
43	**33**	1s 6d multicoloured	. . . .	2·00	1·50
40/3		*Set of 4*	. . . .	4·00	2·75
		First Day Cover	. . . .		3·25
		Presentation Pack.	. . . .	6·00	

See also Nos. 63/6.

Cylinder Nos.: A1–1–1–1 or B1–1–1–1 (all values)

Sheets: 50 (5×10) 4d, 5d; (10×5) others

Quantities sold: 4d 815,737; 5d 668,886; 9d 236,833; 1s 6d 223,907

Withdrawn: 10.11.71

Invalidated: 14.2.72

34 Martello Tower and King John

Decimal Currency

(Photo Harrison (½p to 10p), Delrieu (others))

1971 (6 JAN)–*73. Designs as Type* **4** *etc., but values inscribed in decimal currency as in Type* **34**. *Chalk-surfaced paper. Perf* 14 (½p to 10p) *or* 13½×13 (others), *all comb*

44	**4**	½p deep magenta and black (*b*) . .		10	15
		a. Booklet stamp with margins. Glazed, ordinary paper		15	20
		ab. Ditto. Chalk-surfaced paper (*e*)		15	20
45	**5**	1p bright blue and black (II) (*b*) . .		10	10
46	**6**	1½p yellow-brown and black (*b*) . .		15	15

47	**9**	2p multicoloured (b)	15	15
		a. Booklet stamp with margins. Glazed, ordinary paper	20	20
		ab. Ditto. Chalk-surfaced paper (e)	20	20
		ac. Emerald (stem) omitted	£1200	
		b. Booklet stamp with margins (b)	20	20
48	**10**	2½p gold, bright vermilion, bluish violet and black (be)	15	10
		a. Bright vermilion omitted	£500	
		b. Booklet stamp with margins. Glazed, ordinary paper	20	20
		ba. Ditto. Chalk-surfaced paper (e)	20	20
49	**8**	3p gold, pale greenish yellow, orange-red and black (be)	20	20
50	**14**	3½p mult (glazed, ordinary paper) (b)	25	25
51	**7**	4p multicoloured (b)	35	25
52	**5**	5p turquoise-green & black (II) (b)	30	25
53	**11**	6p gold, pale greenish yellow, lt bronze-green and black (b) . .	30	35
54	**13**	7½p gold, brt verm, bistre & blk (b)	40	45
55	**12**	9p gold, brt red, crimson & blk (b)	50	75
56	**34**	10p bright reddish violet & blk (a)	2·25	1·75
		a. Ordinary paper. Bright reddish violet and deep black (c)	1·75	1·75
57	**16**	20p mult (glazed, ordinary paper) (af)	1·00	1·00
		a. Shade* (d)	1·00	1·00
58	**17**	50p mult (glazed, ordinary paper) (adg)	2·00	2·00
44/58		Set of 15	7·00	7·00
		First Day Covers (2)		8·50
44/58, 28a		Presentation Packs (3)	8·00	
44/56		Set of 13 Gutter Pairs	16·00	

*No. 57 has the sky in a pale turquoise-blue; on No. 57a it is pale turquoise-green.

Printings: (a) 6.1.71; (b) 15.2.71; (c) 1.9.72; (d) 25.1.73; (e) 2.4.73; (f) 10.74; (g) 7.75

Cylinder Nos.: ½p, 1p, 1½p, 5p, 10p 1A–1A, 1B–1B; 2p, 3½p 1A, 1B (each ×5); 2½p, 3p, 4p, 6p, 7½p, 9p 1A, 1B (each ×4); 20p none; 50p 21–22–23–24. Sheets from ptg (g) have and additional S99 (reversed)
On the 3½p only four '1A' Nos. are shown in the margin, the black '1A' being omitted in error.

Sheets: 50 (2 panes 5×5) ½p to 10p; 30 (5×6) others

Imprint: Central, bottom margin (½p to 10p)

Quantities sold: ½p 980,959; 1p 568,509; 1½p 559,576; 2p 2,512,903; 2½p 4,469,578; 3p 2,245,564; 3½p 317,523; 4p 527,696; 5p 511,742; 6p 346,255; 7½p 322,905; 9p 349,211; 10p 538,153; 20p 630.888; 50p 258,150

Withdrawn: 1.4.75 ½p to 10p (½p, 9p, 10p and Presentation Packs sold out by 5.74); 31.3.76 20p, 50p

36 Great Britain 4d of 1855–7

37 Italy 5c of 1862

38 Confederate States 5c of 1862

Thomas De La Rue Commemoration

(Des and recess De La Rue)

1971 (2 JUNE). Perf 14×13½ (C)

59	**35**	2p dull purple to brown-purple* . .	50	30
60	**36**	2½p carmine-red	50	30
61	**37**	4p deep bluish green.	2·50	2·25
62	**38**	7½p deep blue.	2·75	2·25
59/62		Set of 4	5·50	4·50
		First Day Cover		5·00
		Presentation Pack.	6·50	

*These colours represent the extreme range of shades of this value. The majority of the printing, however, is an intermediate shade.

Plate Nos.: 1A, 1B each

Sheets: 25 (5×5)

Imprint: Central, bottom margin

Quantities sold: 2p 897,742; 2½p 1,404,085; 4p 210,691; 7½p 199,424

Withdrawn: 1.6.72

35 Hong Kong 2c of 1862

39 Ebenezer Church, St. Peter Port

40 Church of St. Pierre du Bois

8

41 St. Joseph's Church, St. Peter Port

42 Church of St. Philippe de Torteval

Christmas. Guernsey Churches (2nd series)

(Des and photo Courvoisier)

1971 (27 OCT). *Granite paper. Perf* 11½ (C)

63	**39**	2p multicoloured	. . . .	25	25
64	**40**	2½p multicoloured	. . . .	25	25
65	**41**	5p multicoloured	. . . .	2·25	1·75
66	**42**	7½p multicoloured	. . . .	2·25	1·75
63/6		Set of 4	. . . .	4·50	3·50
		First Day Cover	. . . .		4·00
		Presentation Pack.	. . . .	5·50	
		Set of 4 Gutter Pairs.	. . . .	25·00	

Cylinder Nos.: A1–1–1–1, B1–1–1–1, C1–1–1–1, D1–1–1–1 (all values)

Sheets: 50 (2 panes 5×5)

Imprint: Central, bottom margin (2p, 2½p) or left-hand corner, bottom margin (5p, 7½p)

Quantities sold: 2p 991,155; 2½p 916,004; 5p 223,412; 7½p 215,768

Withdrawn: 26.10.72

43 *Earl of Chesterfield* (1794)

44 *Dasher* (1827)

45 *Ibex* (1891)

46 *Alberta* (1900)

Mail Packet Boats (1st series)

(Des and photo Courvoisier)

1972 (10 FEB). *Granite paper. Perf* 11½ (C)

67	**43**	2p multicoloured	. . . .	15	15
68	**44**	2½p multicoloured	. . . .	20	20
69	**45**	7½p multicoloured	. . . .	90	1·00
70	**46**	9p multicoloured	. . . .	1·50	1·40
67/70		Set of 4	. . . .	2·50	2·50
		First Day Cover	. . . .		4·00
		Presentation Pack.	. . . .	3·50	

See also Nos. 80/3.

Cylinder Nos.: A1–1–1–1 or B1–1–1–1 (all values)

Sheets: 25 (5×5)

Imprint: Central, bottom margin

Quantities sold: 2p 973,503; 2½p 954,263; 7½p 288,929; 9p 289,340

Withdrawn: 9.2.73

47 Guernsey Bull

World Conference of Guernsey Breeders, Guernsey

(Photo Courvoisier)

1972 (22 MAY). *Granite paper. Perf* 11½ (C)

71	**47**	5p multicoloured	. . . .	75	60
		First Day Cover*	. . . .		1·75
		Gutter Pair	. . . .	15·00	

*Prepared by the Royal Guernsey Agricultural and Horticultural Society.

Cylinder Nos.: A1–1–1–1, B1–1–1–1

Sheets: 50 (2 panes 5×5)

48 Bermuda Buttercup

49 Heath Spotted Orchid

50 Kaffir Fig   **51** Scarlet Pimpernel

Wild Flowers

(Des and photo Courvoisier)

1972 (24 MAY). *Granite paper. Perf* 11½ (C)

72	**48**	2p multicoloured	15	20
73	**49**	2½p multicoloured	15	20
74	**50**	7½p multicoloured	1·00	90
75	**51**	9p multicoloured	1·40	1·25
72/5		Set of 4	2·50	2·25
		First Day Cover		3·25
		Presentation Pack..........	4·00	
		Set of 4 Gutter Pairs........	9·00	

Cylinder Nos.: A1–1–1–1, B1–1–1–1, C1–1–1–1, D1–1–1–1 (all values)

Sheets: 50 (2 panes 5×5)

Imprint: 2p, 7½p Central, bottom margin; others left-hand corner, bottom margin

Quantities sold: 2p 1,006,041; 2½p 1,028,826; 7½p 249,471; 9p 244,839

Withdrawn: 23.5.73

52 Angels adoring   **53** The Epiphany
Christ

54 The Virgin Mary   **55** Christ

Royal Silver Wedding and Christmas

(Des and photo Courvoisier)

1972 (20 NOV). *Designs show stained glass windows from Guernsey Churches. Granite paper. Perf* 11½ (C)

76	**52**	2p multicoloured	10	10
77	**53**	2½p multicoloured	15	15
78	**54**	7½p multicoloured	60	55
79	**55**	9p multicoloured	75	60
76/9		Set of 4	1·50	1·25
		First Day Cover		1·75
		Presentation Pack..........	2·00	
		Set of 4 Gutter Pairs........	6·00	

Cylinder Nos.: A1–1–1–1–1, B1–1–1–1–1 each

Sheets: 50 (2 panes 5×5)

Imprint: Central, bottom margin of each pane

Quantities sold: 2p 878,893; 2½p 1,037,387; 7½p 314,972; 9p 313,367

Sold out: By 31.3.73

56 *St. Julien* (1925)

57 *Isle of Guernsey* (1930)

58 *St. Patrick* (1947)

59 *Sarnia* (1961)

Mail Packet Boats (2nd series)

(Des and photo Courvoisier)

1973 (9 MAR). *Granite paper. Perf* 11½ (C)

80	**56**	2½p multicoloured	....	20	10
81	**57**	3p multicoloured	....	30	20
82	**58**	7½p multicoloured	....	1·10	60
83	**59**	9p multicoloured	....	1·25	75
80/3		Set of 4	....	2·50	1·50
		First Day Cover	....		1·60
		Presentation Pack..........		2·75	
		Set of 4 Gutter Pairs........		6·50	

Cylinder Nos.: All values A1–1–1–1, B1–1–1–1, C1–1–1–1, D1–1–1–1

Sheets: 50 (2 panes 5×5)

Imprint: Central, bottom margin of each pane

Quantities sold: 2½p 947,888; 3p 1,274,699; 7½p 278,998; 9p 263,569

Withdrawn: 8.3.74 (3p and Presentation Pack sold out earlier)

60 Supermarine Sea Eagle

61 Westland Wessex Trimotor

62 De Havilland D.H.89 Dragon Rapide

63 Douglas DC-3

64 Vickers Viscount 800 *Anne Marie*

50th Anniversary of Air Service

(Des and photo Courvoisier)

1973 (4 JULY). *Granite paper. Perf* 11½ (C)

84	**60**	2½p multicoloured	....	10	10
85	**61**	3p multicoloured	....	15	15
86	**62**	5p multicoloured	....	30	25
87	**63**	7½p multicoloured	....	90	50
88	**64**	9p multicoloured	....	1·00	55
84/8		Set of 5	....	2·25	1·40
		First Day Cover	....		2·00
		Presentation Pack..........		2·50	
		Set of 5 Gutter Pairs........		5·00	

Cylinder Nos.: A1–1–1–1, B1–1–1–1 each

Sheets: 50 (2 panes 5×5)

Imprint: Central, bottom margin of each pane

Quantities sold: 2½p 918,953; 3p 1,285,890; 5p 313,882; 7½p 294,369; 9p 288,225

Withdrawn: 3.7.74 (5p and Presentation Pack sold out earlier)

65 'The Good Shepherd'

66 Christ at the Well of Samaria

67 St. Dominic

68 Mary and the Child Jesus

Christmas

(Des and photo Courvoisier)

1973 (24 OCT). *Designs show stained glass windows from Guernsey Churches. Granite paper. Perf* 11½ (C)

89	**65**	2½p multicoloured	....	10	10
90	**66**	3p multicoloured	....	10	10

91	**67**	7½p multicoloured	. . . .	30	30
92	**68**	20p multicoloured	. . . .	60	60
89/92		*Set of* 4	. . . .	1·00	1·00
		First Day Cover	. . . .		1·00
		Presentation Pack	. . . .	1·75	
		Set of 4 *Gutter Pairs*	. . . .	3·25	

Cylinder Nos.: A1–1–1–1, B1–1–1–1 each

Sheets: 50 (2 panes 5×5)

Imprint: Central, bottom margin of each pane

Quantities sold: 2½p 1,284,342; 3p 1,285,851; 7½p 367,714; 20p 367,625

Withdrawn: 23.10.74

69 Princess Anne and Capt. Mark Phillips

Royal Wedding

(Des G. Anderson. Photo Courvoisier

1973 (14 NOV). *Granite paper. Perf* 11½ (C)

93	**69**	25p multicoloured	. . . .	1·00	75
		First Day Cover	. . . .		75
		Presentation Pack	. . . .	1·40	
		Gutter Pair	. . . .	2·25	

Cylinder Nos.: A1–1–1–1, B1–1–1–1

Sheets: 50 (2 panes 5×5)

Imprint: Central, bottom margin of each pane

Quantity sold: 392,767

Withdrawn: 13.11.74

70 *John Lockett*, 1875

71 *Arthur Lionel*, 1912

72 *Euphrosyne Kendal*, 1954

73 *Arun*, 1972

150th Anniversary of Royal National Life-boat Institution

(Des and photo Courvoisier)

1974 (15 JAN). *Granite paper. Perf* 11½ (C)

94	**70**	2½p multicoloured	. . . .	10	10
95	**71**	3p multicoloured	. . . .	10	10
96	**72**	8p multicoloured	. . . .	45	45
97	**73**	10p multicoloured	. . . .	45	45
94/97		*Set of* 4	. . . .	1·00	1·00
		First Day Cover	. . . .		1·00
		Presentation Pack	. . . .	1·25	
		Set of 4 *Gutter Pairs*	. . . .	2·00	

Cylinder Nos.: A1–1–1–1, B1–1–1–1 each

Sheets: 50 (2 panes 5×5)

Imprint: Central, bottom margin of each pane

Quantities sold: 2½p 1,016,058; 3p 1,162,020; 8p 393,660; 10p 393,668

Withdrawn: 14.1.75 (8p, 10p and Presentation Pack sold out earlier)

74 Private, East Regt., 1815

75 Officer, 2nd North Regt., 1825

76 Gunner, Guernsey Artillery, 1787

77 Gunner, Guernsey Artillery, 1815

78 Corporal, Royal Guernsey Artillery, 1868

79 Field Officer, Royal Guernsey Artillery, 1895

80 Sergeant, 3rd Regt., 1867

81 Officer, East Regt., 1822

82 Field Officer, Royal Guernsey Artillery, 1895

83 Colour-Sergeant of Grenadiers, 1833

84 Officer, North Regt., 1832

85 Officer, East Regt., 1822

86 Field Officer, Rifle Company, 1868

87 Private, 4th West Regt., 1785

88 Field Officer, 4th West Regt., 1824

89 Driver, Field Battery, Royal Guernsey Artillery, 1848

90 Officer, Field Battery, Royal Guernsey Artillery, 1868

91 Cavalry Trooper, Light Dragoons, 1814

Militia Uniforms

(Photo Courvoisier (½p to 10p), Delrieu (others))

1974 (2 APR)–**78**. *Granite paper (½p to 10p). Perf 11½ (½p to 10p), 13×13½ (20, 50p) or 13½×13 (£1), all comb*

98	**74**	½p multicoloured (*aj*)	10	10
		a. Booklet strip of 8 (98×5 and 102×3)†	30	
		b. Booklet pane of 16 (98×4, 102×6 and 103×6)†	65	
99	**75**	1p multicoloured (*aci*)	10	10
		a. Booklet strip of 8 (99×4, 103, 105×2 and 105a) (8.2.77)† . .	80	
		b. Booklet strip of 4 (99, 101×2, and 105a) (7.2.78)†	50	
100	**76**	1½p multicoloured (*a*)	10	10
101	**77**	2p multicoloured (*ak*)	10	10
102	**78**	2½p multicoloured (*a*)	10	10
103	**79**	3p multicoloured (*a*)	10	10
104	**80**	3½p multicoloured (*a*)	10	10
105	**81**	4p multicoloured (*abc*)	15	15
105a	**82**	5p multicoloured (*f*)	15	15
106	**83**	5½p multicoloured (*a*)	20	25
107	**84**	6p multicoloured (*ae*)	20	25
107a	**85**	7p multicoloured (*f*)	25	25
108	**86**	8p multicoloured (*ag*)	25	30
109	**87**	9p multicoloured (*al*)	30	30
110	**88**	10p multicoloured (*ah*)	30	30
111	**89**	20p multicoloured (*d*)	55	40
112	**90**	50p multicoloured (*d*)	1·50	1·25
113	**91**	£1 multicoloured (*d*)	3·25	2·50
98/113		*Set of 18*	7·00	6·00
		First Day Covers (3)		7·50
		Presentation Packs (3)	8·00	
		Set of 15 Gutter Pairs (Nos. 98/110)	5·50	

†Nos. 98*a*/*b* come from a special booklet sheet of 88 (8×11), and Nos. 99*a*/*b* from booklet sheets of 80 (two panes 8×5). These sheets were put on sale in addition to the normal sheets. The strips and panes have the left-hand selvedge stuck into booklet covers, except for No. 99*b* which had the strip loose, and then folded and supplied in plastic wallets.

Printings: (*a*) 2.4.74; (*b*) 10.74; (*c*) 12.74; (*d*) 1.4.75; (*e*) 12.75; (*f*) 29.5.76; (*g*) 7.76; (*h*) 11.76; (*i*) 8.2.77; (*j*) 7.77; (*k*) 12.77; (*l*) 7.2.78

Plate Nos: 20p to £1 none; A1–1–1–1–1, B1–1–1–1–1 1½p, 2p, 6p; A1–1–1–1, B1–1–1–1 others

Sheets: 20p to £1, 25 (5×5); others, 100 (2 panes 10×5)

Imprint: Central, bottom margin of each page

Quantities sold: ½p 1,173,560; 1p 1,367,828; 1½p 525,248; 2p 1,098,053; 2½p 1,124,091; 3p 1,953,796; 3½p 1,891,493; 4p 3,435,614; 5p 2,920,246; 5½p 634,870; 6p 2,006,983; 7p 3,103,925; 8p 811,418; 9p 717,815; 10p 1,133,141; 20p 788,840; 50p 570,505; £1 464,428

Withdrawn: 12.2.80 ½p to 20p; 4.2.81 50p, £1

92 Badge of Guernsey and U.P.U. Emblem

93 Map of Guernsey

94 U.P.U. Building, Berne, and Guernsey Flag

95 'Salle des Etats'

Centenary of Universal Postal Union

(Photo Courvoisier)

1974 (7 JUNE). *Granite paper. Perf* 11½ (C)

114	**92**	2½p multicoloured	. . . .	10	10
115	**93**	3p multicoloured	. . . .	10	10
116	**94**	8p multicoloured	. . . .	45	45
117	**95**	10p multicoloured	. . . .	45	45
114/17		Set of 4	. . . .	1·00	1·00
		First Day Cover			1·00
		Presentation Pack		1·25	
		Set of 4 Gutter Pairs		2·00	

Cylinder Nos.: 2½p, 8p A1–1–1, B1–1–1; 3p A1–1–1–1. B1–1–1–1; 10p A1–1–1–1–1, B1–1–1–1–1

Sheets: 50 (2 panes 5×5)

Imprint: Central, bottom margin

Quantities sold: 2½p 1,231,657; 3p 1,839,674; 8p 345,271; 10p 356,501

Withdrawn: 6.6.75

96 'Cradle Rock'

97 'Moulin Huet Bay'

98 'Au Bord de la Mer'

99 Self-portrait

Renoir Paintings

(Des and photo Delrieu)

1974 (21 SEPT). *Perf* 13 (C)

118	**96**	3p multicoloured	. . . .	10	10
119	**97**	5½p multicoloured	. . . .	15	15
120	**98**	8p multicoloured	. . . .	40	40
121	**99**	10p multicoloured	. . . .	45	45
118/21		Set of 4	. . . .	1·00	1·00
		First Day Cover			1·00
		Presentation Pack		1·25	

Sheets: 25 (5×5)

Imprint: Right-hand corner, top margin (3p and 5½p), and bottom corner, right-hand margin (others)

Quantities sold: 3p 670,648; 5½p 422,677; 8p 377,615; 10p 391,095

Withdrawn: 20.9.75

100 Guernsey Spleenwort

101 Sand Quillwort

102 Guernsey Fern

103 Least Adder's Tongue

Guernsey Ferns

(Des and photo Courvoisier)

1975 (7 JAN). *Granite paper. Perf* 11½ (C)

122	**100**	3½p multicoloured	. . . .	15	10
123	**101**	4p multicoloured	. . . .	15	10

24	**102**	8p multicoloured	40	40
25	**103**	10p multicoloured	60	50
22/5		Set of 4	1·25	1·00
		First Day Cover..........		1·00
		Presentation Pack........	1·50	
		Set of 4 Gutter Pairs	2·50	

Cylinder Nos.: 3½p, 4p, 8p each A1–1–1–1, B1–1–1–1, C1–1–1–1, D1–1–1–1; 10p A1–1–1–1–1, B1–1–1–1–1, C1–1–1–1–1, D1–1–1–1–1

Sheets: 50 (2 panes 5×5)

Imprint: Central, bottom margin

Quantities sold: 3½p 1,089,142; 4p 1,370,743; 8p 430,672; 10p 443,636

Withdrawn: 6.1.76

104 Victor Hugo House

105 Candie Gardens

106 United Europe Oak, Hauteville

107 Tapestry Room, Hauteville

Victor Hugo's Exile in Guernsey

(Des and photo Courvoisier)

1975 (6 JUNE). Granite paper. Perf 11½ (C)

126	**104**	3½p multicoloured	10	10
127	**105**	4p multicoloured	20	10
128	**106**	8p multicoloured	40	40
129	**107**	10p multicoloured	50	50
126/9		Set of 4	1·10	1·00
		First Day Cover..........		1·00
		Presentation Pack........	1·25	
MS130		114×143 mm. Nos. 126/9........	1·10	1·00

Cylinder Nos.: A1–1–1–1, B1–1–1–1 each

Sheets: 50 (5×10) 3½p, 10p; (10×5) others

Imprint: Central, left-hand margin (3½p, 10p) or central, bottom margin (4p, 8p).

Quantities sold: 3½p 810,327; 4p 1,346,628; 8p 377,637; 10p 369,282; miniature sheet 269,217.

Withdrawn: 5.6.76

108 Globe and Seal of Bailiwick

109 Globe and Guernsey Flag

110 Globe, Guernsey Flag and Alderney Shield

111 Globe, Guernsey Flag and Sark Shield

Christmas

(Des and photo Delrieu)

1975 (7 OCT). Perf 13 (C)

131	**108**	4p multicoloured	10	10
132	**109**	6p multicoloured	15	15
133	**110**	10p multicoloured	45	35
134	**111**	12p multicoloured	50	50
131/4		Set of 4	1·10	1·00
		First Day Cover..........		1·00
		Presentation Pack........	1·25	

Sheets: 25 (5×5)

Imprint: Central, left-hand margin (4p, 6p); central, bottom margin (10p, 12p).

Quantities sold: 4p, 678,619; 6p 667,413; 10p 392,529; 12p 361,548

Withdrawn: 6.10.76·

112 Les Hanois

113 Les Casquets

114 Quesnard

115 Point Robert

Lighthouses

(Des and photo Courvoisier)

1976 (10 FEB). *Granite paper. Perf* 11½ (C)

135	**112**	4p multicoloured	. . . .	10	10
136	**113**	6p multicoloured	. . . .	20	25
137	**114**	11p multicoloured	. . . .	50	45
138	**115**	13p multicoloured	. . . .	55	60
135/8		*Set of* 4	. . . .	1·25	1·25
		First Day Cover			1·25
		Presentation Pack		1·50	
		Set of 4 *Gutter Pairs*		2·50	

Cylinder Nos.: A1–1–1–1, B1–1–1–1 each
Sheets: 50 (2 panes 5×5)
Quantities sold: 4p 846,362; 6p 900,899; 11p 366,468; 13p 348,358
Withdrawn: 9.2.77

116 Milk Can

117 Christening Cup

Europa

(Des and photo Courvoisier)

1976 (29 MAY). *Granite paper. Perf* 11½ (C)

139	**116**	10p brown and green	. . . .	40	40
140	**117**	25p grey and blue	. . . .	85	85
139/40		*Set of* 2	. . . .	1·25	1·25
		First Day Cover			1·25
		Presentation Pack		1·40	

Sheets: 9 (3×3)
Quantities sold: 1,185,014 of each
Sold out: 4.6.76

118 Pine Forest, Guernsey

119 Herm and Jethou

120 Grand Greve
Bay, Sark

121 Trois Vaux Bay,
Alderney

Views

(Des and photo Courvoisier)

1976 (3 AUG). *Granite paper. Perf* 11½ (C)

141	**118**	5p multicoloured	. . . .	15	10
142	**119**	7p multicoloured	. . . .	15	20
143	**120**	11p multicoloured	. . . .	55	45
144	**121**	13p multicoloured	. . . .	55	65
141/4		*Set of* 4	. . . .	1·25	1·25
		First Day Cover			1·25
		Presentation Pack		1·50	
		Set of 4 *Gutter Pairs*		2·50	

Cylinder Nos.: A1–1–1–1, B1–1–1–1 each
Sheets: 50 (2 panes 5×5)
Quantities sold: 5p 661,771; 7p 1,016,350; 11p 349,773; 13p 336,027
Withdrawn: 2.8.77

122 Royal Court House, Guernsey

123 Elizabeth College, Guernsey

124 La Seigneurie, Sark

125 Island Hall, Alderney

Christmas. Buildings

(Des and photo Courvoisier)

1976 (14 OCT). *Granite paper. Perf* 11½ (C)

145	**122**	5p multicoloured	....	15	10
146	**123**	7p multicoloured	....	15	15
147	**124**	11p multicoloured	....	55	50
148	**125**	13p multicoloured	....	55	65
145/8		*Set of 4*	....	1·25	1·25
		First Day Cover	....		1·25
		Presentation Pack	....	1·50	
		Set of 4 Gutter Pairs	......	2·50	

Cylinder Nos.: A1–1–1–1, B1–1–1–1 each

Sheets: 50 (2 panes 5×5)

Imprint: Central, bottom margin

Quantities sold: 5p 1,097,445; 7p 1,051,184; 11p 371,155; 13p 352,347

Withdrawn: 13.10.77

126 Queen Elizabeth II **127**

Silver Jubilee

(Des R. Granger Barrett. Photo Courvoisier)

1977 (8 FEB). *Granite paper. Perf* 11½ (C)

149	**126**	7p multicoloured	....	25	25
150	**127**	35p multicoloured	....	1·00	1·00
149/50		*Set of 2*	....	1·25	1·25
		First Day Cover	....		1·25
		Presentation Pack	....	1·50	

Cylinder Nos.: 7p A1–1–1–1–1, B1–1–1–1–1; 35p A1–1–1–1–1–1

Sheets: 25 (5×5)

Imprint: Central, bottom margin

Quantities sold: 7p 1,004,250; 35p 536,971

Withdrawn: 7.2.78

128 Woodland, Talbots Valley

129 Pastureland, Talbots Valley

Europa

(Des and photo Courvoisier)

1977 (17 MAY). *Granite paper. Perf* 11½ (C)

151	**128**	7p multicoloured	....	35	35
152	**129**	25p multicoloured	....	90	90
151/2		*Set of 2*	....	1·25	1·25
		First Day Cover	....		1·25
		Presentation Pack	....	1·50	
		Set of 2 Gutter Pairs	......	2·50	

Cylinder Nos.: A1–1–1–1, B1–1–1–1 each

Sheets: 50 (2 panes 5×5)

Imprint: Right-hand corner, bottom margin

Quantities sold: 7p 1,371,463; 25p 598,453

Withdrawn: 16.5.78

130 Statue-menhir, Castel

131 Megalithic Tomb, St. Saviour

135 Mobile Radar Unit

136 Marine Ambulance *Flying Christine II*

137 Cliff Rescue

132 Cist, Tourgis

133 Statue-menhir, St. Martin

Prehistoric Monuments

(Des and photo Courvoisier)

1977 (2 AUG). *Granite paper. Perf* 11½ (C)

153	**130**	5p multicoloured	10	10
154	**131**	7p multicoloured	15	15
155	**132**	11p multicoloured	55	55
156	**133**	13p multicoloured	60	60
153/6		*Set of* 4	1·25	1·25
		First Day Cover		1·25
		Presentation Pack	1·50	
		Set of 4 Gutter Pairs	2·50	

Cylinder Nos.: A1–1–1–1, B1–1–1–1 each

Sheets: 50 (2 panes 5×5)

Imprint: Central, right-hand margin (5p and 13p); Central, bottom margin (others)

Quantities sold: 5p 747,236; 7p 1,077,714; 11p 390,927; 13p 373,063;

Withdrawn: 1.8.78

Christmas. St John Ambulance Centenary

(Des P. Slade and M. Horder. Photo Courvoisier)

1977 (25 OCT). *Granite paper. Perf* 11½ (C)

157	**134**	5p multicoloured	10	10
158	**135**	7p multicoloured	15	15
159	**136**	11p multicoloured	55	55
160	**137**	13p multicoloured	60	60
157/60		*Set of 4*	1·25	1·25
		First Day Cover		1·25
		Presentation Pack	1·50	
		Set of 4 Gutter Pairs	2·50	

Cylinder Nos.: 5p A1–1–1–1, B1–1–1–1; others A1–1–1–1, B1–1–1–1

Sheets: 50 (2 panes 5×5)

Imprint: Right-hand corner, bottom margin (7p and 11p); top, right-hand margin (others)

Quantities sold: 5p 1,218,293; 7p 1,155,448; 11p 406,244; 13p 383,489

Withdrawn: 24.10.78

134 Mobile First Aid Unit

138 View from Clifton, *c* 1830

139 Market Square, St. Peter Port, *c* 1838

140 Petit-Bo Bay, *c* 1839

141 The Quay, St. Peter Port, *c* 1830

Old Guernsey Prints (1st series)

(Des, recess and litho De La Rue)

1978 (7 FEB). *Perf* 14×13½ (C)

61	**138**	5p black and light stone	10	10
62	**139**	7p black and cream	15	15
63	**140**	11p black and light pink	55	55
64	**141**	13p black and light azure	60	60
61/4		Set of 4	1·25	1·25
		First Day Cover		1·25
		Presentation Pack	1·50	
		Set of 4 Gutter Pairs	2·50	

See also Nos. 249/52.

Plate Nos.: All values 1A–1A, 1B–1B, 1C–1C, 1D–1D

Sheets: 50 (2 panes 5×5)

Imprint: Left-hand corner, bottom margin

Quantities sold: 5p 858,816; 7p 930,955; 11p 442,009; 13p 388,163

Withdrawn: 6.2.79

42 *Prosperity* Memorial

143 Victoria Monument

Europa. Monuments

(Des R. Granger Barrett. Litho Questa)

1978 (2 MAY). *Perf* 14½ (C)

165	**142**	5p multicoloured	35	35
166	**143**	7p multicoloured	40	40
165/6		Set of 2	75	75
		First Day Cover		1·00
		Presentation Pack	1·00	

Sheets: 20 (5p 5×4; 7p 4×5)

Quantities sold: 5p 2,581,345; 7p 2,370,766

Withdrawn: 1.5.79

144 Queen Elizabeth **145**

25th Anniversary of Coronation

(Des R. Granger Barrett from bust by Arnold Machin. Photo Courvoisier)

1978 (2 MAY). *Granite paper. Perf* 11½ (C)

167	**144**	20p black, grey and bright blue	75	75
		First Day Cover		1·00
		Presentation Pack	1·00	
		Gutter Pair	1·50	

Cylinder Nos.: A1–1–1, B1–1–1

Sheets: 50 (2 panes 5×5)

Imprint: Right-hand corner, bottom margin

Quantity sold: 488,466

Withdrawn: 1.5.79

Royal Visit

(Des R. Granger Barrett from bust by Arnold Machin. Photo Courvoisier)

1978 (28 JUNE). *Granite paper. Perf* 11½ (C)

168	**145**	7p black, grey and bright green	50	50
		First Day Cover		1·00
		Presentation Pack	1·00	
		Gutter Pair	1·00	

Cylinder Nos.: A1–1–1, B1–1–1

Sheets: 50 (2 panes 5×5)

Imprint: Top corner, right-hand margin

Quantity sold: 1,149,768

Withdrawn: 27.6.79

146 Northern Gannet

147 Firecrest

148 Dartford Warbler

149 Spotted Redshank

Birds

(Des John Waddington Ltd. Photo Courvoisier)

1978 (29 AUG). *Granite paper. Perf* 11½ (C)

169	**146**	5p multicoloured	. . . .	15	15
170	**147**	7p multicoloured	. . . .	25	25
171	**148**	11p multicoloured	. . . .	60	45
172	**149**	13p multicoloured	. . . .	70	55
169/72		*Set of 4*	. . . .	1·50	1·25
		First Day Cover	. . . .		1·75
		Presentation Pack	. . . .	1·75	
		Set of 4 Gutter Pairs	. . . . . .	3·00	

Cylinder Nos.: All values A1–1–1–1, B1–1–1–1, C1–1–1–1, D1–1–1–1
Sheets: 50 (2 panes 5×5)
Imprint: Right-hand corner, bottom margin
Quantities sold: 5p 750,011; 7p 924,627; 11p 442,395; 13p 432,106
Withdrawn: 28.8.79

150 Solanum

151 Christmas Rose

152 Holly

153 Mistletoe

Christmas

(Des and photo Courvoisier)

1978 (31 OCT). *Granite paper. Perf* 11½ (C)

173	**150**	5p multicoloured	. . . .	10	10
174	**151**	7p multicoloured	. . . .	20	20
175	**152**	11p multicoloured	. . . .	40	40
176	**153**	13p deep blue-green, grey and greenish yellow.	50	50
173/6		*Set of 4*	. . . .	1·10	1·10
		First Day Cover			1·25
		Presentation Pack	1·40	
		Set of 4 Gutter Pairs	2·25	

Cylinder Nos.: 13p A1–1–1, B1–1–1; others A1–1–1–1, B1–1–1–1
Sheets: 50 (2 panes 5×5)
Imprint: 5, 7p central, bottom margin; others central, right-hand margin
Quantities sold: 5p 1,222,140; 7p 1,246,261; 11p 409,168; 13p 372,991
Withdrawn: 30.10.79

154 One Double, 1830

155 Two Doubles, 1899

156 Four Doubles, 1902

157 Eight Doubles, 1959

158 Three Pence, 1956

159 Five New Pence, 1968

160 Fifty New Pence, 1969

161 Ten New Pence, 1970

162 Half New Penny, 1971

163 One New Penny, 1971

164 Two New Pence, 1971

165 Half Penny, 1979

166 One Penny, 1977

167 Two Pence, 1977

168 Five Pence, 1977

169 Ten Pence, 1977

170 Twenty-five Pence, 1972

171 Ten Shillings William I Commem, 1966

172 Silver Jubilee Commemorative Crown, 1977

173 Royal Silver Wedding Commemorative Crown, 1972

174 Seal of the Bailiwick

Coins

(Des R. Reid and Courvoisier (£5). Photo Courvoisier)

1979 (13 FEB)–**83**. *Granite paper. Perf 11½ (C)*

177	**154**	½p multicoloured (*a*)	10	10
		a. Booklet pane. Nos. 177×2, 178×3, 179×2, 181, 183 and 187 (*c*)	1·00	
		b. Booklet pane. Nos. 177×2, 178, 179×2, 183×2 and 187×3 (*c*)	1·50	
178	**155**	1p multicoloured (*al*).	10	10
		a. Booklet strip of 4. Nos. 178×2, 179 and 182	60	
179	**156**	2p multicoloured (*a*)	10	10
		a. Booklet strip of 5. Nos. 179, 182×2 and 184×2 . .	1·25	
180	**157**	4p multicoloured (*a*)	10	10
		a. Booklet pane of 10. Nos. 180 and 184, each ×5 (*d*)	1·75	
		b. Booklet pane of 15. Nos. 180, 184 and 190, each ×5 (*d*)	3·50	
		c. Booklet pane of 10. Nos. 180×2, 185×3 and 191×5 (*k*)	3·00	
		d. Booklet pane of 15. Nos. 180, 185 and 191, each ×5 (*k*)	3·75	
181	**158**	5p grey-black, silver and chestnut (*a*).	15	10
		a. Grey-black, silver and yellowish brown (*f*)	30	30
		b. Booklet pane of 10. Nos. 181*a*×5, 184×4 and 191 (*f*)	2·25	
		c. Booklet pane of 15. Nos. 181*a*, 184, and 191, each ×5 (*f*)	3·75	

21

182	**159**	6p grey-black, silver and brown-red (*a*)	15	15
183	**160**	7p grey-black, silver & grn (*a*)	15	20
184	**161**	8p grey-blk, silver & brn (*agij*)	20	20
185	**162**	9p multicoloured (*a*)	25	20
186	**163**	10p mult (green background) (*a*)	50	50
187		10p mult (orge background) (*b*)	35	30
188	**164**	11p multicoloured (*a*)	25	30
189	**165**	11½p multicoloured (*b*)	25	30
190	**166**	12p multicoloured (*a*)	30	30
191	**167**	13p multicoloured (*ah*)	30	30
192	**168**	14p grey-blk, silver & dull bl (*a*)	30	30
193	**169**	15p grey-blk, silver & bistre (*a*)	35	35
194	**170**	20p grey-black, silver and dull brown (*a*)	50	45
195	**171**	50p grey-black, orange-red and silver (*b*)	1·00	75
196	**172**	£1 grey-black, yellowish green and silver (*b*)	2·00	1·50
197	**173**	£2 grey-black, new blue and silver (*b*)	4·00	2·50
198	**174**	£5 multicoloured (*e*)	10·00	8·50
177/98		Set of 22	19·00	16·00
		First Day Covers (4).		17·00
		Presentation Packs (4). . . .	22·00	
		Set of 22 Gutter Pairs	38·00	

Nos. 177*a*/*b*, 178*a*, 179*a*, 180*a*/*d* and 181*b*/*c* come from special booklet sheets of 40 (80×5) (Nos. 177*a* and 178*a*), 30 (6×5) (Nos. 177*b*, 180*a*/*b*, 180*d* and 181*b*/*c*), 25 (5×5) (No. 179*a*) or 20 (4×5) (No. 180*c*). These were put on sale as complete sheets or separated into strips, folded and either affixed by the selvedge to booklet covers or supplied loose in plastic wallets.

The booklet sheets containing Nos. 177*a*/*b* show either four (No. 177*a*) or three (No. 177*b*) different arrangements of the same stamps.

Printings: (*a*) 13.2.79; (*b*) 5.2.80; (*c*) 6.5.80; (*d*) 24.2.81; (*e*) 22.5.81; (*f*) 2.2.82; (*g*) 4.82; (*h*) 5.82; (*i*) 7.82; (*j*) 11.82; (*k*) 14.3.83; (*l*) 6.83.

Cylinder Nos.: 5, 6, 7, 8, 14, 15, 20, 50p, £1, £2 A1–1–1, B1–1–1; others A1–1–1–1, B1–1–1–1

Sheets: ½ to 20p 100 (2 panes 10×5); 50p to £5 50 (2 panes 5×5)

Imprint: 50p top corner, left-hand margin; £1, £2 right-hand corner, bottom margin; £5 bottom corner, right-hand margin; others central margin

Quantities sold: ½p 1,285,162; 1p 1,888,850; 2p 1,249,506; 4p 650,195; 5p 1,110,783; 6p 1,678,775; 7p 1,683,430; 8p 3,059,366; 9p 1,952,892; 10p (No. 186) 484,956; 10p (No. 187) 1,751,126; 11p 711,268; 11½p 351,422; 12p 957,197; 13p 1,459,086; 14p 595,744; 15p 677,289; 20p 960,124; 50p 863,760; £1 537,871; £2 375,786

Withdrawn: 4.2.81 10p (No. 186); 22.7.85 (all other values except £5); 31.12.98 £5

175 Pillar Box and Postmark, 1853, Mail Van and Postmark, 1979

176 Telephone, 1897 and Telex Machine, 1979

Europa. Communications

(Des R. Granger Barrett. Photo Courvoisier)

1979 (8 MAY). *Granite paper. Perf* 11½ (C)

201	**175**	6p multicoloured	30	30
202	**176**	8p multicoloured	30	30
201/2		Set of 2	60	60
		First Day Cover		1·00
		Presentation Pack	1·00	

Cylinder Nos.: Both values A1–1–1–1–1, B1–1–1–1–1

Sheets: 20 (5×4)

Quantities sold: 6p 1,863,564; 8p 2,293,379

Withdrawn: 7.5.80

177 Steam Tram, 1879

178 Electric Tram, 1896

179 Motor Bus, 1911

180 Motor Bus, 1979

184 'Philately'

History of Public Transport

(Photo Courvoisier)

1979 (7 AUG). *Granite paper. Perf* 11½ (C)

203	**177**	6p multicoloured	....	15	15
204	**178**	8p multicoloured	....	20	20
205	**179**	11p multicoloured	....	55	55
206	**180**	13p multicoloured	....	60	60
203/6		*Set of 4*	....	1·25	1·25
		First Day Cover	....		1·50
		Presentation Pack	....	1·50	
		Set of 4 Gutter Pairs	......	2·50	

Cylinder Nos.: 6p A1–1–1–1–1, B1–1–1–1–1; others A1–1–1–1, B1–1–1–1

Sheets: 50 (2 panes 5×5)

Imprint: Central, bottom margin

Quantities sold: 6p 676,046; 8p 981,431; 11p 384,701; 13p 371,882

Withdrawn: 6.8.80

10th Anniversary of Guernsey Postal Administration

(Des R. Granger Barrett. Photo Courvoisier)

1979 (1 OCT). *Granite paper. Perf* 11½ (C)

207	**181**	6p multicoloured	....	15	15
208	**182**	8p multicoloured	....	25	15
209	**183**	13p multicoloured	....	50	55
210	**184**	15p multicoloured	....	60	60
207/10		*Set of 4*	....	1·25	1·25
		First Day Cover	....		1·25
		Presentation Pack	....	1·60	
		Set of 4 Gutter Pairs		2·50	
MS211		120×80 mm. Nos. 207/10	....	1·00	70
		First Day Cover	....		1·50

One copy of a pre-release sample as No. 210, but with a face value of 11p, is known. Such stamps were not sold for postal purposes

Cylinder Nos.: All values A1–1–1–1, B1–1–1–1

Sheets: 50 (2 panes 5×5)

Imprint: Central, bottom margin

Quantities sold: 6p 1,254,914; 8p 1,376,682; 13p 389,524; 15p 386,234; miniature sheet 398,443

Withdrawn: 30.9.80

181 Bureau and Postal Headquarters

182 'Mails and Telegrams'

183 'Parcels'

185 Major-General Le Marchant

186 Admiral Lord De Saumarez

Europa. Personalities

(Des and photo Courvoisier)

1980 (6 MAY). *Granite paper. Perf* 11½ (C)

212	**185**	10p multicoloured	....	45	45
213	**186**	13½p multicoloured	....	55	50
212/13		*Set of 2*	....	1·00	1·00
		First Day Cover	....		1·00
		Presentation Pack	......	1·25	

Cylinder Nos.: Both values A1–1–1–1–1, B1–1–1–1–1, C1–1–1–1–1, D1–1–1–1–1

Sheets: 20 (5×4)

Quantities sold: 10p 2,794,871; 13½p 1,715,880

Withdrawn: 5.5.81

187 Policewoman with Lost Child

188 Police Motorcyclist escorting Lorry

189 Police Dog-handler

60th Anniversary of Guernsey Police Force

(Litho John Waddington Ltd)

1980 (6 MAY). *Perf* 13½×14 (C)

214	**187**	7p multicoloured	20	20
215	**188**	15p multicoloured	55	55
216	**189**	17½p multicoloured	65	65
214/16		*Set of* 3	1·25	1·25
		First Day Cover		1·50
		Presentation Pack	1·50	
		Set of 3 *Gutter Pairs*	2·50	

Plate Nos.: All values 1A, 1B, 1C, 1D (each ×4)
Sheets: 50 (2 panes 5×5)
Imprint: Central, bottom margin
Quantities sold: 7p 907,714; 15p 352,802; 17½p 337,551
Withdrawn: 5.5.81

190

191

192

193

T **190/3** show Golden Guernsey Goats.

Golden Guernsey Goats

(Des P. Lambert. Photo Delrieu)

1980 (5 AUG). *Perf* 13 (C)

217	**190**	7p multicoloured	20	2(
218	**191**	10p multicoloured	30	3!
219	**192**	15p multicoloured	55	4!
220	**193**	17½p multicoloured	65	6(
217/20		*Set of* 4	1·50	1·4(
		First Day Cover		1·4(
		Presentation Pack	1·75	
		Set of 4 *Gutter Pairs*	3·00	

Cylinder Nos.: 7p 598–599–600–601–602–603; 10p 578–580–581–
583; 15p 605–606–607–608–609–610; 17½p 621–622–623–624–
625–626
Sheets: 50 (2 panes 5×5)
Imprint: Bottom margin
Quantities sold: 7p 779,424; 10p 931,214; 15p 364,917; 17½p 329,13:
Withdrawn: 4.8.81

194 'Sark Cottage'

195 'Moulin Huet'

196 'Boats at Sea'

197 'Cow Lane'

198 'Peter le Lievre''

Christmas. Peter le Lievre Paintings

(Photo Courvoisier)

1980 (15 NOV). *Granite paper. Perf* 11½ (C)

221	**194**	7p multicoloured	. . . .	25	20
222	**195**	10p multicoloured	. . . .	35	25
223	**196**	13½p multicoloured	. . . .	40	30
224	**197**	15p multicoloured	. . . .	50	40
225	**198**	17½p multicoloured	. . . .	65	50
221/5		*Set of 5*	. . . .	2·00	1·50
		First Day Cover	. . . .		1·50
		Presentation Pack	. . . . .	2·25	
		Stamp-cards (set of 5)	. . . .	2·00	5·50
		Set of 5 Gutter Pairs	. . . .	4·50	

Cylinder Nos.: All values A1–1–1–1, B1–1–1–1

Sheets: 50 (2 panes 5×5)

Imprint: 15, 17½p top corner, right-hand margin; others right-hand corner, bottom margin

Quantities sold: 7p 1,199,280; 10p 1,159,622; 13½p 397,812; 15p 432,182; 17½p 359,116

Withdrawn: 14.11.81

199 *Polyommatus icarus*

200 *Vanessa atalanta*

201 *Aglais urticae*

202 *Lasiommata megera*

Butterflies

(Photo Harrison)

1981 (24 FEB). *Perf* 14 (C)

226	**199**	8p multicoloured	. . . .	25	25
227	**200**	12p multicoloured	. . . .	40	40
228	**201**	22p multicoloured	. . . .	90	70
229	**202**	25p multicoloured	. . . .	1·00	90
226/9		*Set of 4*	. . . .	2·25	2·00
		First Day Cover	. . . .		2·00
		Presentation Pack	. . . .	2·75	
		Set of 4 Gutter Pairs	. . . . . .	4·50	

Cylinder Nos.: All values 1A, 1B (each ×5)

Sheets: 50 (2 panes 5×5)

Imprint: Right-hand corner, bottom margin

Quantities sold: 8p 986,229; 12p 971,801; 22p 438,478; 25p 438,575

Withdrawn: 23.2.82

203 Sailors paying respect to 'Le Petit Bonhomme Andriou' (rock resembling head of a man)

204 Fairies and Guernsey Lily

Europa. Folklore

(Des C. Abbott. Litho Questa)

1981 (22 MAY). *Perf* 14½ (C)

230	**203**	12p gold, red-brown & cinnamon	45	45
231	**204**	18p gold, indigo and azure	55	55
230/1		*Set of 2*	1·00	1·00
		First Day Cover		1·25
		Presentation Pack	1·40	
		Set of 2 Gutter Pairs	2·00	

Plate Nos.: 12p 1B, 1F, 1G, 1H (each ×3); 18p 1B, 1D, 1F, 1G, 1H (each ×3)

Sheets: 20 (2 panes 5×2)

Imprint: Central, left-hand margin

Quantities sold: 12p 2,516,514; 18p 1,937,023

Withdrawn: 21.5.82

205 Prince Charles

206 Prince Charles and Lady Diana Spencer

207 Lady Diana

208 Royal Family

Royal Wedding

(Des C. Abbott. Litho Questa)

1981 (29 JULY). *Perf* 14½ (C)

232	**205**	8p multicoloured	50	50
		a. Strip of 3. Nos. 232/4	1·50	1·50
233	**206**	8p multicoloured	50	50
234	**207**	8p multicoloured	50	50
235	**205**	12p multicoloured	90	90
		a. Strip of 3. Nos. 235/7	2·75	2·75
236	**206**	12p multicoloured	90	90
237	**207**	12p multicoloured	90	90
238	**208**	25p multicoloured	1·50	1·50
232/8		Set of 7	5·00	5·00
		First Day Cover		5·50
		Presentation Pack	6·00	
		Stamp-cards (set of 7)	3·50	12·00
MS239		104×127 mm. Nos. 232/8. P 14 (C)	6·50	6·50
		First Day Cover		7·00

Plate Nos.: 8p 1A, 1C (each ×6); 12p 1B (×6); 25p 1A (×6)

Sheets: 8p, 12p 60 (6×10) each value in *se-tenant* strips of 3 across sheet, 25p 30 (3×10)

Imprint: Bottom corner, right-hand side margin

Quantities sold: 8p 2,115,103; 12p 2,235,005; 25p 510,608; miniature sheet 432,743

Withdrawn: 28.7.82

209 Sark Launch

210 Britten Norman 'short nose' Trislander Airplane

211 Hydrofoil

212 Herm Catamaran

213 *Sea Trent* (coaster)

Inter-island Transport

(Des and photo Courvoisier)

1981 (25 AUG). *Granite paper. Perf* 11½ (C)

240	**209**	8p multicoloured	20	2
241	**210**	12p multicoloured	40	4
242	**211**	18p multicoloured	60	5
243	**212**	22p multicoloured	75	6
244	**213**	25p multicoloured	90	7
240/4		Set of 5	2·50	2·2
		First Day Cover		2·2
		Presentation Pack	2·75	
		Set of 5 Gutter Pairs	5·00	

Cylinder Nos.: All values A1–1–1–1, B1–1–1–1

Sheets: 50 (2 panes 5×5)

Imprint: Right-hand corner, bottom margin

Quantities sold: 8p 790,215; 12p 785,488; 18p 457,763; 22p 469,31 25p 466,112

Withdrawn: 24.8.82

214 Rifle Shooting

215 Riding

216 Swimming

217 Circuit Construction

International Year for Disabled Persons

(Des P. le Vasseur. Litho Questa)

1981 (17 NOV). *Perf* 14½ (C)

245	**214**	8p multicoloured	20	20
246	**215**	12p multicoloured	35	35
247	**216**	22p multicoloured	65	55
248	**217**	25p multicoloured	75	60
245/8		*Set of 4*	1·75	1·50
		First Day Cover		1·50
		Presentation Pack	2·00	
		Set of 4 Gutter Pairs	3·50	

Plate Nos.: All values 1A, 1B, 1C, 1D, 1E, 1F, 1G, 1H (each ×4)

Sheets: 50 (2 panes 5×5)

Imprint: Foot of right-hand margin on each pane

Quantities sold: 8p 912,908; 12p 910,614; 22p 280,882; 25p 287,725

Withdrawn:16.11.82

218 Jethou

219 Fermain Bay

220 The Terres

221 St. Peter Port

Old Guernsey Prints (2nd series)

(Des, recess and litho De La Rue)

1982 (2 FEB). *Perf* 14×13½ (C)

249	**218**	8p black and pale blue	20	20
250	**219**	12p black & pale turquoise-grn	35	35
251	**220**	22p black and pale yellow-brown	65	65
252	**221**	25p black and pale rose-lilac....	75	75
249/52		*Set of 4*	1·75	1·75
		First Day Cover		2·25
		Presentation Pack	2·00	
		Set of 4 Gutter Pairs	3·50	

Plate Nos.: All values 1A–1A, 1B–1B, 1C–1C, 1D–1D

Sheets: 50 (2 panes 5×5)

Imprint: Left-hand corner, bottom margin

Quantities sold: 8p 350,198; 12p 346,515; 22p 346,661; 25p 244,669

Withdrawn: 1.2.83

222 Sir Edgar MacCulloch (founder-president) and Guille-Allès Library, St. Peter Port

223 Norman Invasion Fleet crossing English Channel, 1066 ('history')

224 H.M.S. *Crescent*, 1793 ('history')

225 Dragonfly ('entomology')

226 Common Snipe caught for Ringing ('ornithology')

227 Samian Bowl 160–200 A.D. ('archaeology')

27

Centenary of La Société Guernesiaise

(Des G. Drummond. Photo Courvoisier)

1982 (28 APR). *Granite paper. Perf* 11½ (C)

253	**222**	8p multicoloured	20	20
254	**223**	13p multicoloured	35	35
255	**224**	20p multicoloured	45	45
256	**225**	24p multicoloured	70	70
257	**226**	26p multicoloured	80	80
258	**227**	29p multicoloured	85	85
253/8		Set of 6	3·00	3·00
		First Day Cover		3·00
		First Day Cover (Nos. 254/5)		1·50
		Presentation Pack	3·50	
		Presentation Pack (Nos. 254/5)	1·75	
		Stamp-cards (set of 6)	1·50	5·50

The 13p and 20p (Nos. 254/5) also include the Europa C.E.P.T. emblem in the designs

Cylinder Nos.: 24p A1–1–1–1, B1–1–1–1, C1–1–1–1; D1–1–1–1; others A1–1–1–1–1; B1–1–1–1–1, C1–1–1–1–1, D1–1–1–1–1

Sheets: 20 (5×4)

Quantities sold: 8p 921,095; 13p 2,820,311; 20p 1,491,351; 24p 315,735; 26p 309,919; 29p 298,761

Withdrawn: 27.4.83

228 Sea Scouts

229 Scouts

230 Cub Scouts

231 Air Scouts

75th Anniversary of Boy Scout Movement

(Des W.L.G. Creative Services Ltd. Litho Questa)

1982 (13 JULY). *Perf* 14½×14 (C)

259	**228**	8p multicoloured	20	25
260	**229**	13p multicoloured	50	50
261	**230**	26p multicoloured	70	70
262	**231**	29p multicoloured	85	80
259/62		Set of 4	2·25	2·25
		First Day Cover		2·50
		Presentation Pack	2·50	
		Set of 4 Gutter Pairs	4·50	

Plate Nos.: 8p 1A, 1B, 1C, 1D (each ×6); others 1A, 1B, 1C, 1D (each ×7)

Sheets: 50 (2 panes 5×5)

Imprint: Bottom corner, right-hand margin

Quantities sold: 8p 796,018; 13p 930,924; 26p 237,958; 29p 233,204

Withdrawn: 12.7.83

232 Midnight Mass

233 Exchanging Gifts

234 Christmas Meal

235 Exchanging Cards

236 Queen's Christmas Message

Christmas

(Des Lynette Hammant. Photo Harrison)

1982 (12 OCT). *Perf* 14½ (C)

263	**232**	8p multicoloured	20	20
		a. Black (Queen's head, value and Inscr) omitted		
264	**233**	13p multicoloured	30	30
265	**234**	24p multicoloured	75	75
266	**235**	26p multicoloured	75	75
267	**236**	29p multicoloured	80	80
263/7		Set of 5	2·50	2·50
		First Day Cover		3·00
		Presentation Pack	3·50	
		Set of 5 Gutter Pairs	5·00	

Cylinder Nos.: All values 1A, 1B (each ×5)

Sheets: 50 (2 panes 5×5)

Imprint: Right-hand corner, bottom margin

Quantities sold: 8p 944,560; 13p 927,844; 24p 227,145; 26p 249,110; 29p 232,323

Withdrawn: 11.10.83

237 Flute Player and Boats

238 Cymbal Player and Tug 'o' war

239 Trumpet Player and Bible Class

240 Drummer and Cadets marching

241 Boys' Brigade Band

Centenary of Boys' Brigade

(Des Sally Stiff. Photo Harrison)

1983 (18 JAN). *Perf* 14 (C)

268	**237**	8p multicoloured	. . . .	25	25
269	**238**	13p multicoloured	. . . .	40	40
270	**239**	24p multicoloured	. . . .	85	85
271	**240**	26p multicoloured	. . . .	90	90
272	**241**	29p multicoloured	. . . .	95	95
268/72		Set of 5	. . . .	3·00	3·00
		First Day Cover	. . . .		3·75
		Presentation Pack	. . . .	3·25	
		Set of 5 Gutter Pairs	. . . . . .	6·00	

Cylinder Nos.: All values 1A, 1B (each ×5)

Sheets: 50 (2 panes 5×5)

Imprint: Bottom margin, right-hand corner

Quantities sold: 8p 671,921; 13p 538,257; 24p 223,069; 26p 234,482; 29p 214,723

Withdrawn: 17.1.84

242 Building Albert Pier Extension, 1850s

243 St. Peter Port Harbour, 1983

244 St. Peter Port, 1680

245 Artist's Impression of Future Development Scheme

Europa. Development of St. Peter Port Harbour

(Des C. Abbott. Photo Courvoisier)

1983 (14 MAR). *Granite paper. Perf* 11½ (C)

273	**242**	13p multicoloured	. . . .	35	35
		a. Horiz pair. Nos. 273/4	. . . .	70	70
274	**243**	13p multicoloured	. . . .	35	35
275	**244**	20p multicoloured	. . . .	75	75
		a. Horiz pair. Nos. 275/6	. . . .	1·50	1·50
276	**245**	20p multicoloured	. . . .	75	75
273/6		Set of 4	. . . .	2·00	2·00
		First Day Cover	. . . .		2·50
		Presentation Pack	. . . .	3·00	

Cylinder Nos.: Both values A1–1–1–1–1, B1–1–1–1–1

Sheets: 20 (4×5). The two designs of each value were printed together, *se-tenant*, in horizontal pairs throughout

Quantities sold: 13p 1,884,714; 20p 1,676,250

Withdrawn: 13.3.84

246 'View at Guernsey'

247 'Children on the Seashore'

248 'Marine, Guernesey'

249 'La Baie du Moulin Huet à travers les Arbres'

250 'Brouillard à Guernesey'

Centenary of Renoir's Visit to Guernsey

(Des and photo Courvoisier)

1983 (6 SEPT). *Granite paper. Perf* 11×11½ (13p) *or* 11½ (*others*), *all comb*

277	**246**	9p multicoloured	25	25
278	**247**	13p multicoloured	45	45
279	**248**	26p multicoloured	80	80
280	**249**	28p multicoloured	1·10	1·10
281	**250**	31p multicoloured	1·25	1·25
277/81		Set of 5	3·50	3·50
		First Day Cover		4·25
		Presentation Pack	4·00	
		Stamp-cards (set of 5)	1·10	5·00
		Set of 5 Gutter Pairs	7·00	

Cylinder Nos.: 13p A1–1–1–1–1, B1–1–1–1–1, C1–1–1–1–1, D1–1–1–1–1; others A1–1–1–1–1, B1–1–1–1–1

Sheets: 40 (2 panes 4×5)

Quantities sold: 9p 547,148; 13p 757,838; 26p 185,045; 28p 219,830; 31p 305,219

Withdrawn: 5.9.84

251 Launching *Star of the West*, 1869, and Capt. J. Lenfestey

252 Leaving St. Peter Port

253 Off Rio Grande Bar

254 Off St. Lucia

255 Map of 1879–80 Voyage

Guernsey Shipping (1st series). **Star of the West (brigantine)**

(Des R. Granger Barrett. Litho Questa)

1983 (15 NOV). *Perf* 14 (C)

282	**251**	9p multicoloured	25	25
283	**252**	13p multicoloured	40	40
284	**253**	26p multicoloured	80	80
285	**254**	28p multicoloured	1·10	1·10
286	**255**	31p multicoloured	1·25	1·25
282/6		Set of 5	3·50	3·50
		First Day Cover		4·00
		Presentation Pack	4·00	
		Set of 5 Gutter Pairs	7·00	

See also Nos. 415/19

Plate Nos.: 26p, 31p 1C, 1D (each ×5); others 1A, 1B (each ×5)

Sheets: 50 (2 panes 5×5)

Imprint: Bottom corner, right-hand margin

Quantities sold: 9p 706,809; 13p 974,736; 26p 236,974; 28p 216,279 31p 218,647

Withdrawn: 14.11.84

256 Dame of Sark as Young Woman

257 German Occupation, 1940–45

258 Royal Visit, 1957

259 Chief Pleas

260 Dame of Sark Rose

Birth Centenary of Sibyl Hathaway, Dame of Sark

(Des Jennifer Toombs. Litho Questa)

1984 (7 FEB). *Perf* 14½ (C)

287	**256**	9p multicoloured	25	25
288	**257**	13p multicoloured	40	45
289	**258**	26p multicoloured	90	90

290	**259**	28p multicoloured	. . . .	95	95
291	**260**	31p multicoloured	. . . .	1·10	1·10
287/91		Set of 5	. . . .	3·25	3·25
		First Day Cover	. . . .		4·00
		Presentation Pack	. . . .	4·00	
		Set of 5 Gutter Pairs	. . . . . .	6·50	

Plate Nos.: 13p 1A, 1B, 1C, 1D (each ×5); others 1A, 1B, 1C, 1D, (each ×7)

Sheets: 50 (2 panes 5×5)

Imprint: Bottom margin, right-hand corner

Quantities sold: 9p 637,566; 13p 836,270; 26p 315,561; 28p 293,716; 31p 270,742

Withdrawn: 6.2.85

261 C.E.P.T. 25th
Anniversary Logo

Europa

(Des J. Larrivière. Litho Questa)

1984 (10 APR). Perf 15×14½ (C)

292	**261**	13p cobalt, dull ultramarine & blk	65	65
293		20½p emerald, deep dull grn & blk	85	85
292/3		Set of 2	1·50	1·50
		First Day Cover		2·25
		Presentation Pack	2·00	

Plate Nos.: Both values 1A, 1B (each ×3)

Sheets: 20 (4×5)

Imprint: Bottom corner, right-hand margin

Quantities sold: 13p 1,680,033; 20½p 903,972

Withdrawn: 9.4.85

262 The Royal Court and
St. George's Flag

263 Castle Cornet and
Union Flag

Links with the Commonwealth

(Des C. Abbott. Litho Questa)

1984 (10 APR). Perf 14×14½ (C)

294	**262**	9p multicoloured	. . . .	40	40
295	**263**	31p multicoloured	. . . .	1·10	1·10
294/5		Set of 2	. . . .	1·50	1·50
		First Day Cover		2·00
		Presentation Pack	2·25	

Plate Nos.: Both values 1A, 1B, 1C, 1D (each ×6)

Sheets: 20 (4×5)

Imprint: Bottom corner, right-hand margin

Quantities sold: 9p 1,419,845, 31p 285,099

Withdrawn: 9.4.85

264 Little Chapel

265 Fort Grey

266 St. Apolline
Chapel

267 Petit Port

268 Little Russel

269 The Harbour, Herm

270 Saints

271 St. Saviour

272 New Jetty (inscr
'Cambridge Berth')

273 Belvoir, Herm

31

GUERNSEY 11ᴾ

274 La Seigneurie, Sark

GUERNSEY 13ᴾ

276 St. Saviour's Reservoir

GUERNSEY 12ᴾ

275 Petit Bot

GUERNSEY 14ᴾ

277 St. Peter Port

GUERNSEY 15ᴾ

278 Havelet

GUERNSEY 16ᴾ

279 Hostel of St. John

GUERNSEY 18ᴾ

280 Le Variouf

GUERNSEY 20ᴾ

281 La Coupee, Sark

GUERNSEY 21ᴾ

282 King's Mills

GUERNSEY 26ᴾ

283 Town Church

GUERNSEY 30ᴾ

284 Grandes Rocques

GUERNSEY 40ᴾ

285 Torteval Church

GUERNSEY 50ᴾ

286 Bordeaux

GUERNSEY £1

287 Albecq

GUERNSEY £2

288 L'Ancresse

Views

(Des C. Abbott. Litho Questa)

1984 (18 SEPT)–**91.** *Perf* 14½ (C)

296	**264**	1p multicoloured (c)	20	10
297	**265**	2p multicoloured (c)	20	10
		a. *Booklet pane. Nos.* 297×2, 299×4, 300×2 *and* 305×2 (d)	2·75	
298	**266**	3p multicoloured (a)	20	10
		a. *Booklet pane. Nos.* 298, 299×2, 306×4 *and* 309×3 (f)	4·00	
299	**267**	4p multicoloured (a)	20	10
		a. *Booklet pane. Nos.* 299×2, 304×3 *and* 307×5	3·50	
		b. *Booklet pane. Nos.* 299, 304 *and* 307, *each* ×5	4·50	
		c. *Booklet pane. Nos.* 299×4, 306b×3 *and* 309c×3 (g) . .	3·75	
		d. *Booklet pane. Nos.* 299, 301, 306b×3 *and* 309d×3 (h) . .	4·25	
		e. *Black ptg double*		
300	**268**	5p multicoloured (c)	20	10
		a. *Booklet pane. Nos.* 300×2, 301×2, 309×3 *and* 310b×3 (j)	4·00	
301	**269**	6p multicoloured (c)	20	15
		a. *Booklet pane. Nos.* 301×4, 308×4 *and* 310×2 (i)	4·25	
		b. *Uncoated paper*		
		c. *Black ptg double*		
302	**270**	7p multicoloured (c)	20	20
303	**271**	8p multicoloured (c)	20	20
304	**272**	9p multicoloured (a)	20	25
		a. *Booklet pane. Nos.* 304×4 *and* 308×6 (b)	4·25	
		b. *Booklet pane. Nos.* 304×2 *and* 308×8 (b)	4·25	
305	**273**	10p multicoloured (a)	25	25
		a. *Booklet pane. Nos.* 305 *and* 308, *each* ×5 (e)	4·25	

06	**274**	11p multicoloured (c)	25	25
		a. Booklet pane. Nos. 306 and 309, each × 5 (f)	4·25	
06b	**275**	12p multicoloured (g)	40	30
		ba. Booklet pane. Nos. 306b and 309c, each ×5	4·25	
		bb. Booklet pane. Nos. 306b and 309d, each ×4 (h)	4·75	
		bc. Black ptg double		
07	**276**	13p multicoloured (a)	30	30
08	**277**	14p multicoloured (a)	30	35
		a. Booklet pane. Nos. 308 and 310, each ×5 (i)	4·75	
		b. Uncoated paper		
09	**278**	15p multicoloured (c)	30	35
		a. Booklet pane. Nos. 309 and 310b, each ×5 (j)	5·75	
		b. Imperf at sides and foot (horiz pair)		
09c	**279**	16p multicoloured (g)	30	35
		ca. Black and red ptgs double . .		
09d	**280**	18p multicoloured (h)	35	40
		da. Black ptg double		
10	**281**	20p multicoloured (a)	50	45
		a. Uncoated paper		
10b	**282**	21p multicoloured (j)	50	45
10c	**283**	26p multicoloured (j)	70	55
		ca. Imperf at sides and foot (horiz pair)	£900	
11	**284**	30p multicoloured (c)	60	65
12	**285**	40p multicoloured (a)	80	85
13	**286**	50p multicoloured (a)	1·00	1·10
14	**287**	£1 multicoloured (a)	2·00	2·10
15	**288**	£2 multicoloured (c)	4·25	4·25
96/315		Set of 25	12·50	12·50
		First Day Covers (5)		17·00
		Presentation Packs (3)	12·50	
		Stamp-cards (set of 25)	4·50	21·00
		Set of 25 Gutter Pairs	25·00	

For 11p, 12p, 15p and 16p stamps in a smaller size see Nos. 298/9a.

Booklet panes Nos. 297a, 298a, 299a/c, 304a/b, 305a, 306a and 306ba have margins all round and were issued, folded and loose, within the booklet covers.

Booklet panes Nos. 299d, 300a, 301a, 306bb, 308a and 309a have the outer edges imperforate on three sides and were also issued loose within the booklet covers.

Nos. 299e, 301c, 306bc and 309da come from an example of booklet pane No. 299d.

Nos. 301b, 308b and 310a come from examples of booklet panes Nos. 301a and 308a.

Printings: (a) 18.9.84; (b) 19.3.85; (c) 23.7.85; (d) 2.12.85; (e) 1.4.86; (f) 30.3.87; (g) 28.3.88; (h) 28.2.89; (i) 27.12.89; (j) 2.4.91

Plate Nos.: All values 1A, 1B, 1C, 1D (each ×5)

Sheets: 1p, 3p, 8p, 12p, 14p, 15p, 18p, 26p, 40p, 100 (2 panes 10×5): others 100 (2 panes 5×10)

Imprint: Bottom, right-hand margin of each pane

Quantities sold: 1p 1,397,906; 2p 1,240,037; 3p 460,949; 4p 478,679; 5p 690,128; 6p 560,950; 7p 302,367; 8p 425,421; 9p 1,959,119; 10p 1,692,125; 11p 1,510,077; 12p 2,837,219; 13p 730,405; 14p 3,925,313; 15p 2,631,599; 16p 1,322,353; 18p 1,398,065; 20p 2,149,053; 21p 1,675,329; 26p 210,575; 30p 790,261; 40p 604,514; 50p 765,831; £1 647,055; £2 666,177

Withdrawn: 21.5.93

289 'A Partridge in a Pear Tree' **290** 'Two Turtle Doves' **291** 'Three French Hens'

292 'Four Colly Birds' **293** 'Five Gold Rings' **294** 'Six Geese a-laying'

295 'Seven Swans a-swimming' **296** 'Eight Maids a-milking' **297** 'Nine Drummers drumming'

298 'Ten Pipers piping' **299** 'Eleven Ladies dancing' **300** 'Twelve Lords a-leaping'

'The Twelve Days of Christmas'

(Des R. Downer. Litho Questa)

1984 (20 NOV). *Perf* 14½ (C)

316	**289**	5p multicoloured		20	20
		a. Sheetlet of 12. Nos. 316/27		2·50	
317	**290**	5p multicoloured		20	20
318	**291**	5p multicoloured		20	20
319	**292**	5p multicoloured		20	20
320	**293**	5p multicoloured		20	20
321	**294**	5p multicoloured		20	20
322	**295**	5p multicoloured		20	20
323	**296**	5p multicoloured		20	20
324	**297**	5p multicoloured		20	20
325	**298**	5p multicoloured		20	20
326	**299**	5p multicoloured		20	20
327	**300**	5p multicoloured		20	20
316/27		Set of 12		2·50	2·50
		First Day Cover			3·00
		Presentation Pack		3·75	

Sheets: 12 (4×3) containing Nos. 316/27 *se-tenant*

Imprint: Bottom, left-hand margin

Quantity sold: 271,168 sheetlets

Withdrawn: 19.11.85

301 Sir John Doyle and Coat of Arms   **302** Battle of Germantown, 1777

303 Reclaiming Braye du Valle, 1806   **304** Mail for Alderney, 1812

150th Death Anniversary of Lieutenant-General Sir John Doyle

(Des E. Stemp. Photo Courvoisier)

1984 (20 NOV). *Granite paper. Perf* 11½ (C)

328	**301**	13p multicoloured		40	40
329	**302**	29p multicoloured		1·00	1·00
330	**303**	31p multicoloured		1·25	1·25
331	**304**	34p multicoloured		1·25	1·25
328/31		Set of 4		3·50	3·00
		First Day Cover			4·00
		Presentation Pack		4·00	
		Set of 4 Gutter Pairs		7·00	

Cylinder Nos.: All values A1–1–1–1–1, B1–1–1–1–1 C1–1–1–1–1, D1–1–1–1–1

Sheets: 50 (2 panes 5×5)

Quantities sold: 13p 642,178; 29p 460,535; 31p 450,051; 34p 465,982

Withdrawn: 19.11.85

Yearbook 1984

1984 (1 DEC). *Comprises Nos.* 287/95, 298/9, 304/5, 307/8 310, 312/14, 316/31 *and* A13/17

	Yearbook		40·00

Withdrawn: 29.3.86

305 Cuckoo Wrasse   **306** Red Gurnard

307 Red Mullet   **308** Mackerel

309 Oceanic Sunfish

Fishes

(Des P. Barrett. Photo Courvoisier)

1985 (22 JAN). *Granite paper. Perf* 11½ (C)

332	**305**	9p multicoloured		40	40
333	**306**	13p multicoloured		60	60
334	**307**	29p multicoloured		1·50	1·10
335	**308**	31p multicoloured		1·50	1·10
336	**309**	34p multicoloured		1·60	1·25
332/6		Set of 5		5·00	4·00
		First Day Cover			5·00
		Presentation Pack		5·25	
		Set of 5 Gutter Pairs		10·00	

Cylinder Nos.: 13p, 29p A1–1–1–1, B1–1–1–1, C1–1–1–1,
D1–1–1–1–1; others A1–1–1–1, B1–1–1–1, C1–1–1–1, D1–1–1–1

Sheets: 50 (2 panes 5×5)

Quantities sold: 9p 465,322; 13p 724,941; 29p 221,392; 31p 174,948;
34p 157,422

Withdrawn: 21.1.86

310 Dove

40th Anniversary of Peace in Europe

(Des C. Abbott. Litho Questa)

1985 (9 MAY). *Perf* 14×14½ (C)

337	**310**	22p multicoloured	1·10	1·10
		First Day Cover		1·50
		Presentation Pack	1·50	
		Gutter Pair	2·25	

Plate Nos.: 1A, 1B, 1C, 1D (each ×4)

Sheets: 50 (2 panes 5×5)

Imprint: Bottom. right-hand margin of each pane

Quantity sold: 246,024

Withdrawn: 8.5.86

311 I.Y.Y. Emblem and
Young People of
Different Races

312 Girl Guides cooking
over Fire

International Youth Year

(Des Suzanne Brehaut (9p), Mary Harrison (31p). Litho
Questa)

1985 (14 MAY). *Perf* 14 (C)

338	**311**	9p multicoloured	40	40
339	**312**	31p multicoloured	1·00	1·00
338/9		*Set of 2*	1·40	1·40
		First Day Cover		2·00
		Presentation Pack (with No.		
		342)	3·25	

Plate Nos.: Both values 1A, 1B, 1C, 1D, 1E, 1F (each ×6)

Sheets: 20 (5×4)

Imprint: Bottom, right-hand margin

Quantities sold: 9p 1,246,421; 31p 264,938

Withdrawn: 13.5.86

313 Stave of Music
enclosing Flags

314 Stave of Music and
Musical Instruments

Europa. European Music Year

(Des Fiona Sloan (14p), Katie Lillington (22p). Litho Questa)

1985 (14 MAY). *Perf* 14×14½ (C)

340	**313**	14p multicoloured	45	40
341	**314**	22p multicoloured	95	1·00
340/1		*Set of 2*	1·40	1·40
		First Day Cover		2·00
		Presentation Pack	2·25	

Plate Nos.: Both values 1A, 1B, 1C, 1D, 1E, 1F (each ×6)

Sheets: 20 (4×5)

Imprint: Bottom, right-hand margin

Quantities sold: 14p 1,742,651; 22p 879,421

Withdrawn: 13.5.86

315 Guide Leader, Girl Guide and
Brownie

75th Anniversary of Girl Guide Movement

(Des Karon Mahy. Litho Questa)

1985 (14 MAY). *Perf* 14 (C)

342	**315**	34p multicoloured	1·50	1·50
		First Day Cover		2·00

Plate Nos.: 1A, 1B, 1C, 1D (each ×6)

Sheets: 20 (5×4)

Imprint: Bottom, right-hand margin

Quantity sold: 182,426

Withdrawn: 13.5.86

316 Santa Claus

317 Lussibruden
(Sweden)

318 King
Balthazar

319 Saint Nicholas (Netherlands)

320 La Befana (Italy)

321 Julenisse (Denmark)

322 Christkind (Germany)

323 King Wenceslas (Czechoslovakia)

324 Shepherd of Les Baux (France)

325 King Caspar

326 Baboushka (Russia)

327 King Melchior

Christmas. Gift-bearers

(Des C. Abbott. Photo Courvoisier)

1985 (19 NOV). *Granite paper. Perf* 12½ (C)

343	**316**	5p multicoloured	40	35
		a. *Sheetlet of* 12. *Nos.* 343/54	4·25	
344	**317**	5p multicoloured	40	35
345	**318**	5p multicoloured	40	35
346	**319**	5p multicoloured	40	35
347	**320**	5p multicoloured	40	35
348	**321**	5p multicoloured	40	35
349	**322**	5p multicoloured	40	35
350	**323**	5p multicoloured	40	35
351	**324**	5p multicoloured	40	35
352	**325**	5p multicoloured	40	35
353	**326**	5p multicoloured	40	35
354	**327**	5p multicoloured	40	35
343/54		Set of 12	4·25	4·00
		First Day Cover		4·00
		Presentation Pack	4·75	

Sheets: 12 (4×3) containing Nos. 343/54 *se-tenant*
Imprint: Central, bottom margin
Quantity sold: 236,937 sheetlets
Withdrawn: 18.11.86

328 'Vraicing'

329 'Castle Corne'

330 'Rocquaine Bay'

331 'Little Russel'

332 'Seaweed-gatherers'

Paintings by Paul Jacob Naftel

(Des and photo Harrison)

1985 (19 NOV). *Perf* 15×14 (C)

355	**328**	9p multicoloured	30	30
356	**329**	14p multicoloured	40	40
357	**330**	22p multicoloured	90	90
358	**331**	31p multicoloured	1·40	1·40
359	**332**	34p multicoloured	1·50	1·50
355/9		Set of 5	4·00	4·00
		First Day Cover		5·50
		Presentation Pack	5·25	
		Set of 5 Gutter Pairs	8·00	

Cylinder Nos.: All values 1A, 1B (each ×5)

Sheets: 50 (2 panes 5×5)

Imprint: Left-hand margin of each pane

Quantities sold: 9p 398,472; 14p 452,728; 22p 164,922; 31p 197,422; 34p 173,428

Withdrawn: 18.11.86

36

85 (DEC). *Comprises Nos.* 296/7, 300/3, 306, 309, 311, 315, 332/59 *and* A18/27

	Yearbook	. . . .	60·00

Withdrawn: 31.12.86

33 Squadron off Nargue Island, 1809

334 Battle of the Nile, 1798

35 Battle of St. Vincent, 1797

336 H.M.S. *Crescent* off Cherbourg, 1793

337 Battle of the Saints, 1782

50th Death Anniversary of Admiral Lord De Saumarez

(Des T. Thompson. Photo Courvoisier)

986 (4 FEB). *Granite paper. Perf* 11½ (C)

60	**333**	9p multicoloured	. . . .	40	40
61	**334**	14p multicoloured	. . . .	50	50
62	**335**	29p multicoloured	. . . .	1·25	1·25
63	**336**	31p multicoloured	. . . .	1·40	1·40
64	**337**	34p multicoloured	. . . .	1·40	1·40
60/4		Set of 5	. . . .	4·50	4·00
		First Day Cover			5·50
		Presentation Pack	5·75	
		Set of 5 Gutter Pairs	9·00	

Cylinder Nos.: All values A1–1–1–1–1, B1–1–1–1–1

Sheets: 40 (2 panes 5×4)

Quantities sold: 9p 456,518; 14p 706,727; 29p 157,693; 31p 163,612; 34p 160,724

Withdrawn: 3.2.87

338 Profile of Queen Elizabeth II (after R. Maklouf)

60th Birthday of Queen Elizabeth II

(Des C. Abbott. Litho Questa)

1986 (21 APR). *Perf* 14 (C)

365	**338**	60p multicoloured	. . . .	2·50	2·50
		First Day Cover			3·75
		Presentation Pack	4·00	
		Gutter Pair	. . . .	5·00	

Plate Nos.: 1A, 1B, 1C, 1D (each ×4)

Sheets: 40 (2 panes 5×4)

Imprint: Bottom, right-hand margin of each pane

Quantity sold: 169,661

Withdrawn: 20.4.87

339 Northern Gannet and Nylon Net ('Operation Gannet')

340 Loose-flowered Orchid

341 Guernsey Elm

Europa. Nature and Environmental Protection

(Des P. Newcombe. Photo Courvoisier)

1986 (22 MAY). *Granite paper. Perf* 11½ (C)

366	**339**	10p multicoloured	. . . .	45	45
367	**340**	14p multicoloured	. . . .	75	75
368	**341**	22p multicoloured	. . . .	1·00	1·00
366/8		Set of 3	. . . .	2·00	2·00
		First Day Cover			3·25
		Presentation Pack	3·00	

Cylinder Nos.: All values A1–1–1–1–1–1, B1–1–1–1–1–1,
C1–1–1–1–1–1, D1–1–1–1–1–1

Sheets: 20 (4×5)

Quantities sold: 10p 977,212; 14p 995,123; 22p 662,565

Withdrawn: 21.5.87

342   Prince Andrew and Miss Sarah Ferguson   **343**

Royal Wedding

(Des C. Abbott. Litho Questa)

1986 (23 JULY). *Perf* 14 (14p) *or* 13½×14 (34p), *both comb*

369	**342**	14p multicoloured	75	75
370	**343**	34p multicoloured	1·50	1·50
369/70		Set of 2	2·25	2·25
		First Day Cover..........		3·50
		Presentation Pack........	3·25	
		Set of 2 Gutter Pairs......	4·50	

Plate Nos.: Both values 1A, 1B, 1C, 1D, 1E, 1F (each ×5)

Sheets: 50 (2 panes 5×5)

Imprint: Bottom right-hand margin of each pane

Quantities sold: 14p 292,018; 34p 199,297

Withdrawn: 22.7.87

344 Bowls   **345** Cricket

346 Squash   **347** Hockey

348 Swimming   **349** Shooting

Sport in Guernsey

(Des R. Goldsmith. Litho Questa)

1986 (24 JULY). *Perf* 14½ (C)

371	**344**	10p multicoloured	30	30
372	**345**	14p multicoloured	50	50
		a. Black (face value, inscr etc.) printed treble		
373	**346**	22p multicoloured	75	75
		a. Black (face value, inscr etc.) printed treble		
374	**347**	29p multicoloured	1·25	1·25
375	**348**	31p multicoloured	1·40	1·40
376	**349**	34p multicoloured	1·50	1·50
371/6		Set of 6	5·00	5·00
		First Day Cover..........		5·75
		Presentation Pack........	6·00	
		Set of 6 Gutter Pairs......	10·00	

Plate Nos.: All values 1A, 1B, 1C, 1D (each ×4)

Sheets: 50 (2 panes 5×5)

Imprint: Bottom right-hand margin of each pane

Quantities sold: 10p 399,897; 14p 985,699; 22p 212,203; 29p 141,882; 31p 157,751; 34p 156,164

Withdrawn: 23.7.87

350 Guernsey Museum and Art Gallery, Candie Gardens   **351** Fort Grey Maritime Museum

352 Castle Cornet   **353** National Trust of Guernsey Folk Museum

Centenary of Guernsey Museums

(Des Sir Hugh Casson. Litho Questa)

1986 (18 NOV). *Perf* 14 (C)

377	**350**	14p multicoloured	....	60	60
378	**351**	29p multicoloured	....	1·10	1·10
379	**352**	31p multicoloured	....	1·10	1·10
380	**353**	34p multicoloured	....	1·40	1·40
377/80		Set of 4	....	3·75	3·75
		First Day Cover	....		5·50
		Presentation Pack	....	4·75	
		Set of 4 Gutter Pairs	......	7·50	

Plate Nos.: All values 1A, 1B, 1C, 1D (each ×5)

Sheets: 50 (2 panes 5×5)

Imprint: Bottom right-hand margin of each pane

Quantities sold: 14p 796,879; 29p 141,974; 31p 159,326; 34p 144,074

Withdrawn: 17.11.87

354 'While Shepherds Watched their Flocks by Night'

355 'In the Bleak Mid-Winter'

356 'O Little Town of Bethlehem'

357 'The Holly and the Ivy'

358 'O Little Christmas Tree'

359 'Away in a Manger'

360 'Good King Wenceslas'

361 'We Three Kings of Orient Are'

362 'Hark the Herald Angels Sing'

363 'I Saw Three Ships'

364 'Little Donkey'

365 'Jingle Bells'

Christmas. Carols

(Des Wendy Bramall. Photo Courvoisier)

1986 (18 NOV). *Granite paper. Perf* 12½ (C)

381	**354**	6p multicoloured	....	40	40
		a. Sheetlet of 12. Nos. 381/92		4·00	
382	**355**	6p multicoloured	....	40	40
383	**356**	6p multicoloured	....	40	40
384	**357**	6p multicoloured	....	40	40
385	**358**	6p multicoloured	....	40	40
386	**359**	6p multicoloured	....	40	40
387	**360**	6p multicoloured	....	40	40
388	**361**	6p multicoloured	....	40	40
389	**362**	6p multicoloured	....	40	40
390	**363**	6p multicoloured	....	40	40
391	**364**	6p multicoloured	....	40	40
392	**365**	6p multicoloured	....	40	40
381/92		Set of 12	....	4·00	4·00
		First Day Cover	....		4·25
		Presentation Pack		4·25	

Sheets: 12 (4×3) containing Nos. 381/92 *se-tenant*

Imprint: Central bottom margin

Quantity sold: 226,119 sheetlets

Withdrawn: 17.11.87

Yearbook 1986

1986 (DEC). *Comprises Nos.* 360/92 *and* A28/31

	Yearbook	40·00

Withdrawn: 31.12.87

366a Duke of Richmond and Map of 1787
(*illustration reduced to half size*)

Bicentenary of Duke of Richmond's Survey of Guernsey

(Des J. Cooter. Litho Questa)

1987 (10 FEB). *Perf* 14½×14 (C)
MS393 134×103 mm **366a** 14p, 29p, 31p,
34p multicoloured . . . . 4·00   4·00
First Day Cover . . . .   5·00
Presentation Pack . . . . 5·00

Quantity sold: 176,655
Withdrawn: 9.2.88

367 Post Office
Headquarters

368 Architect's Elevation
of Post Office
Headquarters

369 Guernsey Grammar
School

370 Architect's Elevation
of Grammar School

Europa. Modern Architecture

(Des R. Reed. Litho Cartor)

1987 (5 MAY). *Perf* 13×13½ (C)

394	**367**	15p multicoloured		55	55
		a. Horiz pair. Nos. 394/5		1·10	1·10
395	**368**	15p multicoloured		55	55
396	**369**	22p multicoloured		80	80
		a. Horiz pair. Nos. 396/7		1·75	1·75
397	**370**	22p multicoloured		80	80
394/7		Set of 4		2·50	2·50
		First Day Cover			4·00
		Presentation Pack	4·00		

Plate Nos.: Both values 1A, 1B, 1C, 1D (each ×4)

Sheets: 20 (4 x 5), the two designs for each value printed together, *se-tenant*, in horizontal pairs throughout the sheets

Quantities sold: 15p 595,661 pairs; 22p 434,886 pairs

Withdrawn: 4.5.88

Coil Stamps

(Photo Harrison)

1987 (15 MAY)–**88**. *As Nos.* 306, 306b, 309 *and* 309c, *but smaller.* 22×18 mm (11p, 16p) *or* 18×22 mm (12p, 15p). *Perf* 14×14½ (11p, 16p) *or* 14½×14 (12p, 15p), all comb

398	**274**	11p multicoloured (a)		30	40
398a	**275**	12p multicoloured (b)		25	25
399	**278**	15p multicoloured (a)		45	55
399a	**279**	16p multicoloured (b)		35	35
398/9a		Set of 4		1·40	1·25
		First Day Covers (2)			3·00

Printings: (a) 15.5.87; (b) 28.3.88

Coils: Rolls of 1000 (a) or 500 (b)

Withdrawn: 26.12.89 11p, 15p; 22.5.92 12p, 16p

371 Sir Edmund Andros
and La Plaiderie,
Guernsey

372 Governor's Palace,
Virginia

373 Governor Andros in
Boston

374 Map of New Amsterdam
(New York), 1661

350th Birth Anniversary of Sir Edmund Andros (colonial administrator)

(Des B. Sanders. Photo Courvoisier)

1987 (7 JULY). *Granite paper. Perf 12 (C)*

400	371	15p multicoloured	45	45
401	372	29p multicoloured	1·00	1·00
402	373	31p multicoloured	1·10	1·10
403	374	34p multicoloured	1·40	1·40
400/3		Set of 4	3·50	3·50
		First Day Cover		4·25
		Presentation Pack	4·50	
		Set of 4 Gutter Pairs	7·00	

Cylinder Nos.: All values A1–1–1–1–1–1, B1–1–1–1–1–1

Sheets: 40 (2 panes 5×4)

Quantities sold: 15p 707,843; 29p 129,462; 31p 136,308; 34p 129,527

Withdrawn: 6.7.88

375 The Jester's Warning to Young William

376 Hastings Battlefield

377 Norman Soldier with Pennant

378 William the Conqueror

379 Queen Matilda and Abbaye aux Dames, Caen

380 William's Coronation Regalia and Halley's Comet

900th Death Anniversary of William the Conqueror

(Des P. le Vasseur. Litho Cartor)

1987 (9 SEPT). *Perf 13½×14 (C)*

404	375	11p multicoloured	45	35
405	376	15p multicoloured	50	50
		a. Horiz pair. Nos. 405/6	1·00	1·00
406	377	15p multicoloured	50	50
407	378	22p multicoloured	80	75
		a. Horiz pair. Nos. 407/8	1·60	1·50

408	379	22p multicoloured	80	80
409	380	34p multicoloured	1·25	1·25
404/9		Set of 6	4·00	3·75
		First Day Cover		5·00
		Presentation Pack	5·00	
		Set of 4 Gutter Pairs	8·00	

Plate Nos.: All values 1A, 1B, 1C, 1D (each ×4)

Sheets: 40 (2 panes 4×5), The two designs for the 15p and 22p values were printed together, *se-tenant*, in horizontal pairs throughout the sheets

Imprint: Bottom, left-hand margin

Quantities sold: 11p 639,904; 15p 241,572 pairs; 22p 142,718 pairs; 34p 131,655

Withdrawn: 8.9.88

381 John Wesley preaching on the Quay, Alderney

382 Preaching at Mon Plaisir, St. Peter Port

383 Preaching at Assembly Rooms

384 Wesley and La Ville Baudu (early Methodist meeting place)

385 Wesley and first Methodist Chapel, St. Peter Port

Bicentenary of John Wesley's Visit to Guernsey

(Des R. Geary. Litho Questa)

1987 (17 NOV). *Perf 14½ (C)*

410	381	7p multicoloured	30	30
411	382	15p multicoloured	45	45
412	383	29p multicoloured	1·25	1·25
413	384	31p multicoloured	1·25	1·25
414	385	34p multicoloured	1·25	1·25
410/14		Set of 5	4·00	4·00
		First Day Cover		5·00
		Presentation Pack	5·00	
		Set of 5 Gutter Pairs	8·00	

Plate Nos.: All values 1A, 1B, 1C, 1D (each ×4)

Sheets: 50 (2 panes 5×5)

Imprint: Bottom, right-hand margin of each pane

Quantities sold: 7p 762,772; 15p 887,797; 29p 122,322; 31p 126,591; 34p 125,863

Withdrawn: 16.11.88

Yearbook 1987

1987 (DEC). *Comprises Nos.* **MS**393/7, 400/14 *and* A32/6

               Yearbook . . . . 40·00

Withdrawn: 31.12.88

386 *Golden Spur* off St. Sampson Harbour

387 Entering Hong Kong Harbour

388 Anchored off Macao

389 In China Tea Race

390 *Golden Spur* and Map showing Voyage of 1872–74

Guernsey Shipping (2nd series). Golden Spur (full- rigged ship)

(Des R. Granger Barrett. Litho B.D.T.)

1988 (9 FEB). *Perf* 13½ (C)

415	**386**	11p multicoloured	. . . .	35	35
416	**387**	15p multicoloured	. . . .	50	50
417	**388**	29p multicoloured	. . . .	1·25	1·25
418	**389**	31p multicoloured	. . . .	1·25	1·25
419	**390**	34p multicoloured	. . . .	1·25	1·25
415/19		*Set of 5*	. . . .	4·00	4·00
		First Day Cover			5·00
		Presentation Pack	5·00	
		Set of 5 Gutter Pairs	8·00	

Plate Nos.: All values 1A, 1B, 1C, 1D (each ×4)

Sheets: 50 (2 panes 5×5)

Imprint: Central, side margins of each pane

Quantities sold: 11p 213,291; 15p 214,048; 29p 136,246; 31p 143,815; 34p 141,177

Withdrawn: 8.2.89

391 Rowing Boat and Bedford 'Rascal' Mail Van

392 Rowing Boat and Vickers Viscount 800 Mail Plane

393 Postman on Bicycle and Horse-drawn Carriages, Sark

394 Postmen on Bicycles and Carriage

Europa. Transport and Communications

(Des C. Abbott. Litho Questa)

1988 (10 MAY). *Perf* 14½ (C)

420	**391**	16p multicoloured	. . . .	60	60
		a. Horiz pair. Nos. 420/1	. . . .	1·25	1·25
421	**392**	16p multicoloured	. . . .	60	60
422	**393**	22p multicoloured	. . . .	95	95
		a. Horiz pair. Nos. 422/3	. . . .	1·90	1·90
423	**394**	22p multicoloured	. . . .	95	95
420/3		*Set of 4*	. . . .	2·75	2·75
		First Day Cover			4·00
		Presentation Pack	3·75	

Plate Nos.: Both values 1A, 1B, 1C, 1D (each ×5)

Sheets: 20 (4×5), the two designs for each value printed together, *se-tenant*, in horizontal pairs throughout the sheets

Imprint: Top, right-hand margin

Quantities sold: 16p 387,699 pairs: 22p 359,634 pairs

Withdrawn: 9.5.89

395 Frederick Corbin Lukis and Lukis House, St Peter Port

396 Natural History Books and Reconstructed Pot

397 Lukis directing Excavation of Le Creux ès Faies and Prehistoric Beaker

398 Lukis House Observatory and Garden

399 Prehistoric Artifacts

Birth Bicentenary of Frederick Corbin Lukis (archaeologist)

(Des Wendy Bramall. Photo Courvoisier)

1988 (12 JULY). *Granite paper. Perf 12½ (C)*

424	**395**	12p multicoloured	40	40
425	**396**	16p multicoloured	50	50
426	**397**	29p multicoloured	1·10	1·10
427	**398**	31p multicoloured	1·25	1·25
428	**399**	34p multicoloured	1·25	1·25
424/8		*Set of 5*	4·00	4·00
		First Day Cover		5·25
		Presentation Pack	5·00	
		Set of 5 Gutter Pairs	8·00	

Cylinder Nos.: 29p, 34p, A1–1–1–1, B1–1–1–1, C1–1–1–1, D1–1–1–1; others A1–1–1–1–1, B1–1–1–1–1, C1–1–1–1–1, D1–1–1–1–1

Sheets: 40 (2 panes 5×4)

Quantities sold: 12p 634,056; 16p 510,713; 29p 120,538; 31p 114,192; 34p 134,358

Withdrawn: 11.7.89

400 Powerboats and Westland Wessex Rescue Helicopter off Jethou

401 Powerboats in Gouliot Passage

402 Start of Race at St. Peter Port

403 Admiralty Chart showing Course

World Offshore Powerboat Championships

(Des and photo Courvoisier)

1988 (6 SEPT). *Granite paper. Perf 12 (C)*

429	**400**	16p multicoloured	60	60
430	**401**	30p multicoloured	1·10	1·10
431	**402**	32p multicoloured	1·25	1·25
432	**403**	35p multicoloured	1·50	1·50
429/32		*Set of 4*	4·00	4·00
		First Day Cover		5·00
		Presentation Pack	5·00	
		Set of 4 Gutter Pairs	8·00	

Cylinder Nos.: 16p, 32p A1–1–1–1, B1–1–1–1; 30p, 35p C1–1–1–1, D1–1–1–1

Sheets: 40 (2 panes 5×4) 16p, 30p or (2 panes 4×5) others

Quantities sold: 16p 582,190; 30p 127,183; 32p 166,804; 35p 128,552

Withdrawn: 5.9.89

404 Joshua Gosselin and Herbarium

405 Hares-tail Grass

406 Dried Hares-tail Grass

407 Variegated Catchfly

408 Dried Variegated
Catchfly

409 Rock Sea
Lavender

Bicentenary of *Joshua Gosselin's* **Flora Sarniensis**

(Des M. Oxenham. Litho Cartor)

1988 (15 NOV). *Perf* 13½×14 (C)

433	**404**	12p multicoloured	40	40
434	**405**	16p multicoloured	55	55
		a. *Horiz pair. Nos.* 434/5	1·10	1·10
435	**406**	16p multicoloured	55	55
436	**407**	23p multicoloured	80	80
		a. *Horiz pair. Nos.* 436/7	1·60	1·60
437	**408**	23p multicoloured	80	80
438	**409**	35p multicoloured	1·40	1·40
433/8		*Set of* 6	4·00	4·00
		First Day Cover		5·00
		Presentation Pack	4·25	
		Set of 4 *Gutter Pairs*	8·00	

Plate Nos.: All values 1A, 1B, 1C, 1D (each ×4)

Sheets: 40 (2 panes 4×5), the two designs for the 16p and 23p values printed together, *se-tenant*, in horizontal pairs throughout the sheets

Imprint: Bottom, left-hand margin

Quantities sold: 12p 562,702; 16p 378,679 pairs; 23p 141,152 pairs; 35p 133,205

Withdrawn: 14.11.89

410 Coutances
Cathedral,
France

411 Interior of
Notre Dame
du Rosaire
Church,
Guernsey

412 Stained
Glass, St.
Sampson's
Church,
Guernsey

413 Dol-de-
Bretagne
Cathedral,
France

414 Bishop's
Throne, Town
Church,
Guernsey

415 Winchester
Cathedral

416 St. John's
Cathedral,
Portsmouth

417 High Altar,
St. Joseph's
Church,
Guernsey

418 Mont Saint-
Michel,
France

419 Chancel, Vale
Church,
Guernsey

420 Lychgate,
Forest
Church,
Guernsey

421 Marmoutie
Abbey,
France

Christmas. *Ecclesiastical Links*

(Des R. Downer. Litho Questa)

1988 (15 NOV). *Perf* 14½ (C)

439	**410**	8p multicoloured	35	35
		a. *Sheetlet of* 12. *Nos.* 439/50	3·75	
440	**411**	8p multicoloured	35	35
441	**412**	8p multicoloured	35	35
442	**413**	8p multicoloured	35	35
443	**414**	8p multicoloured	35	35
444	**415**	8p multicoloured	35	35
445	**416**	8p multicoloured	35	35
446	**417**	8p multicoloured	35	35
447	**418**	8p multicoloured	35	35
448	**419**	8p multicoloured	35	35
449	**420**	8p multicoloured	35	35
450	**421**	8p multicoloured	35	35
439/50		*Set of* 12	3·75	3·75
		First Day Cover		4·50
		Presentation Pack	4·00	

Sheets: 12 (4×3) containing Nos. 439/50 *se-tenant*
Imprint: Bottom, left-hand margin
Quantity sold: 185,939 sheetlets
Withdrawn: 14.11.89

earbook 1988

988 (DEC). *Comprises Nos. 306b, 309c and 415/50*
Yearbook . . . . 26·00

Withdrawn: 31.12.89

22 Lé Cat (Tip Cat)

423 Girl with Cobo Alice Doll

424 Lé Colimachaön (hopscotch)

uropa. Children's Toys and Games

(Des P. le Vasseur. Litho Cartor)

989 (28 FEB). *Perf 13½* (C)

51	**422**	12p multicoloured	40	40
52	**423**	16p multicoloured	60	60
53	**424**	23p multicoloured	1·25	1·25
51/3		Set of 3	2·00	2·00
		First Day Cover		2·75
		Presentation Pack	2·75	

Plate Nos.: All values 1A, 1B, 1C (each ×4)
Sheets: 20 (4×5)
Imprint: Top, right-hand margin
Quantities sold: 12p 839,111; 16p 829,156; 23p 448,761
Withdrawn: 27.2.90

425 Outline Map of Guernsey

Coil Stamps

(Photo Harrison)

1989 (3 APR–27 DEC). *No value expressed. Perf 14½×14* (C)

454	**425**	(–) ultramarine (b)	40	40
455		(–) emerald (a)	60	60
454/5		Set of 2	1·00	1·00
		First Day Covers (2)		2·00

No. 454 is inscribed 'MINIMUM BAILIWICK POSTAGE PAID' and No. 455 'MINIMUM FIRST CLASS POSTAGE TO UK PAID'. They were originally sold at 14p. and 18p., but this was changed in line with postage rate rises.

Printings: (a) 3.4.89; (b) 27.12.89
Coils: Rolls of 500, numbered on the reverse of every fifth stamp
Withdrawn: 30.6.96

426 Guernsey Airways De Havilland D.H.86 Dragon Express and Mail Van

427 Supermarine Southampton II Flying Boat at Mooring

428 B.E.A. De Havilland D.H.89 Dragon Rapide

429 Short S.25 Sunderland Mk V Flying Boat taking off

430 Air U.K. British Aerospace BAe 146

431 Avro Shackleton M.R.3

50th Anniversaries of Guernsey Airport (Nos. 456, 458 and 460) and 201 Squadron's Affiliation with Guernsey (Nos. 457, 459 and 461)

(Des N. Foggo. Litho B.D.T.)

1989 (5 MAY). *Perf 13½* (C)

456	**426**	12p multicoloured	50	40
		a. Booklet pane. No. 456×6	2·00	
457	**427**	12p multicoloured	50	40
458	**428**	18p multicoloured	75	75
		a. Booklet pane. No. 458×6	3·00	
459	**429**	18p multicoloured	75	75

460	**430**	35p multicoloured	1·25	1·25
		a. Booklet pane. No. 460×6	6·00	
461	**431**	35p multicoloured	1·25	1·25
456/61		Set of 6	4·50	4·50
		First Day Cover..........		5·50
		Presentation Pack........	5·00	
		Set of 6 Gutter Pairs	9·00	

Each booklet pane has margins all round with text printed at the foot.

Plate Nos.: All values 1A, 1B (each ×4)

Sheets: 50 (2 panes 5×5)

Imprint: Central, side margins of each pane

Quantities sold: No. 456, 461,080; No. 457, 362,154; No. 458, 436,134; No. 459, 388,274; No. 460, 172,574; No. 461, 149,134

Withdrawn: 4.5.90

432 'Queen Elizabeth II' (June Mendoza)

Royal Visit

(Des A. Theobald. Litho B.D.T.)

1989 (23 MAY). *Perf* 15×14

462	**432**	30p multicoloured	1·25	1·25
		First Day Cover..........		2·25
		Presentation Pack........	2·25	

Plate Nos.: 1A (×5)

Sheets: 20 (5×4)

Imprint: Top, right-hand margin

Quantity sold: 180,900

Withdrawn: 22.5.90

433 *Ibex* at G.W.R. Terminal, St. Peter Port

434 *Great Western* (paddle-steamer) in Little Russel

435 *St. Julien* passing Casquets Light

436 *Roebuck* off Portland

437 *Antelope* and Boat Train on Weymouth Quay

Centenary of Great Western Railway Steamer Service to Channel Islands

(Des C. Jaques. Litho B.D.T.)

1989 (5 SEPT). *Perf* 13½ (C)

463	**433**	12p multicoloured	30	30
464	**434**	18p multicoloured	65	65
465	**435**	29p multicoloured	90	90
466	**436**	34p multicoloured	1·25	1·25
467	**437**	37p multicoloured	1·40	1·40
463/7		Set of 5	4·00	4·00
		First Day Cover..........		5·50
		Presentation Pack........	4·75	
		Set of 5 Gutter Pairs	8·00	
MS468	115×117 mm. Nos. 463/7........		4·00	4·00
		First Day Cover..........		5·50

Plate Nos.: All values 1A, 1B (each ×4)

Sheets: 50 (2 panes 5×5)

Imprint: Central, side margins of each pane

Quantities sold: 12p 741,870; 18p 666,520; 29p 223,570; 34p 202,570; 37p 209,020; miniature sheet 74,127

Withdrawn 4.9.90

438 Two-toed Sloth

439 Capuchin Monkey

440 White-lipped Tamarin

441 Common Squirrel-Monkey

442 Common Gibbon

0th Anniversary of Guernsey Zoological Trust. Animals f the Rainforest

(Des Anne Farncombe. Litho Cartor)

989 (17 NOV). *Perf* 13½×14 (C)

69	**438**	18p multicoloured	1·10	90
		a. *Strip of* 5. *Nos.* 469/73	5·00	
70	**439**	29p multicoloured	1·10	90
71	**440**	32p multicoloured	1·10	90
72	**441**	34p multicoloured	1·10	90
73	**442**	37p multicoloured	1·10	90
69/73		*Set of* 5	5·00	4·00
		First Day Cover		5·50
		Presentation Pack	6·00	
		Stamp-cards (*set of* 5)	1·00	6·00

Plate Nos.: 1B (×4)

Sheets: 20 (5×4). Nos. 469/73 were printed in *se-tenant* strips of 5 across the sheet

Imprint: Top, right-hand margin

Quantities sold: 148,505 of each value

Withdrawn: 16.11.90

Christmas. Christmas Tree Decorations

(Des Wendy Bramall. Litho B.D.T.)

1989 (17 NOV). *Perf* 13 (C)

474	**443**	10p multicoloured	35	35
		a. *Sheetlet of* 12. *Nos.* 474/85	3·75	
475	**444**	10p multicoloured	35	35
476	**445**	10p multicoloured	35	35
477	**446**	10p multicoloured	35	35
478	**447**	10p multicoloured	35	35
479	**448**	10p multicoloured	35	35
480	**449**	10p multicoloured	35	35
481	**450**	10p multicoloured	35	35
482	**451**	10p multicoloured	35	35
483	**452**	10p multicoloured	35	35
484	**453**	10p multicoloured	35	35
485	**454**	10p multicoloured	35	35
474/85		*Set of* 12	3·75	3·75
		First Day Cover		4·75
		Presentation Pack	4·50	

Sheets: 12 (3×4) containing Nos. 474/85 *se-tenant*

Imprint: Central, left-hand margin

Quantity sold: 229,000 sheetlets

Withdrawn: 16.11.90

Yearbook 1989

1989 (17 NOV). *Comprises Nos.* 309d, 451/3, 456/62, **MS**468/85 *and* A37/41

Yearbook . . . . 28·00

Withdrawn: 31.12.90

43 Star

444 Fairy

445 Candles

46 Bird

447 Present

448 Carol-singer

455 Sark Post Office, *c* 1890

49 Christmas Cracker

450 Bauble

451 Christmas Stocking

456 Sark Post Office, 1990

52 Bell

453 Fawn

454 Church

457 Arcade Post Office Counter, St. Peter Port, *c* 1840

458 Arcade Post Office
Counter, St. Peter Port,
1990

Europa. Post Office Buildings

(Des C. Abbott. Litho Enschedé)

1990 (27 FEB). *Perf* 13½×14 (C)

486	**455**	20p blackish brown, sepia and pale cinnamon	60	60
487	**456**	20p multicoloured	60	60
488	**457**	24p blackish brown, sepia and pale cinnamon	75	75
489	**458**	24p multicoloured	75	75
486/9		Set of 4	2·50	2·50
		First Day Cover..........		3·50
		Presentation Pack........	3·50	

Plate Nos.: Nos. 486 and 488 1A, 1B (each ×3); Nos. 487 and 489 1A, 1B (each ×4)

Sheets: 20 (4×5)

Imprint: Central, side margins

Quantities sold: No. 486, 498,819; No. 487, 398,759; No. 488, 495,039; No. 489, 397,759

Withdrawn: 26.2.91

459 Penny Black and Mail
Steamer off St. Peter
Port, 1840

460 Penny Red, 1841, and
Pillar Box of 1853

461 Bisected 2d., 1940,
and German Army
Band

462 Regional 3d., 1958,
and Guernsey
Emblems

463 Independent Postal
Administration 1½d., 1969,
and Queue at Main Post
Office

150th Anniversary of the Penny Black

(Des Jennifer Toombs. Litho Questa)

1990 (3 MAY). *Perf* 14 (C)

490	**459**	14p multicoloured	45	45
491	**460**	20p multicoloured	60	60
492	**461**	32p multicoloured	1·00	90
493	**462**	34p multicoloured	1·10	95
494	**463**	37p multicoloured	1·10	1·00
490/4		Set of 5	3·75	3·50
		First Day Cover..........		5·00
		Presentation Pack........	4·50	
		Set of 5 Gutter Pairs......	7·50	
MS495		151×116 mm. Nos. 490/4........	4·00	3·75
		First Day Cover..........		5·00

No. **MS**495 also commemorates 'Stamp World London 90' International Stamp Exhibition. It was reissued on 24 August 1990 overprinted for 'NEW ZEALAND 1990' and sold at this international stamp exhibition in Auckland.

Plate Nos.: 14p, 32p 1A, 1B (each ×4); 20p, 34p 1C, 1D (each ×4); 37p 1A, 1B, 1C, 1D (each ×4)

Sheets: 50 (2 panes 5×5)

Imprint; Bottom corner, right-hand margin of each pane

Quantities sold: 14p 687,850; 20p 662,800; 32p 155,960; 34p 143,850; 37p 174,830; miniature sheet 92,701

Withdrawn: 2.5.91

464 Lt. Philip Saumarez
writing Log Book

465 Anson's Squadron
leaving Portsmouth,
1740

466 Ships at St. Catherine's
Island, Brazil

467 H.M.S. *Tryal* (sloop) dismasted, Cape Horn, 1741

468 Crew of H.M.S. *Centurion* on Juan Fernandez

250th Anniversary of Anson's Circumnavigation

(Des R. Granger Barrett. Litho Enschedé)

1990 (26 JULY). *Perf* 13½×14 (C)

496	**464**	14p multicoloured	....	45	45
497	**465**	20p multicoloured	....	60	60
498	**466**	29p multicoloured	....	1·00	90
499	**467**	34p multicoloured	....	1·10	95
500	**468**	37p multicoloured	....	1·10	1·00
496/500		Set of 5	....	3·75	3·50
		First Day Cover	....		5·00
		Presentation Pack	....	4·50	
		Stamp-cards (set of 5)	....	2·00	5·00
		Set of 5 Gutter Pairs	......	7·50	

Plate Nos.: 14p, 20p, 29p 1A, 1B, 1C, 1D (each ×4); 34p, 37p 1A, 1B (each ×4)

Sheets: 50 (2 panes 5×5)

Imprint: Central, side margins of each pane

Quantities sold: 14p 985,850; 20p 481,400; 29p 162,800; 34p 143,500; 37p 138,450

Withdrawn: 25.7.91

469 Grey Seal and Pup

470 Bottle-nosed Dolphin

471 Basking Shark

472 Common Porpoise

Marine Life

(Des Jennifer Toombs. Litho Questa)

1990 (16 OCT). *Perf* 14½ (C)

501	**469**	20p multicoloured	....	60	60
502	**470**	26p multicoloured	....	1·10	1·10
503	**471**	31p multicoloured	....	1·25	1·25
504	**472**	37p multicoloured	....	1·50	1·50
501/4		Set of 4	....	4·00	4·00
		First Day Cover	....		4·50
		Presentation Pack	....	4·50	
		Set of 4 Gutter Pairs	......	8·00	

Plate Nos.: 20p, 31p 1A, 1B (each ×4); 26p, 37p 1C, 1D (each ×4)

Sheets: 50 (2 panes 5×5)

Imprint: Top, right-hand margin of each pane

Quantities sold: 20p 973,900; 26p 478,200; 31p 328,650; 37p 303,600

Withdrawn: 15.10.91

473 Blue Tit and Great Tit

474 Snow Bunting

475 Common Kestrel

476 Common Starling

477 Greenfinch

478 European Robin

479 Winter Wren

480 Barn Owl

481 Mistle Thrush

482 Grey Heron

483 Chaffinch

484 Common Kingfisher

Christmas. Winter Birds

(Des Wendy Bramall, Litho B.D.T.)

1990 (16 OCT). *Perf* 13 (C)

505	**473**	10p multicoloured	. . . .	40	40
		a. *Sheetlet of* 12. *Nos.* 505/16		4·50	
506	**474**	10p multicoloured	. . . .	40	40
507	**475**	10p multicoloured	. . . .	40	40
508	**476**	10p multicoloured	. . . .	40	40
509	**477**	10p multicoloured	. . . .	40	40
510	**478**	10p multicoloured	. . . .	40	40
511	**479**	10p multicoloured	. . . .	40	40
512	**480**	10p multicoloured	. . . .	40	40
513	**481**	10p multicoloured	. . . .	40	40
514	**482**	10p multicoloured	. . . .	40	40
515	**483**	10p multicoloured	. . . .	40	40
516	**484**	10p multicoloured	. . . .	40	40
505/16		*Set of* 12	. . . .	4·50	4·50
		First Day Cover	. . . .		4·75
		Presentation Pack	. . . .	4·75	

Sheets: 12 (3×4) containing Nos. 505/16 *se-tenant*

Imprint: Central, left-hand margin

Quantity sold: 237,602 sheetlets

Withdrawn: 15.10.91

Yearbook 1990

1990 (1 NOV). *Comprises Nos.* 486/9, **MS**495, 496/516, A12a *and* A42/6

Yearbook . . . . 24·00

Withdrawn: 31.12.91

485 Air Raid and 1941
½d. Stamp

486 1941 1d. Stamp

487 1944 2½d Stamp

50th Anniversary of First Guernsey Stamps

(Des C. Abbott. Litho B.D.T.)

1991 (18 FEB). *Perf* 13½ (C)

517	**485**	37p multicoloured	. . . .	1·25	1·2
		a. *Booklet pane. Nos.* 517/19		4·00	
518	**486**	53p multicoloured	. . . .	1·60	1·6
519	**487**	57p multicoloured	. . . .	1·60	1·6
517/19		*Set of* 3	. . . .	4·00	4·0
		First Day Cover	. . . .		5·5
		Presentation Pack	. . . .	5·00	
		Set of 3 *Gutter Pairs*	. . . . . .	8·00	

Booklet pane No. 517a exists in three versions, which differ in the order of the stamps from left to right and in the information printed on the pane margins.

Plate Nos.: 37p, 53p 1A, 1B (each ×4); 57p 1A, 1B, 1C, 1D (each ×4

Sheets: 40 (2 panes 5×4)

Imprint: Central, side margins

Quantities sold: 37p 260,015; 53p 250,536; 57p 250,219

Withdrawn: 17.2.92

488 Visit of Queen Victori
to Guernsey, and
Discovery of Neptune
1846

489 Visit of Queen
Elizabeth II and Prince
Philip to Sark, and
Flight of 'Sputnik' (1st
artificial satellite,
1957)

490 Maiden Voyage of
Sarnia (ferry), and
'Vostok 1' (first
manned space flight),
1961

491 Cancelling Guernsey
Stamps, and First
Manned Landing on
Moon, 1969

(Des Jennifer Toombs. Litho Enschedé)

1991 (30 APR). *Perf* 13½×14 (C)

20	**488**	21p multicoloured	65	65
21	**489**	21p multicoloured	65	65
22	**490**	26p multicoloured	90	75
23	**491**	26p multicoloured	90	75
20/3		*Set of 4*	2·75	2·50
		First Day Cover		4·00
		Presentation Pack	3·75	

Plate Nos.: Both values 1A, 1B (each ×5)

Sheets: 20 (4×5)

Imprint: Central, side margins

Quantities sold: No. 520, 390,924; No. 521, 390,834; No. 522, 369,404; No. 523, 370,244

Withdrawn: 29.4.92

492 Children in Guernsey Sailing Trust 'GP14' Dinghy

493 Guernsey Regatta

494 Lombard Channel Islands' Challenge Race

495 Rolex Swan Regatta

496 Old Gaffers' Association Gaff-rigged Yacht

Centenary of Guernsey Yacht Club

(Des C. Abbott. Litho B.D.T.)

1991 (2 JULY). *Perf* 14 (C)

524	**492**	15p multicoloured	50	50
525	**493**	21p multicoloured	80	80
526	**494**	26p multicoloured	90	90
527	**495**	31p multicoloured	1·00	1·00
528	**496**	37p multicoloured	1·25	1·25
524/8		*Set of 5*	4·00	4·00
		First Day Cover		4·75
		Presentation Pack	4·75	
		Set of 5 Gutter Pairs	8·00	
MS529		163×75 mm. Nos. 524/8	4·00	4·00
		First Day Cover		4·75

Stamps from No. **MS**529 show 'GUERNSEY' and the face value in yellow.

Plate Nos.: 37p 1C, 1D (each ×5); others 1A, 1B (each ×5)

Sheets: 50 (2 panes 5×5)

Imprint: Top corner, right-hand margin of each pane

Quantities sold: 15p 711,043; 21p 708,743; 26p 188,894; 31p 158,938; 37p 138,543; miniature sheet 81,012

Withdrawn: 1.7.92

497 Pair of Oystercatchers

498 Three Turnstones

499 Dunlins and Turnstones

500 Curlew and Turnstones

501 Ringed Plover with Chicks

502 Gull, Sea Campion and Sea Radish

503 Yellow Horned Poppy

504 Pair of Stonechats, Hare's Foot Clover and Fennel

505 Hare's Foot Clover, Fennel and Slender Oat

506 Sea Kale on Shore

Nature Conservation. L'Eree Shingle Bank Reserve

(Des Wendy Bramall. Litho Questa)

1991 (15 OCT). *Perf* 14½ (C)

530	**497**	15p multicoloured	60	40
		a. *Horiz strip of* 5. *Nos.* 530/4	3·00	
531	**498**	15p multicoloured	60	40
532	**499**	15p multicoloured	60	40
533	**500**	15p multicoloured	60	40
534	**501**	15p multicoloured	60	40
535	**502**	21p multicoloured	60	50
		a. *Horiz strip of* 5. *Nos.* 535/9	3·00	
536	**503**	21p multicoloured	60	50
537	**504**	21p multicoloured	60	50
538	**505**	21p multicoloured	60	50
539	**506**	21p multicoloured	60	50
530/9		Set of 10	5·50	4·00
		First Day Cover		5·50
		Presentation Pack	6·00	
		Stamp-cards (set of 10)	2·00	6·25

Plate Nos.: Both values 1A, 1B, 1C, 1D (each ×4)

Sheets: 20 (5×4), the five designs for each value printed together, *se-tenant*, in horizontal strips throughout the sheets.

Imprint: Bottom, left-hand margin

Quantities sold: 15p 270,830 strips; 21p 272,198 strips

Withdrawn: 14.10.92

507 'Rudolph the Red-nosed Reindeer' (Melanie Sharpe)

508 'Christmas Pudding' (James Quinn)

509 'Snowman' (Lisa Guille)

510 'Snowman in Top Hat' (Jessica Ede-Golightly)

511 'Robins and Christmas Tree' (Sharon Le Page)

512 'Shepherds and Angels' (Anna Coquelin)

513 'Nativity' (Claudine Lihou)

514 'Three Wise Men' (Jonathan Le Noury)

515 'Star of Bethlehem and Angels' (Marcia Mahy)

516 'Christmas Tree' (Laurel Garfield)

517 'Santa Claus' (Rebecca Driscoll)

518 'Snowman and Star' (Ian Lowe)

Christmas. Children's Paintings

(Litho B.D.T.)

1991 (15 OCT). *Perf* 13½×13 (C)

540	**507**	12p multicoloured	35	3
		a. *Sheetlet of* 12. *Nos.* 540/51	4·00	
541	**508**	12p multicoloured	35	3
542	**509**	12p multicoloured	35	3
543	**510**	12p multicoloured	35	3
544	**511**	12p multicoloured	35	3
545	**512**	12p multicoloured	35	3
546	**513**	12p multicoloured	35	3
547	**514**	12p multicoloured	35	3
548	**515**	12p multicoloured	35	3
549	**516**	12p multicoloured	35	3
550	**517**	12p multicoloured	35	3
551	**518**	12p multicoloured	35	3
540/51		Set of 12	4·00	4·0
		First Day Cover		5·5
		Presentation Pack	4·75	

Sheets: 12 (3×4) containing Nos. 540/51 *se-tenant*

Imprint: Central, left-hand margin

Quantity sold: 192,203 sheetlets

Withdrawn: 14.10.92

1991 (1 NOV). *Comprises Nos. 310b/c, 517/51, A12b and 547/51*

              Yearbook . . . . 30·00

Withdrawn: 31.12.92

519 Queen Elizabeth II in 1952

520 In 1977

521 In 1986

522 In 1991

40th Anniversary of Accession

(Des C. Abbott. Litho Questa)

1992 (6 FEB). *Perf* 14 (C)

552	**519**	23p multicoloured	70	70
553	**520**	28p multicoloured	75	75
554	**521**	33p multicoloured	85	85
555	**522**	39p multicoloured	1·10	1·10
552/5		Set of 4	3·00	3·00
		First Day Cover		4·75
		Presentation Pack	4·00	
		Set of 4 Gutter Pairs	6·00	

Plate Nos.: All values 1A, 1B (each ×6)

Sheets: 50 (2 panes 5×5)

Quantities sold: 23p 773,200; 28p 479,095; 33p 212,446; 39p 219,900

Withdrawn: 5.2.93

523 Christopher Columbus

524 Examples of Columbus's Signature

525 *Santa Maria*

526 Map of First Voyage

Europa. 500th Anniversary of Discovery of America by Columbus

(Des R. Ollington. Litho Walsall)

1992 (6 FEB). *Perf* 13½×14 (C)

556	**523**	23p multicoloured	60	60
557	**524**	23p multicoloured	60	60
558	**525**	28p multicoloured	1·10	1·10
559	**526**	28p multicoloured	1·10	1·10
556/9		Set of 4	3·00	3·00
		First Day Cover		3·75
		Presentation Pack	4·00	
MS560		157×77 mm. Nos. 556/9	3·00	3·00
		First Day Cover		4·00

No. **MS**560 was reissued on 22 May 1992 overprinted for 'WORLD COLUMBIAN STAMP EXPO 92' and sold at this international stamp exhibition in Chicago.

Plate Nos.: All values 1A, 1B, 1C (each ×4)

Sheets: 20 (4×5)

Imprint: Bottom, right-hand margin

Quantities sold: No. 556, 543,672; No. 557, 575,633; No. 558, 363,124; No. 559, 364,684; miniature sheet 157,166

Withdrawn: 5.2.93

527a Guernsey Calves

150th Anniversary of Royal Guernsey Agricultural and Horticultural Society

(Des R. Goldsmith. Litho Questa)

1992 (22 MAY). *Sheet* 93×71 *mm. Perf* 14 (C)

MS561 **527***a* 75p multicoloured	2·00	2·00
First Day Cover		3·25
Presentation Pack	3·25	

Quantity sold: 142,549
Withdrawn: 21.5.93

528 *Stephanotis floribunda*

529 Potted Hydrangea

530 Stock

531 Anenomes

532 Gladiolus

533 *Asparagus plumosus, Gypsophila paniculata*

534 Guernsey Lily

535 Enchantment Lily

536 Clematis 'Freckles'

537 Alstroemeria

538 Standard Carnation

539 Standard Rose

540 Spray Rose

541 Mixed Freesia

542 Standard Rose

543 Iris 'Ideal'

544 Freesia 'Pink Glow'

545 Lisianthus

546 Spray Chrysanthemum

547 Spray Carnation

548 Single Freesia

549 Floral Arrangement

550 Chelsea Flower Show Exhibit

551 'Floral Fantasia' (exhibit)

54

orticultural Exports

(Des R. Gorringe. Litho Walsall (Nos. 572a, 572ba, 574a, 575a, 576b and 577a), Questa (No. 576a), Cartor (No. 582a) or B.D.T. (others))

992 (22 MAY)–**97.** *Perf* 14 (£1, £2) *or* 13 (*others*), *all comb*

52	**528**	1p multicoloured (b)	10	10
63	**529**	2p multicoloured (b)	10	10
64	**530**	3p multicoloured (a)	10	10
65	**531**	4p multicoloured (a)	10	10
66	**532**	5p multicoloured (a)	15	15
67	**533**	6p multicoloured (b)	15	15
68	**534**	7p multicoloured (b)	20	20
69	**535**	8p multicoloured (b)	20	20
70	**536**	9p multicoloured (b)	20	25
71	**537**	10p multicoloured (a)	25	25
72	**538**	16p multicoloured (a)	35	35
		a. *Perf* 14 (ab)	50	50
		ab. *Lavender ptg double*		
		ac. *Booklet pane. Nos. 572a×5*		
		and 574a×3 (a)	3·50	
		ad. *Booklet pane of 8 (b)*	3·25	
72b	**539**	18p multicoloured (e)	45	45
		ba. *Perf* 14	45	45
		bb. *Booklet pane of 8*	3·50	
73	**540**	20p multicoloured (a)	50	50
74	**541**	23p multicoloured (a)	55	55
		a. *Perf* 14	60	60
		ab. *Brownish grey ptg double* . .		
		ac. *Booklet pane of 8*	4·25	
75	**542**	24p multicoloured (b)	60	60
		a. *Perf* 14	60	60
		ab. *Booklet pane of 8*	4·25	
76	**543**	25p multicoloured (c)	60	60
		a. *Perf* 14½×15	60	60
		ab. *Booklet pane of 4*	2·50	
76b	**544**	26p multicoloured (e)	60	60
		ba. *Perf* 14	60	60
		bb. *Booklet pane of 4*	2·75	
77	**545**	28p multicoloured (b)	65	65
		a. *Perf* 14	65	65
		ab. *Booklet pane of 4*	2·75	
78	**546**	30p multicoloured (b)	70	70
79	**547**	40p multicoloured (a)	1·00	1·00
80	**548**	50p multicoloured (a)	1·25	1·25
81	**549**	£1 multicoloured (a)	2·50	2·50
82	**550**	£2 multicoloured (b)	4·50	4·50
82a	**551**	£3 multicoloured (d)	6·00	6·25
62/82a		*Set of 24*	19·50	20·00
		First Day Covers (5)		23·00
		Presentation Packs (3)	21·00	
		Stamp-cards (set of 24)	5·00	27·00
		Set of 24 Gutter Pairs	40·00	

Nos. 572a, 572ba, 574a, 575a, 576a, 576ba and 577a were only issued in booklets with the upper and lower edges of the anes imperforate.

For No. 581 in miniature sheets see Nos. **MS**644 and **MS**681.

Printings: (a) 22.5.92; (b) 2.3.93; (c) 18.2.94; (d) 24.1.96; (e) 2.1.97, each with appropriate imprint date.

Plate Nos.: £1 1A, 1B (each ×8); £3 1A, 1B, 1C, 1D (each ×5); others 1A, 1B, 1C, 1D (each ×6)

Sheets: 1p, 2p, 3p, 4p, 5p, 6p, 7p, 8p, 9p, 10p, 18p, 20p, 40p 100 (2 panes 10×5); 16p, 23p, 24p, 25p, 26p, 28p, 30p, 50p (2 panes 5×10); £1, £2, £3 50 (2 panes 5×5)

Imprints: 1p, 2p, 3p, 4p, 5p, 6p, 7p, 8p, 9p, 10p, 18p, 20p, 40p, £1, £2 left-hand corner, top and bottom margin; £3 central, side margins; others top of side margin.

Withdrawn: 31.8.99 1p to £2

552 Building the Ship

553 Loading the Cargo

554 Ship at Sea

555 Ship under Attack

556 Crew swimming Ashore

"Operation Asterix" (excavation of Roman ship)

(Des Studio Legrain. Litho Cartor)

1992 (18 SEPT). *Perf* 13 (C)

583	**552**	16p multicoloured	45	45
		a. *Booklet pane. Nos. 583/7*		
		plus label	3·50	
584	**553**	23p multicoloured	60	60
585	**554**	28p multicoloured	80	80
586	**555**	33p multicoloured	95	95
587	**556**	39p multicoloured	1·10	1·10
583/7		*Set of 5*	3·50	3·50
		First Day Cover		4·75
		Presentation Pack	4·00	
		Set of 5 Gutter Pairs	7·00	

Booklet pane No. 583a has margins all round and exists with marginal inscriptions in either English, French, Italian or German.

Plate Nos.: All values 1A, 1B, 1C, 1D (each ×4)

Sheets: 50 (2 panes 5×5)

Imprint: Central, side margins

Quantities sold: 16p 904,428; 23p 743,228; 28p 308,091; 33p 281,941; 39p 291,841

Withdrawn: 17.9.93

557 Tram No. 10 decorated for Battle of Flowers

558 Tram No. 10 passing Hougue a la Perre

559 Tram No. 1 at St. Sampsons

560 First Steam Tram at St. Peter Port, 1879

561 Last Electric Tram, 1934

Guernsey Trams

(Des A. Peck. Litho Enschedé)

1992 (17 NOV). *Perf* 13½ (C)

588	**557**	16p multicoloured	45	45
589	**558**	23p multicoloured	60	60
590	**559**.	28p multicoloured	80	80
591	**560**	33p multicoloured	95	95
592	**561**	39p multicoloured	1·10	1·10
588/92		*Set of* 5	3·50	3·50
		First Day Cover		4·75
		Presentation Pack	4·00	
		Set of 5 Gutter Pairs	7·00	

Plate Nos.: 39p 1A, 1B, 1C, 1D (each ×6); others 1A, 1B (each ×6)

Sheets: 50 (2 panes 5×5)

Imprint: Central, side margins of each pane

Quantities sold: 16p 366,400; 23p 282,520; 28p 181,670; 33p 130,920; 39p 156,170

Withdrawn: 16.11.93

562 Man in Party Hat

563 Girl and Christmas Tree

564 Woman and Balloons

565 Mince Pies and Champagne

566 Roast Turkey

567 Christmas Pudding

568 Christmas Cake

569 Fancy Cakes

570 Cheese

571 Nuts

572 Ham

573 Chocolate Log

Christmas. Seasonal Fayre

(Des Wendy Bramall. Litho B.D.T.)

1992 (17 NOV). *Perf* 13 (C)

593	**562**	13p multicoloured	35	3
		a. Sheetlet of 12. *Nos.* 593/604	4·00	
		ab. Gold ptg double		
594	**563**	13p multicoloured	35	3
595	**564**	13p multicoloured	35	3
596	**565**	13p multicoloured	35	3
597	**566**	13p multicoloured	35	3
598	**567**	13p multicoloured	35	3
599	**568**	13p multicoloured	35	3
600	**569**	13p multicoloured	35	3
601	**570**	13p multicoloured	35	3
602	**571**	13p multicoloured	35	3
603	**572**	13p multicoloured	35	3
604	**573**	13p multicoloured	35	3
593/604		*Set of* 12	4·00	4·0
		First Day Cover		5·0
		Presentation Pack	4·50	

Sheets: 12 (3×4) containing Nos. 593/604 *se-tenant*, forming composite design showing family during Christmas meal

Imprint: Central, left-hand margin

Quantity sold: 183,550 sheetlets

Withdrawn: 16.11.93

Yearbook 1992

1992 (18 NOV). *Comprises Nos.* 552/61, 564/6, 571/4, 579/8 583/604, A12c *and* A52/5

Yearbook	32·00

Withdrawn: 31.12.93

24 GUERNSEY   **574** Rupert Bear, Bingo and Dog

RUPERT & FRIENDS

574a Rupert and Friends
(*illustration reduced. Actual size* 116×97 *mm*)

Rupert Bear and Friends (cartoon characters created by Mary and Herbert Tourtel)

(Des J. Harold. Litho Walsall)

1993 (2 FEB). *Perf* 13½×13 (C)

605	**574**	24p multicoloured	1·00	1·00
		First Day Cover		2·00
		Gutter Pair	2·00	

MS606 116×97 mm. **574a** 16p Airplane and castle; 16p Professor's servant and Autumn Elf; 16p Algy Pug; 16p Baby Badger on sledge; 24p Bill Badger, Willie Mouse, Reggie Rabbit and Podgy playing in snow; 24p Type **574**; 24p The Balloonist avoiding Gregory on toboggan; 24p Tiger Lily and Edward Trunk .... 5·00 5·00

	a. Black ptg double		
	First Day Cover		5·50
	Presentation Pack (*Nos. 605/6*)	6·50	

The 24p values in No. **MS**606 are as Type **574**; the 16p designs are smaller, each 25½×26 mm.

Plate Nos.: 24p 1A, 1B (each ×4)
Sheets: 50 (2 panes 5×5)
Imprint: Top left-hand margin of each pane
Quantities sold: 24p 523,690; miniature sheet 107,258
Withdrawn: 1.2.94

24 GUERNSEY

575 Tapestry by Kelly Fletcher

24 GUERNSEY

576 'Le Marchi a Paissaon' (etching and aquatint, Sally Reed)

28 GUERNSEY

577 'Red Abstract' (painting, Molly Harris)

28 GUERNSEY

578 'Dress Shop, King's Road' (painting, Damon Bell)

Europa. Contemporary Art

(Des B. Bell. Litho Enschedé)

1993 (7 MAY). *Perf* 13½×14 (C)

607	**575**	24p multicoloured	....	80	80
608	**576**	24p multicoloured	....	80	80
609	**577**	28p multicoloured	....	90	90
610	**578**	28p multicoloured	....	90	90
607/10		Set of 4	....	3·00	3·00
		First Day Cover	....		3·50
		Presentation Pack	....	3·25	

Plate Nos.: 24p (No. 607) 1A, 1B, 1C, 1D (each ×5); others 1A, 1B (each ×5)
Sheets: 20 (4×5)
Imprint: Central, side margins
Quantities sold: No. 607, 289,838; No. 608, 292,450; No. 609, 283,627; No. 610, 280,150
Withdrawn: 6.5.94

16 GUERNSEY

579 Arrest of Guernsey Parliamentarians, Fermain Bay

580 Parliamentary Ships attacking Castle Cornet

581 Parliamentary Captives escaping

582 Castle Cannon firing at St. Peter Port

583 Surrender of Castle Cornet, 19 December 1651

350th Anniversary of Siege of Castle Cornet

(Des C. Abbott. Litho Questa)

1993 (7 MAY). *Perf* 14½×14 (C)

611	**579**	16p multicoloured	40	40
612	**580**	24p multicoloured	65	65
613	**581**	28p multicoloured	85	85
614	**582**	33p multicoloured	95	95
615	**583**	39p multicoloured	1·10	1·10
611/15		*Set of* 5	3·50	3·50
		First Day Cover		4·25
		Presentation Pack	4·00	
		Set of 5 *Gutter Pairs*	7·25	
MS616	203×75 mm. Nos. 611/15		3·50	3·50
		First Day Cover		4·25

Plate Nos.: All values 1A, 1B (each ×5)

Sheets: 40 (2 panes 4×5)

Imprint: Central, right-hand margin

Quantities sold: 16p 253,310; 24p 289,408; 28p 125,877; 33p 124,981; 39p 125,761; miniature sheet 184,308

Withdrawn: 6.5.94

584 Playing Cards

585 Fountain Pens

586 Envelope-folding Machine

587 Great Britain 1855 4d Stamp

588 Thomas de la Rue and Mauritius £1 Banknote

Birth Bicentenary of Thomas de la Rue (printer)

(Des J. Stephenson. Litho (16, 24, 28p) or recess (33, 39p) Enschedé)

1993 (27 JULY). *Perf* 13½ (C)

617	**584**	16p multicoloured	40	4
		a. *Booklet pane of 4 with margins all round*	1·50	
618	**585**	24p multicoloured	65	6
		a. *Booklet pane of 4 with margins all round*	2·25	
619	**586**	28p multicoloured	80	8
		a. *Booklet pane of 4 with margins all round*	3·00	
620	**587**	33p carmine-lake	95	9
		a. *Booklet pane of 4 with margins all round*	3·25	
621	**588**	39p blackish green	1·10	1·1
		a. *Booklet pane of 4 with margins all round*	3·75	
617/21		*Set of* 5	3·50	3·5
		First Day Cover		4·2
		Presentation Pack	4·00	
		Set of 5 *Gutter Pairs*	7·25	

Plate Nos.: 16p, 24p 1A×4; 28p 1A, 1B (each ×4); 33p, 39p 1A

Sheets: 50 (2 panes 5×5)

Imprint: Central, side margins of each pane

Quantities sold: 16p 465,736; 24p 452,982; 28p 111,030; 3 113,299; 39p 119,548

Withdrawn: 26.7.94

589 'The Twelve Pearls'

590 'Healing Rays'

591 'Hand of God over the Holy City'

592 'Wing and Seabirds' (facing left)

593 'Christ the Healer'

594 'Wing and Seabirds' (facing right)

595 'The Young Jesus in the Temple'

596 'The Raising of Jairus' Daughter'

597 'Suffer Little Children to come unto Me'

598 'Pilgrim's Progress'

599 'The Light of the World'

600 'Raphael, Archangel of Healing, with Tobias'

Christmas. Stained Glass Windows by Mary-Eily de Putron from Chapel of Christ the Healer

(Des Jennifer Toombs. Litho B.D.T.)

1993 (2 NOV). *Perf* 13 (C)

622	**589**	13p multicoloured	....	45	45
		a. Sheetlet. Nos. 622/33	....	4·00	
623	**590**	13p multicoloured	....	45	45
624	**591**	13p multicoloured	....	45	45
625	**592**	13p multicoloured	....	45	45
626	**593**	13p multicoloured	....	45	45
627	**594**	13p multicoloured	....	45	45
628	**595**	13p multicoloured	....	45	45
629	**596**	13p multicoloured	....	45	45
630	**597**	13p multicoloured	....	45	45
631	**598**	13p multicoloured	....	45	45
632	**599**	13p multicoloured	....	45	45
633	**600**	13p multicoloured	....	45	45
622/33		Set of 12	....	4·00	4·00
		First Day Cover	....		4·25
		Presentation Pack	....	4·25	

Sheets: 12 (3×4) containing Nos. 622/33 *se-tenant*
Imprint: Central, left-hand margin
Quantity sold: 150,594 sheetlets
Withdrawn: 1.11.94

Yearbook 1993

1993 (2 NOV). *Comprises Nos.* 562/3, 567/70, 575, 577/8, 582, 605/33, A12*d*/*e and* A56/9

Yearbook .... 38·00

Withdrawn: 30.12.94

601 Les Fouaillages (ancient burial ground)

602 Mounted Celtic Warrior

603 Jars, Arrow Heads and Stone Axe from Les Fouaillages

59

604 Sword, Spear Head and
Torque from King's
Road Burial

Europa. Archaeological Discoveries

(Des Miranda Schofield. Litho Cartor)

1994 (18 FEB). *Perf* 13½ (C)

634	**601**	24p multicoloured	. . . .	60	60
635	**602**	24p multicoloured	. . . .	60	60
636	**603**	30p multicoloured	. . . .	80	80
637	**604**	30p multicoloured	. . . .	80	80
634/7		*Set of* 4	. . . .	2·50	2·50
		First Day Cover			2·75
		Presentation Pack		2·75	

Some sheets of No. 635 were overprinted with the 'Hong
Kong '94' emblem on the left margin for sale at this philatelic
exhibition.

Plate Nos.: All values 1A

Sheets: 10 (2×5) with large inscribed margin at left

Quantities sold: No. 634, 241,910; No. 635, 241,943; No. 636,
237,126; No. 637, 232,797; 'Hong Kong '94' margin opt 31,124
sheets.

Withdrawn: 17.2.95

605*a* Canadian Supermarine Spitfires Mk V over Normandy
Beaches

50th Anniversary of D-Day

(Des N. Trudgian. Litho B.D.T.)

1994 (6 JUNE). *Sheet* 93×71 *mm. Perf* 14 (C)

MS638	**605***a*	£2 multicoloured	5·00	5·00
		First Day Cover		5·00
		Presentation Pack	5·25	

Quantity sold: 156,793

Withdrawn: 5.6.95

606 Peugeot 'Type 3',   **607** Mercedes 'Simplex',
1894   1903

608 Humber Tourer, 1906   **609** Bentley Sports Tourer,
1936

610 MG TC Midget, 1948

Centenary of First Car in Guernsey

(Des R. Ollington. Litho B.D.T.)

1994 (19 JULY). *Perf* 14½×14 (C)

639	**606**	16p multicoloured	. . . .	45	45
		a. Booklet pane of 4 with			
		margins all round		1·75	
640	**607**	24p multicoloured	. . . .	70	70
		a. Booklet pane of 4 with			
		margins all round		2·75	
641	**608**	35p multicoloured	. . . .	1·00	1·00
		a. Booklet pane of 4 with			
		margins all round		4·00	
642	**609**	41p multicoloured	. . . .	1·10	1·10
		a. Booklet pane of 4 with			
		margins all round		4·25	
643	**610**	60p multicoloured	. . . .	1·75	1·75
		a. Booklet pane of 4 with			
		margins all round		6·50	
639/43		*Set of* 5	. . . .	4·50	4·50
		First Day Cover			5·00
		Presentation Pack		4·75	
		Set of 5 *Gutter Pairs*		9·00	

Plate Nos.: 60p 1A, 1B, 1C, 1D (each ×5); others 1A, 1B (each ×5)

Sheets: 50 (2 panes 5×5)

Imprint: Central, side margins of each pane

Quantities sold: 16p 279,325; 24p 238,478; 35p 114,668; 41p
116,567; 60p 117,435

Withdrawn: 18.7.95

510a Floral Arrangement
(*illustration reduced. Actual size* 110×90 *mm*)

Philakorea '94' International Stamp Exhibition, Seoul

(Des R. Gorringe and M. Whyte. Litho Cartor)

1994 (16 AUG). *Sheet* 110×90 *mm containing stamp as No. 581 with changed imprint date. Perf* 13 (C)

MS644	**610a**	£1 multicoloured	2·50	2·50
		First Day Cover		2·75
		Presentation Pack	2·75	

Quantity sold: 78,679
Withdrawn: 15.8.95

611 *Trident* (Herm Ferry)

612 Handley Page HPR-7 Super Dart Herald of Channel Express

613 Britten Norman Trislander G-JOEY of Aurigny Air Services

614 *Bon Marin de Serk* (Sark Ferry)

615 Map of Bailiwick

25th Anniversary of Guernsey Postal Administration

(Des A. Copp. Litho Questa)

1994 (1 OCT). *Perf* 14 (C)

645	**611**	16p multicoloured	....	35	35
646	**612**	24p multicoloured	....	55	55
647	**613**	35p multicoloured	....	75	75
648	**614**	41p multicoloured	....	85	85
649	**615**	60p multicoloured	....	1·40	1·40
645/9		Set of 5	....	3·75	3·75
		First Day Cover	....		4·25
		Presentation Pack	....	4·25	
		Stamp-cards (set of 5)	....	1·00	4·75
MS650	150×100 mm. Nos 645/9		....	3·75	3·75
		First Day Cover	....		4·25

Plate Nos.: All values 1A (×5)
Sheets: 20 (5×4)
Imprint: Central, left-hand margin
Quantities sold: 16p 218,779; 24p 188,946; 35p 129,318; 41p 139,622; 60p 140,855; miniature sheet 63,283
Withdrawn: 30.9.95

616 Dolls' House

617 Doll

618 Teddy in Bassinette

619 Sweets in Pillar Box and Playing Cards

620 Spinning Top

621 Building Blocks

622 Rocking Horse

623 Teddy Bear

624 Tricycle

625 Wooden
Duck

626 Hornby Toy
Locomotive

627 Ludo Game

Christmas. Bygone Toys

(Des A. Peck. Litho B.D.T.)

1994 (1 OCT). *Perf* 13 (C)

651	**616**	13p multicoloured	....	40	40
		a. *Sheetlet. Nos.* 651/6	......	2·00	
652	**617**	13p multicoloured	....	40	40
653	**618**	13p multicoloured	....	40	40
654	**619**	13p multicoloured	....	40	40
655	**620**	13p multicoloured	....	40	40
656	**621**	13p multicoloured	....	40	40
657	**622**	24p multicoloured	....	75	75
		a. *Sheetlet. Nos.* 657/62	....	3·50	
658	**623**	24p multicoloured	....	75	75
659	**624**	24p multicoloured	....	75	75
660	**625**	24p multicoloured	....	75	75
661	**626**	24p multicoloured	....	75	75
662	**627**	24p multicoloured	....	75	75
651/62		*Set of* 12	....	5·00	5·00
		First Day Covers (2)	......		5·50
		Presentation Pack	....	5·50	

Sheets: 6 (3×2) containing Nos. 650/5 or 656/61 *se-tenant*

Imprint: Bottom, left-hand margin

Quantities sold: 13p 192,937 sheetlets; 24p 133,416 sheetlets

Withdrawn: 30.9.95

Yearbook 1994

1994 (1 OCT). *Comprises Nos.* 576, 634/62 *and* A60/76

Yearbook (softback) ...... 38·00

Yearbook (hardback) ...... 60·00

Withdrawn: 29.12.95

628 Seafood 'Face'

629 Buckets and
Spade 'Face'

630 Flowers 'Face'

631 Fruit and
Vegetables
'Face'

632 Sea Shells and
Seaweed 'Face'

633 Anchor and Life
Belts 'Face'

634 Glasses, Cork
and Cutlery
'Face'

635 Butterflies and
Caterpillars
'Face'

Greetings Stamps. 'The Welcoming Face of Guernsey'

(Des R. Ollington. Litho Questa)

1995 (28 FEB). *Perf* 14 (C)

663	**628**	24p multicoloured	....	65	6
664	**629**	24p multicoloured	....	65	6
665	**630**	24p multicoloured	....	65	6
666	**631**	24p multicoloured	....	65	6
667	**632**	24p multicoloured	....	65	6
668	**633**	24p multicoloured	....	65	6
669	**634**	24p multicoloured	....	65	6
670	**635**	24p multicoloured	....	65	6
663/70		*Set of* 8	....	4·50	4·5
		First Day Cover	....		5·0
		Presentation Pack	....	5·00	
		Stamp-cards (set of 8)	....	1·60	5·2
		Set of 8 *Gutter Pairs*	......	9·50	
MS671		137×109 mm. Nos. 663/70	......	4·50	4·5
		First Day Cover	....		5·0

Plate Nos.: All values 1A, 1B (each ×5)

Sheets: 50 (2 panes 5×5)

Imprint: Central, left-hand margin

Withdrawn: 27.2.96

636 Winston Churchill and Wireless

637 Union Jack and Royal Navy Ships off St. Peter Port

638 Royal Arms and Military Band

639 *Vega* (Red Cross supply ship)

640 Rejoicing Crowd

50th Anniversary of Liberation

(Des M. Whyte. Litho Enschedé)

1995 (9 MAY). *Perf* 13½×14 (C)

672	**636**	16p multicoloured	. . . .	50	50
673	**637**	24p multicoloured	. . . .	75	75
674	**638**	35p multicoloured	. . . .	1·00	1·00
675	**639**	41p multicoloured	. . . .	1·00	1·00
676	**640**	60p multicoloured	. . . .	1·75	1·75
672/6		*Set of* 5	. . . .	4·50	4·50
		First Day Cover			5·00
		Presentation Pack		5·00	
		Set of 5 *Gutter Pairs*		9·50	
MS677		189×75 mm. Nos. 672/6		4·50	4·50
		First Day Cover			5·00

Plate Nos.: 60p 1A, 1B, 1C, 1D (each ×4); others 1A, 1B (each ×4)

Sheets: 50 (2 panes 5×5)

Imprint: Central, side margins

Withdrawn: 8.5.96

641 Silhouette of Doves on Ground

642 Silhouette of Doves in Flight

Europa. Peace and Freedom

(Des K. Bassford, Litho Walsall)

1995 (9 MAY). *Perf* 14 (C)

678	**641**	25p multicoloured	. . . .	65	65
679	**642**	30p multicoloured	. . . .	85	85
678/9		*Set of* 2	. . . .	1·50	1·50
		First Day Cover			1·75
		Presentation Pack		1·75	

The designs of Nos. 678/9 each provide a stereogram or hidden three-dimensional image of a single dove designed by D. Burder.

Plate Nos.: Both values 1A, 1B, 1C (each ×4)

Sheets: 10 (2×5)

Imprint: Central, bottom margin

Withdrawn: 8.5.96

643 Prince Charles, Castle Cornet and Bailiwick Arms

Royal Visit

(Des C. Abbott. Litho Questa)

1995 (9 MAY). *Perf* 14 (C)

680	**643**	£1.50 multicoloured	4·00	4·00
		First Day Cover		4·25
		Presentation Pack	4·50	
		Gutter Pair	8·25	

Plate Nos.: 1A, 1B, 1C, 1D (each ×5)

Sheets: 40 (2 panes 5×4)

Imprint: Central, left-hand margin

Withdrawn: 8.5.96

643a (illustration reduced. Actual size 110×90 mm)

'Singapore '95' International Stamp Exhibition

(Des R. Gorringe and M. Whyte. Litho Cartor)

1995 (1 SEPT). *Sheet 110×90 mm containing stamp as No. 581 with changed imprint date. Perf 13* (C)
MS681 **643a** £1 multicoloured . . . . 2·50   2·50
            First Day Cover . . . .   2·75
            Presentation Pack . . . . 3·00

Withdrawn: 31.8.96

644

645

646

647

50th Anniversary of United Nations

(Des K. Bassford. Litho and embossed Enschedé)

1995 (24 OCT). *Perf* 14×13½ (C)
682 **644** 50p pale new blue and gold . . . . 1·25 1·25
              a. Block of 4. Nos. 682/5 . . . . 5·00
683 **645** 50p pale new blue and gold . . . . 1·25 1·25
684 **646** 50p pale new blue and gold . . . . 1·25 1·25
685 **647** 50p pale new blue and gold . . . . 1·25 1·25
682/5   *Set of 4* . . . . 5·00 5·00
              First Day Cover . . . .   5·25
              Presentation Pack . . . . 5·25

Plate Nos.: 1A–1A

Sheets: 36 (6×6). Nos. 682/5 were printed together, *se-tenant* throughout the sheet with each block of 4 showing the complete United Nations emblem

Imprint: Central, side margins

Withdrawn: 23.10.96

648 'Christmas Trees for Sale in Bern' **649**
         (Cornelia Nussbrum-Weibel)

650 'Evening Snowfall' **651**
         (Katerina Mertikas)

652 'It came upon a Midnight Clear' **653**
         (Georgia Guback)

654 'Children of the World' **655**

Christmas. 50th Anniversary of U.N.I.C.E.F.

(Adapted M. Whyte from U.N.I.C.E.F. Christmas Cards. Litho B.D.T.)

1995 (16 NOV). *Perf* 13 (C)

686	**648**	13p multicoloured	40	40
		a. *Horiz pair. Nos.* 686/7	80	80
687	**649**	13p multicoloured	40	40
688	**650**	13p + 1p multicoloured	40	40
		a. *Horiz pair. Nos.* 688/9	80	80
689	**651**	13p + 1p multicoloured	40	40
690	**652**	24p multicoloured	70	70
		a. *Horiz pair. Nos.* 690/1	1·40	1·40
691	**653**	24p multicoloured	70	70
692	**654**	24p + 2p multicoloured	70	70
		a. *Horiz pair. Nos.* 692/3	1·40	1·40
693	**655**	24p + 2p multicoloured	70	70
686/93		*Set of 8*	4·00	4·00
		First Day Cover..........		4·25
		Presentation Pack........	4·25	

Sheets: 12 (4×3), the two designs for each value printed together, *se-tenant*, in horizontal pairs throughout the sheets, each pair forming a composite design

Withdrawn: 15.11.96

Yearbook 1995

1995 (1 DEC). *Comprises Nos.* 663/93 *and* A77/84

	Yearbook	45·00

Withdrawn: 31.12.97

656 Princess Anne (President, Save the Children Fund) and Children

657 Queen Elizabeth II and People of the Commonwealth

Europa. Famous Women

(Des D. Miller. Litho B.D.T.)

1996 (21 APR). *Perf* 14 (C)

694	**656**	25p multicoloured	65	65
695	**657**	30p multicoloured	85	85
694/5		*Set of 2*	1·50	1·50
		First Day Cover..........		1·75
		Presentation Pack........	1·75	

The background designs of Nos. 694/5 continue on to the vertical sheet margins.

Plate Nos.: Both values 1A, 1B (each ×4)

Sheets: 10 (2×5)

Withdrawn: 20.4.97

658   England v U.S.S.R., 1968   **659**

660   Italy v Belgium, 1972   **661**

662   Ireland v Netherlands, 1988   **663**

664   Denmark v Germany, 1992 Final   **665**

European Football Championship

(Des M. Whyte. Litho Questa)

1996 (25 APR). *Perf* 14½×14 (C)

696	**658**	16p multicoloured	55	55
		a. *Horiz pair. Nos.* 696/7	1·10	1·10
697	**659**	16p multicoloured	55	55
698	**660**	24p multicoloured	75	75
		a. *Horiz pair. Nos.* 698/9	1·50	1·50
699	**661**	24p multicoloured	75	75
700	**662**	35p multicoloured	80	80
		a. *Horiz pair. Nos.* 700/1	1·60	1·60
701	**663**	35p multicoloured	80	80
702	**664**	41p multicoloured	95	95
		a. *Horiz pair. Nos.* 702/3	1·90	1·90
703	**665**	41p multicoloured	95	95
696/703		*Set of 8*	5·50	5·50
		First Day Cover..........		6·00
		Presentation Pack........	6·00	
		Souvenir Folder (*complete sheets*)	22·00	

Plate Nos.: All values 1A (×4)

Sheets: 8 (2×4), the two designs for each value printed together, *se-tenant*, in horizontal pairs throughout sheets with illustrated margins, each pair forming a composite design

Withdrawn: 24.4.97

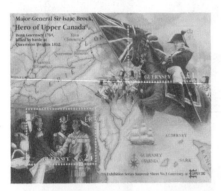

666a Maj-Gen. Brock meeting Tecumseh (Indian Chief) (24p); Maj-Gen. Isaac Brock on Horseback, 1812 (£1) (*illustration reduced. Actual size* 110×90 *mm*)

'CAPEX '96' International Stamp Exhibition, Toronto

(Des A. Peck. Litho Enschedé)

1996 (8 JUNE). *Sheet* 110×90 *mm. Perf* 13½ (C)
MS704 **666a** 24p, £1 multicoloured . . . . . . 2·75 2·75
First Day Cover . . . . 3·25
Presentation Pack . . . . 3·25

Withdrawn: 7.6.97

667 Runner

668 Throwing the Javelin

669 Throwing the Discus

670 Wrestling

671 Jumping

Centenary of Modern Olympic Games. Ancient Gree‑ Athletes

(Des K. Bassford. Litho Questa)

1996 (19 JULY). *Perf* 14 (C)

705	**667**	16p black, orange-yellow & orge	50	5‑
706	**668**	24p black, orange-yellow & orge	95	9
707	**669**	41p black, orange-yellow & orge	1·10	1·1‑
708	**670**	55p black, orange-yellow & orge	1·40	1·4‑
709	**671**	60p black, orange-yellow & orge	1·60	1·6‑
705/9		*Set of* 5	5·00	5·0‑
		First Day Cover		5·5‑
		Presentation Pack	5·50	
		Set of 5 *Gutter Pairs*	10·50	
MS710	192×75 mm. Nos. 705/9		5·00	5·0‑

No. 708 also includes the 'OLYMPHILEX '96' Internationa Stamp Exhibition, Atlanta, logo.

Plate Nos.: All values 1A, 1B (each ×3)
Sheets: 55p 50 (2 panes 5×5); others 100 (2 panes 10×5)
Imprint: Central, right-hand margin of top pane
Withdrawn: 18.7.97

672 Humphrey Bogart as Philip Marlowe

673 Peter Sellers as Inspector Clouseau

674 Basil Rathbone as Sherlock Holmes

675 Margaret Rutherford as Miss Marple

676 Warner Oland as Charlie Chan

(Des R. Ollington. Litho Enschedé)

996 (6 NOV). *Perf* 15×14 (C)

1	**672**	16p multicoloured	40	40
		a. *Booklet pane. No.* 711×3		
		with margins all round	1·00	
		b. *Booklet pane. Nos.* 711/15		
		with margins all round	3·75	
12	**673**	24p multicoloured	60	60
		a. *Booklet pane. No.* 712×3		
		with margins all round	1·75	
13	**674**	35p multicoloured	85	85
		a. *Booklet pane. No.* 713×3		
		with margins all round	2·25	
14	**675**	41p multicoloured	90	90
		a. *Booklet pane. No.* 714×3		
		with margins all round	2·50	
15	**676**	60p multicoloured	1·40	1·40
		a. *Booklet pane. No.* 715×3		
		with margins all round	4·00	
11/15		*Set of 5*	3·75	3·75
		First Day Cover		4·50
		Presentation Pack	4·50	
		Set of 5 Gutter Pairs	7·50	

Plate Nos.: All values 1A, 1B (each ×4)

Sheets: 50 (2 panes 5×5)

Imprint: Central, side margins

Withdrawn: 5.11.97

77 The
Annunciation

678 Journey to
Bethlehem

679 Arrival at
the Inn

680 Angel and
Shepherds

681 Mary, Joseph
and Jesus in
Stable

682 Shepherds
worshipping
Jesus

683 Three Kings
following
Star

684 Three Kings
with Gifts

685 The
Presentation
in the
Temple

686 Mary and
Jesus

687 Joseph
warned by
Angel

688 The Flight
into Egypt

689 Mary cradling
Jesus

690 The Nativity

Christmas

(Des P. le Vasseur. Litho B.D.T.)

1996 (6 NOV). *Perf* 13 (C)

716	**677**	13p multicoloured	30	30
		a. *Sheetlet. Nos.* 716/27	3·50	
717	**678**	13p multicoloured	30	30
718	**679**	13p multicoloured	30	30
719	**680**	13p multicoloured	30	30
720	**681**	13p multicoloured	30	30
721	**682**	13p multicoloured	30	30
722	**683**	13p multicoloured	30	30
723	**684**	13p multicoloured	30	30
724	**685**	13p multicoloured	30	30
725	**686**	13p multicoloured	30	30
726	**687**	13p multicoloured	30	30
727	**688**	13p multicoloured	30	30
728	**689**	24p multicoloured	60	60
729	**690**	25p multicoloured	60	60
716/29		*Set of 14*	4·25	4·25
		First Day Cover		5·25
		Presentation Pack	5·25	
		Set of 2 Gutter Pairs	2·40	

Plate Nos.: 24p, 25p 1A, 1B (each ×4)

Sheets: 13p 12 (4×3) containing Nos. 716/27 *se-tenant*; 24p, 25p 100 (2 panes 5×10)

Imprint: 13p bottom, left-hand margin; 24p, 25p central, side margins

Withdrawn: 5.11.97

Yearbook 1996

1996 (1 DEC). *Comprises Nos. 582a, 694/729 and A85/95*

Yearbook . . . . 50·00

Sold out: 6.99

691 Holly Blue (*Celastrina argiolus*)

692 Hummingbird Hawk-moth (*Macroglossum stellatarum*)

693 Emperor Moth (*Saturnia pavonia*)

694 Brimstone (*Gonepteryx rhamni*)

695a Painted Lady (*Cynthia cardui*)

Endangered Species. Butterflies and Moths

(Des A. Peck. Litho B.D.T.)

1997 (12 FEB). *Perf* 14 (C)

730	**691**	18p multicoloured	. . . .	60	60
731	**692**	25p multicoloured	. . . .	75	75
732	**693**	26p multicoloured	. . . .	90	90
733	**694**	37p multicoloured	. . . .	1·10	1·10
730/3		Set of 4	. . . .	3·00	3·00
		First Day Cover			3·25
		Presentation Pack	3·25		
		Souvenir Folder (*complete sheets*)	25·00		
MS734		92×68 mm. **695a** £1 multicoloured. Perf 13½ (C)	2·50	2·50
		First Day Cover			3·00
		Presentation Pack	3·00		

No. **MS**734 includes the 'HONG KONG '97' International Stamp Exhibition logo on the sheet margin.

Plate Nos.: All values 1A, 1B (each ×4)

Sheets: 10 (2×5) with designs extending into side margins

Withdrawn: 11.2.98

696 Gilliatt fighting Octopus

697 Gilliatt grieving on Rock

Europa. Tales and Legends. Scenes from Les Travailleur de la Mer *by Victor Hugo*

(Des M. Wilkinson. Litho Cartor)

1997 (24 APR). *Perf* 13½ (C)

735	**696**	26p multicoloured	. . . .	65	65
736	**697**	31p multicoloured	. . . .	75	75
735/6		Set of 2	. . . .	1·40	1·40
		First Day Cover			2·25
		Presentation Pack	2·25		

Plate Nos.: Both values 1A, 1B (each ×4)

Sheets: 10 (2×5) with enlarged inscribed margins at left

Withdrawn: 23.4.98

698 Shell Beach, Herm

699 La Seigneurie, Sark

700 Castle Cornet, Guernsey

Guernsey Scenes (1st series)

(Litho B.D.T.)

1997 (24 APR). *Self-adhesive. Perf 9½ (diecut)*

737	**698**	18p multicoloured	50	50
		a. *Booklet pane of 8*	3·75	
738	**699**	25p multicoloured	70	70
		a. *Booklet pane of 8*	5·25	
739	**700**	26p multicoloured	70	70
		a. *Booklet pane of 4*	2·75	
737/9		*Set of 3*	1·75	1·75
		First Day Cover		2·50
		Presentation Pack	2·50	

Nos. 737/9 were issued in stamp booklets or as rolls of 100 (18p and 25p).
See also Nos. 770/3.

Withdrawn: 31.3.98

701a 19th-century Boatyard, St. Peter's Port (30p);
Costa Rica Packet (coffee clipper) (£1)
(illustration reduced. Actual size 110×90 mm)

'PACIFIC '97' World Philatelic Exhibition, San Francisco

(Des C. Abbott. Litho Questa)

1997 (29 MAY). *Sheet 110×90 mm. Perf 14 (C)*

MS740	**701**a	30p. brn-olive & gold; £1 mult. .	3·00	3·00
		First Day Cover		3·50
		Presentation Pack	3·50	

Withdrawn: 28.5.98

702 Transistor Radio,
Microphone and
Radio Logos

703 Television, Video
Camera and Satellite
Dish

704 Fax Machine,
Telephones and
Mobile Phone

705 Printing Press,
Newspaper and Type

706 Stamp, Coding
Machine and Postbox

707 C.D., Computer and
Disk

Methods of Communication

(Des Miranda Schofield. Litho Cartor)

1997 (21 AUG). *Perf 13½×13 (C)*

741	**702**	18p multicoloured	45	45
742	**703**	25p multicoloured	70	70
743	**704**	26p multicoloured	70	70
744	**705**	37p multicoloured	1·00	1·00
745	**706**	43p multicoloured	1·10	1·10
746	**707**	63p multicoloured	1·60	1·60
741/6		*Set of 6*	5·00	5·00
		First Day Cover		5·25
		Presentation Pack	5·25	
		Set of 6 Gutter Pairs	10·00	

Plate Nos.: All values 1A, 1B (each ×4)
Sheets: 50 (2 panes 5×5)
Imprint: Central, side margins
Withdrawn: 20.8.98

708 Teddy Bear making Cake

709 Teddy Bears decorating Christmas Tree

710 Two Teddy Bears in Armchair

711 Teddy Bear as Father Christmas

712 Teddy Bears unwrapping Presents

713 Teddy Bears eating Christmas Dinner

Christmas. Teddy Bears

(Des Sally Diamond. Litho Walsall)

1997 (6 NOV). *Perf* 14½×14 (C)

747	**708**	15p multicoloured	. . . .	45	45
748	**709**	25p multicoloured	. . . .	70	70
749	**710**	26p multicoloured	. . . .	70	70
750	**711**	37p multicoloured	. . . .	1·00	1·00
751	**712**	43p multicoloured	. . . .	1·10	1·10
752	**713**	63p multicoloured	. . . .	1·60	1·60
747/52		*Set of* 6	. . . .	5·00	5·00
		First Day Cover	. . . .		5·25
		Presentation Pack	. . . .	5·25	
		Set of 6 *Gutter Pairs*	. . . . . .	10·00	
MS753		123×107 mm. Nos. 747/52	. . . . .	5·00	5·00
		First Day Cover	. . . .		5·25

Plate Nos.: All values 1A, 1B (each ×4)
Sheets: 50 (2 panes 5×5)
Imprint: Central, right-hand margin
Withdrawn: 5.11.98

714 Visiting Guernsey, 1957

715 Coronation Day, 1953 (inscr '1947')

716 Royal Family, 1957

717 On Royal Yacht, 1972

718 Queen Elizabeth and Prince Philip at Trooping the Colour, 1987

719 Queen Elizabeth and Prince Philip, 1997

Golden Wedding of Queen Elizabeth and Prince Philip

(Des M. Whyte. Litho Questa)

1997 (20 NOV). *Perf* 14½ (C)

754	**714**	18p multicoloured	45	45
		a. Booklet pane. Nos. 754/5, each ×3	3·25	
		b. Booklet pane. Nos. 754/9 . .	5·00	
755	**715**	25p multicoloured	70	70
756	**716**	26p multicoloured	70	70
		a. Booklet pane. Nos. 756/7, each ×3	5·00	
757	**717**	37p multicoloured	1·00	1·00
758	**718**	43p multicoloured	1·10	1·10
		a. Booklet pane. Nos. 758/9, each ×3	8·25	
759	**719**	63p multicoloured	1·60	1·60
754/9		Set of 6	5·00	5·00
		First Day Cover		5·50
		Presentation Pack	5·50	
		Set of 6 Gutter Pairs	10·00	

Plate Nos.: All values 1A, 1B (each ×6)

Sheets: 50 (2 panes 5×5)

Imprint: Central, right-hand margin

Withdrawn: 19.11.98

Yearbook 1997

1997 (1 DEC). *Comprises Nos.* 572b, 576b, 730/59, A70b, A72b/c and A96/101

	Yearbook	50·00

Sold out: 9.99

720 11th-century (St. Martin)

721 12th-century (St. Saviour)

722 13th-century (Vale)

723 14th-century (St. Sampson)

724 15th-century (Torteval)

725 16th-century (Castel)

726 17th-century (St. Andrew)

727 18th-century (Forest)

728 19th-century (St. Pierre du Bois)

729 20th-century (St. Peter Port)

The Millennium Tapestries Project

(Des Sally Diamond. Litho Questa)

1998 (10 FEB). *Perf* 15×14½ (C)

760	**720**	25p multicoloured	60	60
		a. Horiz strip of 10 or two strips of 5. Nos. 760/9	5·50	
		b. Booklet pane. Nos. 760/1, each ×2, and 762/3 with margins all round	3·50	
		c. Booklet pane. Nos. 760/1 and 768/9, each ×2 with margins all round	3·50	
761	**721**	25p multicoloured	60	60
762	**722**	25p multicoloured	60	60
		a. Booklet pane. Nos. 762/3, each ×2, and 764/5 with margins all round	3·50	

71

763	**723**	25p multicoloured	60	60
764	**724**	25p multicoloured	60	60
		a. *Booklet pane. Nos. 764/5, each ×2, and 766/7 with margins all round*	3·50	
765	**725**	25p multicoloured	60	60
766	**726**	25p multicoloured	60	60
		a. *Booklet pane. Nos. 766/7, each ×2, and 768/9 with margins all round*	3·50	
767	**727**	25p multicoloured	60	60
768	**728**	25p multicoloured	60	60
769	**729**	25p multicoloured	60	60
760/9		*Set of 10*	5·50	5·50
		First Day Cover.		6·00
		Presentation Pack.	5·75	

Plate Nos.: 1A, 1B (each ×4)

Sheets: 50 (10×5); the ten designs printed together, *se-tenant*, in horizontal strips throughout the sheet.

Imprint: Central, side margins

Withdrawn: 9.2.99

730 Fort Grey

731 Grand Havre

732 Little Chapel

733 Guernsey Cow

Guernsey Scenes (2nd series)

(Des Joanna Brehaut. Litho B.D.T.)

1998 (25 MAR). *Self-adhesive. Perf 9½ (diecut)*

770	**730**	(20p) multicoloured	40	45
		a. *Horiz pair. Nos. 770/1*	80	
		b. *Booklet pane. Nos. 770/1, each ×4 with margins all round*	3·25	
771	**731**	(20p) multicoloured	40	45
772	**732**	(25p) multicoloured	50	55
		a. *Horiz pair. Nos. 772/3*	90	
		b. *Booklet pane. Nos. 772/3, each × 4 with margins all round*	4·00	
773	**733**	(25p) multicoloured	50	55
770/3		*Set of 4*	1·75	2·00
		First Day Cover.		2·50
		Presentation Pack.	2·50	

Nos. 770/1 are inscribed "Bailiwick Minimum Postage Paid" and were initially sold at 20p. Nos. 772/3 are inscribed "UK Minimum Postage Paid" and were initially sold at 25p.

Nos. 770/3 were issued in stamp booklets or as rolls of 100, each roll containing two designs.

734 Fairey IIIC, Balloon, Sopwith Camel and Avro 504

735 Fairey Swordfish, Tiger Moth, Supermarine Walrus and Gloster Gladiator

736 Hawker Hurricane, Supermarine Spitfire, Vickers Wellington, Short Sunderland (flying boat), Westland Lysander and Bristol Blenheim

737 De Havilland Mosquito, Avro Lancaster, Auster III, Gloster Meteor and Horsa Glider

738 Canberra, Hawker Sea Fury, Bristol Sycamore, Hawker Hunter, Handley Page Victor and BAe Lightning

739 Panavia Tornado GR1, BAe Hawk, BAe Sea Harrier, Westland Lynx (helicopter) and Hawker Siddeley Nimrod

80th Anniversary of the Royal Air Force

(Des C. Abbott. Litho Cartor)

1998 (7 MAY). *Perf* 13½×13 (C)

774	**734**	20p multicoloured	....	50	50
775	**735**	25p multicoloured	....	60	60
776	**736**	30p multicoloured	....	70	70
777	**737**	37p multicoloured	....	85	85
778	**738**	43p multicoloured	....	95	95
779	**739**	63p multicoloured	....	1·40	1·40
774/9		*Set of* 6	....	4·50	4·50
		First Day Cover.			5·50
		Presentation Pack.		5·25	

Plate Nos.: All values 1A (×5)

Sheets: 50 (5×10)

Imprint: Central, side margins

Withdrawn: 6.5.99

740*a* Jules Rimet (first President of FIFA) (30p); Bobby Moore and Queen Elizabeth II, 1966 (£1.75)
(*illustration reduced. Actual size* 110×90 *mm*)

150th Anniversary of the Cambridge Rules for Football

(Des A. Peck. Litho Enschedé)

1998 (7 MAY). *Sheet* 110×90 *mm. Perf* 13½×14 (C)

MS780	**740***a*	30p, £1.75 multicoloured	....	4·50	4·50
		First Day Cover.			5·00
		Presentation Pack.		5·00	

Withdrawn: 6.5.99

741 Girls in Traditional Costume watching Sheep Display, West Show

742 Marching Band and 'Battle of Flowers' Exhibit, North Show

743 Prince Charles, Monument and Tank, Liberation Day

744 Goat, Dahlias and Show-jumping, South Show

Europa. National Festivals

(Des Sally Diamond. Litho Enschedé)

1998 (11 AUG). *Perf* 13½ (C)

781	**741**	20p multicoloured	....	50	50
782	**742**	25p multicoloured	....	60	60
783	**743**	30p multicoloured	....	70	70
784	**744**	37p multicoloured	....	90	90
781/4		*Set of* 4	....	2·50	2·50
		First Day Cover.			3·00
		Presentation Pack.		3·00	

Plate Nos.: All values 1A, 1B, 1C (each ×4)

Sheets: 10 (2×5) with enlarged inscribed margin at left

Imprint: Central, right-hand margin

Withdrawn: 10.8.99

745 Outboard Motorboat

746 St. John Ambulance Inshore Rescue Dinghy

747 Pilot Boat, St. Peter Port

748 *Flying Christine III* (St. John Ambulance launch)

749 Crab-fishing Boat

750 Herm Island Ferry

751 *Sarnia* (St. Peter Port Harbour Authority launch)

752 *Leopardess* (States' fisheries protection launch)

753 Trawler

754 Powerboat

757 Motor Cruiser

758 Ocean-going Sailing Yacht

759 Motor Yacht, Beaucette Marina

760 *Queen Elizabeth 2* (liner)

762 Royal Yacht *Britannia*

Maritime Heritage

(Des M. Wilkinson. Litho and embossed Questa (£5) or litho (£1 also embossed) Walsall (others))

1998 (11 AUG)–**99**. *Perf* 14 (1*p* to 9*p*), 14½×14 (10*p* to 75*p*), 14×14½ (£1) *or* 15×14½ (£5), *all comb*

785	**745**	1p multicoloured (*b*)	. . . .	10	10
786	**746**	2p multicoloured (*b*)	. . . .	10	10
787	**747**	3p multicoloured (*b*)	. . . .	10	10
788	**748**	4p multicoloured (*b*)	. . . .	10	10
789	**749**	5p multicoloured (*b*)	. . . .	10	10
790	**750**	6p multicoloured (*b*)	. . . .	10	10
791	**751**	7p multicoloured (*b*)	. . . .	15	20
792	**752**	8p multicoloured (*b*)	. . . .	15	20
793	**753**	9p multicoloured (*b*)	. . . .	20	25
794	**754**	10p multicoloured (*b*)	. . . .	20	25
797	**757**	40p multicoloured (*b*)	. . . .	80	85
798	**758**	50p multicoloured (*b*)	. . . .	1·00	1·10
799	**759**	75p multicoloured (*b*)	. . . .	1·50	1·75
800	**760**	£1 multicoloured (*b*)	. . . .	2·00	2·10
802	**762**	£5 multicoloured (*a*)	. . . .	10·00	10·50
785/802		*Set of 15*	. . . .	16·00	17·00
		First Day Covers (2)	. . . .		19·25
		Presentation Packs (2)	. . . . . .	18·25	
		Set of 14 Gutter Pairs (1p to £1)	. . . .	32·00	

Printings: (*a*) 11.8.98; (*b*) 27.7.99

Plate Nos.: £5 1A, 1B, 1C, 1D (each ×5); others 1A, 1B (each ×4)

Sheets: 1p to £1 50 (2 panes 5×5); £5 10 (5×2)

Imprint: Side margins (£5) or centre, left-hand margin (others)

769 Modern Tree, Teletubby and Playstation

770 1960s Tinsel Tree, Toy Bus and Doll

771 1930s Gold Foil Tree, Panda and Toy Tank

772 1920s Tree, Model of *Bluebird* and Doll

773 1900 Tree, Teddy Bear and Toy Train

774 1850s Tree, Wooden Doll and Spinning Top

(Des R. Ollington. Litho B.D.T.)

98 (10 NOV). *Perf* 13½ (C)

0	**769**	17p multicoloured	40	40
1	**770**	25p multicoloured	60	60
2	**771**	30p multicoloured	70	70
3	**772**	37p multicoloured	90	90
4	**773**	43p multicoloured	1·00	1·00
5	**774**	63p multicoloured	1·50	1·50
0/15		*Set of* 6	4·50	4·50
		First Day Cover.		5·50
		Presentation Pack.	5·50	
S816		160×94 mm. Nos. 810/15	4·25	4·75
		First Day Cover.		5·50

Plate Nos.: 17p, 25p 1A, 1B (each ×4); others 1A (×4)

Sheets: 50 (5×10)

Imprint: Central, side margins

Withdrawn: 9.11.99

earbook 1998

998 (1 DEC). *Comprises Nos.* 760/816 *and* A110/23
Yearbook . . . . 54·00

75 Elizabeth Bowes-
Lyon, 1907

776 On Wedding Day,
1923

777 Holding Princess
Elizabeth, 1926

778 At Coronation,
1937

779 Visiting Bombed
Areas of London,
1940

780 Fishing near
Auckland, New
Zealand, 1966

781 At Guernsey
Function, 1963

782 Receiving Flowers
on Birthday, 1992

783 Presenting
Trophy, Sandown
Park Races, 1989

784 Opening Royal
Norfolk Regimental
Museum, Norwich,
1990

Life and Times of Queen Elizabeth the Queen Mother

(Des R. Ollington. Litho Cartor)

1999 (4 FEB). *Perf* 13 (C)

817	**775**	25p multicoloured	50	55
		a. Horiz strip of 10 *or two* *strips of* 5. *Nos.* 817/26 . .	5·00	
		b. Booklet pane. Nos. 817/18, *each* ×2, *and* 819/20, *with* *margins all round*	3·00	
		c. Booklet pane. Nos. 817/18, *and* 825/6, *each* ×2, *with* *margins all round*	3·00	
818	**776**	25p multicoloured	50	55

819	**777**	25p multicoloured	. . . .	50	55
		b. Booklet pane. Nos. 819/20, each ×2, and 821/2, with margins all round	3·00	
820	**778**	25p multicoloured	. . . .	50	55
821	**779**	25p multicoloured	. . . .	50	55
		b. Booklet pane. Nos. 821/2, each × 2, and 823/4, with margins all round	3·00	
822	**780**	25p multicoloured	. . . .	50	55
823	**781**	25p multicoloured	. . . .	50	55
		b. Booklet pane. Nos. 823/4, each ×2, and 825/6, with margins all round	3·00	
824	**782**	25p multicoloured	. . . .	50	55
825	**783**	25p multicoloured	. . . .	50	55
826	**784**	25p multicoloured	. . . .	50	55
817/26		Set of 10		5·00	5·25
		First Day Cover.			6·00
		Presentation Pack.		6·00	

Plate Nos.: 1A, 1B (each ×5)

Sheets: 50 (10×5), the ten designs printed together, *se-tenant*, as horizontal strips throughout the sheets

Imprint: Central, side margins

785 *Spirit of Guernsey*, 1995

786 *Sir William Arnold*, 1973

787 *Euphrosyne Kendal*, 1954

788 *Queen Victoria*, 1929

789 *Arthur Lionel*, 1912

790 *Vincent Kirk Ella*, 1888

175th Anniv of Royal National Lifeboat Institution

(Des K. Wisdom. Litho Cartor)

1999 (27 APR). *Perf* 13½×13 (C)

827	**785**	20p multicoloured	. . . .	40	45
828	**786**	25p multicoloured	. . . .	50	55
829	**787**	30p multicoloured	. . . .	60	65
830	**788**	38p multicoloured	. . . .	75	80
831	**789**	44p multicoloured	. . . .	90	95
832	**790**	64p multicoloured	. . . .	1·25	1·40
827/32		Set of 6		4·25	4·75
		First Day Cover.			5·50
		Presentation Pack.		5·50	

Plate Nos.: All values 1A (×5)

Sheets: 50 (5×10)

Imprint: Central, side margins

791 Burnet Rose and Local Carriage Label

792 Puffin

793 Small Heath Butterfly

794 Shells on Shell Beach

Europa. Parks and Gardens. Herm Island

(Des Colleen Corlett. Litho Walsall)

1999 (27 APR). *Perf* 13½×13 (C)

833	**791**	20p multicoloured	. . . .	40	45
834	**792**	25p multicoloured	. . . .	50	55
835	**793**	30p multicoloured	. . . .	60	65
836	**794**	38p multicoloured	. . . .	75	80
833/6		Set of 4		2·25	2·40
		First Day Cover.			3·00
		Presentation Pack.		3·00	

Plate Nos.: All values 1A, 1B (each ×4)

Sheets: 10 (2×5) with enlarged illustrated margin at left (20, 30p) c right (25, 38p)

Imprint: Central right (20, 30p) or left (25, 38p) margin

The Marriage of HRH Prince Edward and Sophie Rhys-Jones, 19th June 1999.

795 Prince Edward and Miss Sophie Rhys-Jones
(*illustration reduced. Actual size 93×70 mm*)

Royal Wedding

(Des Sally Diamond. Litho B.D.T.)

1999 (19 JUNE). *Sheet* 93×70 mm. *Perf* 13 (C)

MS837	**795**	£1 multicoloured	2·00	2·10
		First Day Cover		2·75
		Presentation Pack	2·75	

796 Major-General
Le Marchant
(founder) and
Cadet at Sword
Drill

797 Duke of York
(official sponsor)
and Cadet on
Horseback

798 Field-Marshal
Earl Haig and
Cadets on
Parade

799 Field-Marshal
Viscount
Montgomery
and Bridging
Exercise

800 David Niven
(actor) and
Rifle Practice

801 Sir Winston
Churchill and
Tank

Bicentenary of The Royal Military Academy, Sandhurst

(Des R. Ollington. Litho B.D.T.)

1999 (27 JULY). *Perf* 14 (C)

838	**796**	20p multicoloured	. . . .	40	45
839	**797**	25p multicoloured	. . . .	50	55
840	**798**	30p multicoloured	. . . .	60	65
841	**799**	38p multicoloured	. . . .	75	80
842	**800**	44p multicoloured	. . . .	90	95
843	**801**	64p multicoloured	. . . .	1·25	1·40
838/43		Set of 6	. . . .	4·25	4·75
		First Day Cover	. . . .		5·50
		Presentation Pack	. . . .	5·50	

Plate Nos.: All values 1A (×4)

Sheets: 50 (5×10)

Imprint: Lower side margins

802 The Nativity

803 Virgin Mary and
Child

804 Holy Family

805 Cattle around
Manger

06 Adoration of the
Shepherds

807 Adoration of the
Magi

**hristmas. Wood Carvings by Denis Brehaut from Notre
ame Church**

(Des Sally Diamond. Litho Questa)

999 (19 OCT). *Perf* 14×14½ (C)

14	**802**	17p multicoloured	35	40
15	**803**	25p multicoloured	50	55
16	**804**	30p multicoloured	60	65
17	**805**	38p multicoloured	75	80
18	**806**	44p multicoloured	90	95
19	**807**	64p multicoloured	1·25	1·40
14/9		*Set of* 6	4·25	4·75
		First Day Cover.		5·50
		Presentation Pack.	5·50	
IS850		159×86 mm. Nos. 844/9	4·25	4·75
		First Day Cover.		5·50

Plate Nos.: All values 1A, 1B, 1C (each ×4)

Sheets: 50 (5×10)

Imprint: Bottom, right-hand margin

earbook 1999

999 (1 DEC). *Comprises Nos.* 817/49 *and* A125/39
               Yearbook . . . . 56·00

POSTAGE DUE STAMPS

D **1** Castle Cornet   D **2** Castle Cornet

(Des R. Granger Barrett. Photo Delrieu)

1969 (1 OCT). *Face value in black; background colour given. No wmk. Perf* 12½×12 (C)

D1	D **1**	1d plum	2·25	1·25
D2		2d bright green	2·25	1·25
D3		3d vermilion	3·75	4·00
D4		4d ultramarine	5·00	5·00
D5		5d yellow-ochre	5·50	5·50
D6		6d turquoise-blue	6·50	6·00
D7		1s lake-brown	17·00	17·00
D1/7		*Set of 7*	35·00	35·00

Sheets: 60 (10×6)

Quantities sold: 1d 82,802; 2d 75,340; 3d 74,532; 4d 74,659; 5d 71,129; 6d 72,912; 1s 71,659

Withdrawn and Invalidated: 14.2.72

Decimal Currency

(Des R. Granger Barrett. Photo Delrieu)

1971 (15 FEB)–**76**. *No wmk. Perf* 12½×12 (C)

D8	D **2**	½p plum (a)	10	10
D9		1p bright green (a)	10	10
D10		2p vermilion (a)	10	10
D11		3p ultramarine (a)	15	15
D12		4p yellow-ochre (a)	15	15
D13		5p turquoise-blue (a)	15	15
D14		6p violet (c)	20	20
D15		8p yellow-orange (b)	30	30
D16		10p lake-brown (a)	35	35
D17		15p grey (c)	60	60
D8/17		*Set of 10*	2·00	2·00
D1/13, 16		*Presentation Pack* (a)	85·00	
D8/17		*Presentation Pack* (c)	2·50	

Printings: (a) 15.2.71; (b) 7.10.75; (c) 10.2.76

Sheets: 60 (10×6)

Withdrawn: 14.2.72 Presentation Pack (Nos. D1/13 and D16); 1.8.78 ½p to 15p (½p and 1p sold out by 6.78)

D **3** St. Peter Port

(Photo Delrieu)

1977 (2 AUG)–**80**. *Face value in black; background colour given. Perf* 13 (C)

D18	D **3**	½p lake-brown (a)	10	10
D19		1p bright purple (a)	10	10
D20		2p bright orange (a)	10	10
D21		3p vermilion (a)	10	10
D22		4p turquoise-blue (a)	15	15
D23		5p yellow-green (a)	15	15
D24		6p turquoise-green (a)	20	20
D25		8p brown-ochre (a)	25	25
D26		10p ultramarine (a)	40	40
D27		14p green (b)	45	45
D28		15p bright violet (a)	45	45
D29		16p rose-red (b)	55	55
D18/29		*Set of 12*	2·50	2·50
D18/26, 28		*Presentation Pack*	2·00	

Printings: (a) 2.8.77; (b) 5.2.80

Sheets: 50 (5×10)

Withdrawn: 12.7.83 (Presentation Pack sold out earlier)

D **4** Milking Cow   D **5** Vale Mill

D **6** Sark Cottage   D **7** Quay-side, St. Peter Port

D **8** Well, Water Lane, Moulin Huet   D **9** Seaweed Gathering

D **10** Upper Walk, White Rock   D **11** Cobo Bay

D **12** Saint's Bay

D **13** La Coupee, Sark

D **14** Old Harbour, St.
       Peter Port

D **15** Greenhouse,
       Doyle Road, St.
       Peter Port

Guernsey Scenes, c. 1900

(Des C. Abbott. Litho Questa)

1982 (13 JULY). *Perf* 14½ (C)

D30	D **4**	1p indigo, blue-black & brt grn	10	10
D31	D **5**	2p yellow-brown, sepia & azure	10	10
D32	D **6**	3p blackish green, black & lilac	10	10
D33	D **7**	4p bottle green, blk & dull orge	10	10
D34	D **8**	5p deep violet-blue, blue-black and turquoise-green	10	10
D35	D **9**	16p dp grey-blue, dp bl & cobalt	30	35
D36	D **10**	18p steel bl, indigo & apple grn	35	40
D37	D **11**	20p brown-olive, agate & pale bl	40	45
D38	D **12**	25p Prussian blue, blue-black and rose-pink	50	55
D39	D **13**	30p deep bluish green, blackish olive and bistre-yellow	60	65
D40	D **14**	50p olive-brown, sepia and dull violet-blue	1·00	1·10
D41	D **15**	£1 lt brown, brown & pale brn	2·00	2·10
D30/41		*Set of* 12	5·25	5·75
		Presentation Pack.	5·75	

Sheets: 50 (5×10)

Imprint: Bottom corner, right-hand margin

STAMP BOOKLETS

PRICES given are for complete booklets. Booklets Nos. SB1/12 are stitched.

B **1** Military Uniforms

1969 (12 DEC). *White covers as Type B* **1**, *printed in black*
SB1   2s booklet containing 3×4d (No. 18*a*), 2×5d (No. 19*a*) and 2×1d (No. 14*c*) (*cover showing Trooper, Royal Guernsey Cavalry (Light Dragoons), 1814*) . . . .   1·50
SB2   4s booklet containing 6×4d (No. 18*a*), 4×5d (No. 19*a*) and 4×1d (No. 14*c*) (*cover showing Officer, St. Martin's Company (La Milice Bleue), Guernsey, 1720*) . . . .   2·25
SB3   6s booklet containing 9×4d (No. 18*a*), 6×5d (No. 19*a*) and 6×1d (No. 14*c*) (*cover showing Colour Sergeant of Grenadiers and Rifleman, East (Town) Regiment, Guernsey, 1833*) . . . .   3·75

Withdrawn: 14.2.72

1970 (29 JUNE). *White covers as Type B* **1**. *Printed in black* (SB4), *green* (SB5) *or red* (SB6). *Same composition as Nos.* SB1/3
SB4   2s booklet (*cover showing Officer, Royal Guernsey Horse Artillery, 1793*) . . . .   4·00
SB5   4s booklet (*cover showing Gunner, Royal Guernsey Artillery, 1743*) . . . .   13·00
SB6   6s booklet (*cover showing Sergeant, Royal Guernsey Light Infantry, 1832*) . . . .   12·00

Quantities sold: 2s (SB1, SB4), 81,928; 4s (SB2, SB5), 23,817; 6s (SB3, SB6), 25,123

Withdrawn: 14.2.72

Decimal Currency

1971 (15 FEB). *White covers as Type B* **1**. *Printed in black* (SB7), *green* (SB8) *or red* (SB9)
SB7   10p booklet containing 2×½p (No. 44*a*), 2×2p (No. 47*a*) and 2×2½p (No. 48*b*) (*cover showing Officer, Royal Guernsey Horse Artillery, 1850*)   2·00
SB8   20p booklet containing 4×½p (No. 44*a*), 4×2p (No. 47*a*) and 4×2½p (No. 48*b*) (*cover showing Sergeant, Guernsey Light Infantry (Grenadiers), 1826*) . . . .   1·00
SB9   30p booklet containing 6×½p (No. 44*a*), 6×2p (No. 47*a*) and 6×2½p (No. 48*b*) (*cover showing Sergeant and Bandsman, Royal Guernsey Light Infantry (North Regiment), 1866*) . . . . . . ·. . .   1·75

Withdrawn: 27.6.73 (SB7); 12.3.75 (SB8); 15.1.75 (SB9)

1973 (2 APR). *White covers as Type B* **1**. *Printed in black* (SB10), *green* (SB11) *or red* (SB12)
SB10   10p booklet containing 2×½p (No. 44*ab*), 2×2p (No. 47*ab*) and 2×2½p (No. 48*ba*) (*cover showing Officer, Guernsey Horse Artillery, 1828*) . . . .   1·0
SB11   20p booklet containing 4×½p (No. 44*ab*), 4×2p (No. 47*ab*) and 4×2½p (No. 48*ba*) (*cover showing Grenadier, Guernsey Light Infantry, 1792*) . . . .   1·2
SB12   30p booklet containing 6×½p (No. 44*ab*), 6×2p (No. 47*ab*) and 6×2½p (No. 48*ba*) (*cover showing Insignia, Royal Guernsey Light Infantry*) . . . .   1·5

Nos. SB10/12 are inscribed 'January 1973' on back cover.

Withdrawn: 1.4.75

B **2** Arms of Guernsey

1974 (2 APR). *Silver* (SB13) *or gold cover* (SB14) *as Type B*
SB13   10p booklet containing five ½p stamps and three 2½p in *se-tenant* strip (No. 98*a*) . . . . .
SB14   35p booklet containing four ½p stamps, six 2½p and six 3p in *se-tenant* pane (No. 98*b*)   1·2

The strips and panes have the left-hand selvedge stuck in booklet covers and then folded and supplied in plastic wallet

Withdrawn 6.2.79

1977 (8 FEB). *Green cover as Type B* **2**
SB15   20p booklet containing No. 99*a* . . . .

The note beneath SB14 also applies here.

Withdrawn: 12.2.80

BOOKLET PANES from Nos. SB16/18 are loose within ca covers supplied in plastic sachets.

1978 (7 FEB). *Blue cover as Type B* **2**
SB16   10p booklet containing No. 99*b* . . . .

Withdrawn: 12.2.80

1979 (13 FEB). *Covers as Type B* **2**
SB17   10p booklet containing No. 178*a* (*black and green cover*) . . . .
SB18   30p booklet containing No. 179*a* (*black and red cover*) . . . .   1·2

Withdrawn: 23.2.82

B **3** Castle Cornet

980 (6 MAY). *Horiz covers as Type B* **3**. *Folded*
B19 30p booklet containing No. 177a (*blue printed cover, Type* C). . . . . 1·00
B20 50p booklet containing No. 177b (*brown printed cover showing view from the sea*) . . 1·50

Withdrawn: 4.5.83

981 (24 FEB). *Covers similar to Type B* **3**, *but vert. Folded*
B21 60p booklet containing No. 180a (*red printed cover showing Fort Grey*) . . . . 1·75
B22 £1.20 booklet containing No. 180b (*green printed cover showing Rokaine Castle*) . . . . 3·50

Withdrawn 23.2.84

982 (2 FEB). *Covers similar to Type B* **3** *showing Fort George. Folded*
B23 70p booklet containing No. 181b (*orange printed cover showing main entrance*) . . . . . . 2·25
B24 £1.30 booklet containing No. 181c (*magenta printed cover showing aerial view of Citadel*) 3·75

Withdrawn: 22.7.85

983 (14 MAR). *Covers similar to Type B* **3**. *Folded*
B25 £1 booklet containing No. 180c (*new blue printed cover showing States Office, St. Peter Port*) . . . . 3·00
B26 £1.30 booklet containing No. 180d (*sepia printed cover showing Constable's Office, St. Peter Port*) . . . . 3·75

Withdrawn: 22.7.85

BOOKLET PANES from Nos. SB27/38 are loose within card covers.

B **4** View of Post Office Headquarters, St. Peter Port

1984 (18 SEPT). *Multicoloured covers as Type B* **4**
SB27 £1 booklet containing No. 299a . . . . 3·50
SB28 £1.30 booklet containing No. 299b (*cover showing Head Post Office, St. Peter Port*) . . 4·50

Quantities sold: SB27 50,393; SB28 25,372
Withdrawn: 1.87

1985 (19 MAR). *Multicoloured covers as Type B* **4**
SB29 £1.20 booklet containing No. 304a (*cover showing French Halles, St. Peter Port*) . . . 4·25
SB30 £1.30 booklet containing No. 304b (*cover showing Market Halls, St. Peter Port*) . . . . . . 4·25

Quantities sold: SB29 49,248; SB30 45,463
Withdrawn: 8.87

1985 (2 DEC). *Multicoloured cover as Type B* **4**, *but vert*
SB31 50p booklet containing No. 297a (*cover showing Victoria Tower, St. Peter Port*) . . . . 2·75

Quantity sold: 55,768
Withdrawn: 8.87

1986 (1 APR). *Multicoloured cover as Type B* **4**, *but vert*
SB32 £1.20 booklet containing No. 305a (*cover showing St. James-the-Less, St. Peter Port*) 4·25

Quantity sold: 32,627
Withdrawn: 2.89

1987 (30 MAR). *Multicoloured covers as Type B* **4**, *but vert*
SB33 £1 booklet containing No. 298a (*cover showing Lukis Observatory, St. Peter Port*) . . 4·00
SB34 £1.30 booklet containing No. 306a (*cover showing Weighbridge, St. Peter Port*) . . . . . . 4·25

Quantities sold: SB33 42,478; SB34 36,369
Withdrawn: 2.89

1988 (28 MAR). *Multicoloured covers as Type B* **4**, *but vert*
SB35 £1 booklet containing No. 299c (*cover showing North Pier Light, St. Peter Port*) . . . . 3·75
SB36 £1.40 booklet containing No. 306ba (*cover showing Castle Light, St. Peter Port*) . . . . . . 4·25

Quantities sold: SB35 41,092; SB36 39,478
Withdrawn: 2.90

1989 (28 Feb). *Multicoloured covers as Type B* **4**, *but vert*
SB37 £1 booklet containing No. 299d (*cover showing Town Church, St. Peter Port*) . . . . . 4·25
SB38 £1.20 booklet containing No. 306bb (*cover showing St. Barnabas Church, St. Peter Port*) 4·75

Quantities sold: SB37 47,175; SB38 41,235
Withdrawn: 12.90

B **5** Opening Ceremony, 1939
(*illustration reduced. Actual size 163×97 mm*)

50th Anniversary of Guernsey Airport

1989 (5 MAY). *Multicoloured cover, Type B* **5**. *Booklet contains text and illustrations on panes and interleaving pages. Stitched*
SB39 £3.90 booklet containing Nos. 456a, 458a and 460a . . . . 11·00

Quantity sold: 38,025
Sold out: By 11.89

1989 (27 DEC). *Multicoloured covers as Type B* **4**, *but vert*
SB40 £1.20 booklet containing No. 301a (*cover showing Fish Market, St. Peter Port*) . . . . . . 4·25
SB41 £1.70 booklet containing No. 308a (*cover showing Lloyds Bank, St. Peter Port*) . . . . . . 4·75

Quantities sold: SB40 31,736; SB41 31,743
Withdrawn: 21.5.92

B **6** Crown Hotel
(*illustration reduced. Actual size 163×97 mm*)

50th Anniversary of First Guernsey Stamps

1991 (18 FEB). *Multicoloured cover, Type B* **6**. *Booklet contains text on panes and text and illustrations on interleaving pages. Stitched*
SB42 £4.41 booklet containing No. 517a×3 . . . . . . 12·00

Quantity sold: 31,955
Withdrawn: 17.2.92

1991 (2 APR). *Multicoloured covers as Type B* **4**, *but vert*
SB43 £1.30 booklet containing No. 300a (*cover showing Golden Lion Inn, St. Peter Port*) . . . . 4·0
SB44 £1.80 booklet containing No. 309a (*cover showing National Trust Building, St. Peter Port*) . . . . 5·7

Quantities sold: SB43 36,066; SB44 26,029
Withdrawn: 21.5.92

B **7** Carnations

1992 (22 MAY). *Multicoloured covers as Type B* **7**. *Pane attached by selvedge*
SB45 £1.45 booklet containing pane No. 572ac (*cover Type B* **7**) . . . . 3·5
SB46 £1.80 booklet containing pane No. 574ac (*cover showing mixed freesias*) . . . . 4·2

Withdrawn: 31.8.99

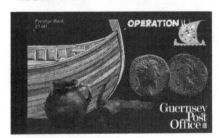

B **8** Bow of Ship and Relics
(*illustration reduced. Actual size 163×97 mm*)

"Operation Asterix"

1992 (18 SEPT). *Multicoloured cover, Type B* **8**. *Booklet contains text and illustrations on interleaving pages. Stitched*
SB47 £5.60 booklet containing No. 583a×4 . . . . . . 13·0

Quantity sold: 24,211
Withdrawn: 17.9.93

1993 (2 MAR)–**95**. *Multicoloured covers as Type B* **7**, *but different Guernsey Post Office logo. Without barcode on the reverse. Panes attached by selvedge*
SB48 £1.12 booklet containing pane No. 577ab (*cover showing Lisianthus*) . . . . 2·

SB49 £1.28 booklet containing pane No. 572*ad*
(*cover Type* B **7**) . . . . 3·25
　a. With barcode sticker on reverse (6.95) . . . . 3·25
　b. Barcode printed on reverse (10.95) . . . . . . 3·25
SB50 £1.92 booklet containing pane No. 575*ab*
(*cover showing standard roses*) . . . . 4·75
　a. With barcode sticker on reverse (3.95) . . . . 4·75
　b. Barcode printed on reverse (6.95) . . . . . . 4·75

Withdrawn: 31.8.99

9 Thomas de la Rue
(*Illustration reduced. Actual size 163×97 mm*)

Birth Bicentenary of Thomas de la Rue (printer)

1993 (27 JULY). *Multicoloured cover as Type B* **9**. *Booklet contains text and illustrations on interleaving pages. Stapled*
SB51 £5.60 booklet containing panes Nos. 617*a*/21*a* 13·00

Withdrawn: 26.7.94

1994 (18 FEB). *Multicoloured cover as Type B* **7**, *but different Guernsey Post Office logo. With barcode on reverse. Pane attached by selvedge*
SB52 £1 booklet containing pane No. 576*ab* (*cover showing Iris "Ideal"*) . . . . 2·50

Withdrawn: 31.8.99

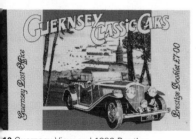

10 Guernsey View and 1936 Bentley
(*Illustration reduced. Actual size 162×97 mm*)

Centenary of First Car in Guernsey

1994 (19 JULY). *Black and grey cover as Type B* **10**. *Booklet contains text and illustrations on labels attached to panes and on interleaving pages. Stitched*
SB53 £7 booklet containing panes Nos. 639*a*/43*a* 18·00

Withdrawn 18.7.95

B **11** Coins, Postbox and Stamps "Face"

Greetings Stamps. "The Welcoming Face of Guernsey"

1995 (28 FEB). *Multicoloured cover as Type B* **11**. *Miniature sheet folded and attached by selvedge*
SB54 £1.92 booklet containing No. **MS**671 . . . . . . 4·50

Withdrawn: 27.2.96

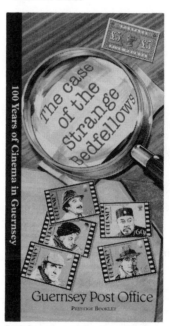

B **12** Stamps and Magnifying Glass

Centenary of Cinema. Screen Detectives

1996 (6 NOV). *Multicoloured cover as Type B* **12**. *Booklet contains text and illustrations on margins of panes and interleaving pages. Stitched*
SB55 £7.04 booklet containing panes Nos. 711*a*/15*a* 15·00
　Withdrawn: 5.11.97

4 stamps £1.04
European Community rate

B **13** Freesia 'Pink Glow'

1997 (2 JAN). *Multicoloured covers as Type* B **13**. *Panes attached by selvedge*

SB56 £1.04 booklet containing pane No. 576*bb* (*cover Type* B **13**) .... 2·75
SB57 £1.44 booklet containing pane No. 572*bb* (*cover showing Standard Rose*) .... 3·50
SB58 £2 booklet containing No. 576*ab*×2 (*cover showing Iris 'Ideal'*) .... 4·75

Withdrawn: 31.8.99

B **14** Castle Cornet, Guernsey

Guernsey Scenes (1st series)

1997 (24 APR). *Multicoloured covers as Type* B **14**. *Self-adhesive*

SB59 £1.04 booklet containing pane No. 739*a* (*cover as Type* B **14**) .... 2·75
SB60 £1.44 booklet containing pane No. 737*a* (*cover showing Shell Beach, Herm*) .... 3·75
SB61 £2 booklet containing pane No. 738*a* (*cover showing La Seigneurie, Sark*) .... 5·25

Withdrawn: 31.3.98

B **15** Queen Elizabeth and Prince Philip
(*illustration reduced. Actual size* 162×95 *mm*)

Golden Wedding

1997 (20 NOV). *Multicoloured cover as Type* B **15**. *Booklet contains text and illustrations on panes and interleaving pages. Stitched*

SB62 £8.48 booklet containing Nos. 754*a*/*b*, 756*a* and 758*a*. .... 20·0

Withdrawn: 19.11.98

B **16** Millennium Tapestry
(*illustration reduced. Actual size* 162×97 *mm*)

The Millennium Tapestries Project

1998 (10 FEB). *Multicoloured cover as Type* B **16**. *Booklet contains text and illustrations on pane margins and interleaving pages. Stitched*

SB63 £7.50 booklet containing Nos. 760*b*/*c*, 762*a*, 764*a* and 766*a* .... 17·

Withdrawn: 9.2.99

17 Fort Grey

uernsey Scenes (2nd series)

98 (25 MAR). *Multicoloured covers as Type* B **17**. *Self-adhesive*

364	£1.60 booklet containing pane No. 770*b* (*cover as Type* B **17**)	3·25
365	£2 booklet containing pane No. 772*b* (*cover showing Guernsey cow*)	4·00

18 Queen Elizabeth the Queen Mother
  (*illustration reduced. Actual size* 160×100 *mm*)

ife and Times of Queen Elizabeth the Queen Mother

99 (4 FEB). *Multicoloured cover as Type* B **18**. *Booklet contains text and illustrations on pane margins and interleaving pages. Stitched*

366	£7.50, booklet containing panes Nos. 817*b*/*c*, 819*b*, 821*b* and 823*b*	15·00

ALDERNEY

The following issues are provided by the Guernsey Post Office for use on Alderney. They are also valid for postal purposes throughout the rest of the Bailiwick of Guernsey.

A **1** Island Map

A **2** Hanging Rock

A **3** States' Building, St. Anne

A **4** St. Anne's Church

A **5** Yachts in Braye Bay

A **6** Victoria St, St. Anne

A **7** Map of Channel

A **8** Fort Clonque

A **9** Corblets Bay and Fort

A **10** Old Tower, St. Anne

A **11** Golf Course and Essex Castle

A **12** Old Harbour

A **12**a Quesnard Lighthouse

A **12**b Braye Harbour

A **12**c Island Hall

A **12**d J. T. Daly (steam locomotive)

A **12**e Louis Marchesi of Round Table (lifeboat)

Island Scenes

(Des G. Drummond. Litho B.D.T. (20p to 28p) or photo Courvoisier (others))

1983 (14 JUNE)–**93**. *Granite paper* (1p to 18p). *Perf* 15× (20p to 28p) *or* 11½ (others), *both comb*

A1	A **1**	1p multicoloured (a)	10
A2	A **2**	4p multicoloured (a)	10
A3	A **3**	9p multicoloured (a)	25
A4	A **4**	10p multicoloured (a)	25
A5	A **5**	11p multicoloured (a)	25
A6	A **6**	12p multicoloured (a)	30
A7	A **7**	13p multicoloured (a)	30
A8	A **8**	14p multicoloured (a)	35
A9	A **9**	15p multicoloured (a)	40
A10	A **10**	16p multicoloured (a)	40
A11	A **11**	17p multicoloured (a)	45
A12	A **12**	18p multicoloured (a)	45

2a	A **12a**	20p multicoloured (b)	1·00	1·00
2b	A **12b**	21p multicoloured (c)	1·00	1·00
2c	A **12c**	23p multicoloured (d)	90	90
2d	A **12d**	24p multicoloured (e)	2·00	2·00
2e	A **12e**	28p multicoloured (e)	2·25	2·25
/12e		Set of 17	9·50	9·50
		First Day Covers (5)		25·00
		Presentation Packs (2) . .	11·00	
		Set of 17 Gutter Pairs	19·00	

Printings: (a) 14.6.83; (b) 27.12.89; (c) 2.4.91; (d) 6.2.92; (e) 2.3.93

Plate and Cylinder Nos.: 1p, 12p, 13p, 17p, 20p to 28p 1A, 1B, 1C, 1D (each ×4); others 1A, 1B, 1C, 1D (each ×5)

Sheets: 40 (2 panes 5×4)

Imprint: Central, bottom margin

Quantities sold: 1p 1,337,865; 4p 465,887; 9p 680,896; 10p 709,197; 11p 778,483; 12p 573,124; 13p 671,772; 14p 1,027,248; 15p 740,519; 16p 542,970; 17p 404,323; 18p 491,877; 20p 248,694; 21p 233,975; 23p 237,345; 24p 311,144; 28p 134,765

Withdrawn: 4.6.94

13 Oystercatcher

A **14** Turnstone

15 Ringed Plover

A **16** Dunlin

A **17** Curlew

rds

(Des and photo Harrison)

84 (12 JUNE). Perf 14½ (C)

3	A **13**	9p multicoloured	1·50	1·50
4	A **14**	13p multicoloured	1·50	2·00
5	A **15**	26p multicoloured	5·00	4·00
6	A **16**	26p multicoloured	5·00	4·00
7	A **17**	31p multicoloured	5·00	4·00
3/17		Set of 5	16·00	14·00
		First Day Cover		14·00
		Presentation Pack	20·00	
		Set of 5 Gutter Pairs	32·00	

Cylinder Nos.: All values 1A, 1B (each ×5)

Sheets: 50 (2 panes 5×5)

Imprint: Bottom margin, right-hand corner

Quantities sold: 9p 285,931; 13p 360,619; 26p 246,916; 28p 261,370; 31p 334,484

Withdrawn: 11.6.85

A **18** Westland Wessex Hu Mk 5 Helicopter of the Queen's Flight

A **19** Britten Norman 'long-nose' Trislander

A **20** De Havilland D.H.114 Heron 1B

A **21** De Havilland D.H.89A Dragon Rapide *Sir Henry Lawrence*

A **22** Saro A.21 Windhover Flying Boat *City of Portsmouth*

50th Anniversary of Alderney Airport

(Des A. Theobald. Photo Courvoisier)

1985 (19 MAR). Granite paper. Perf 11½ (C)

A18	A **18**	9p multicoloured	2·50	2·25
A19	A **19**	13p multicoloured	2·50	3·00
A20	A **20**	29p multicoloured	6·00	5·00
A21	A **21**	31p multicoloured	6·50	6·00
A22	A **22**	34p multicoloured	7·00	6·00
A18/22		Set of 5	22·00	20·00
		First Day Cover		20·00
		Presentation Pack	25·00	

Cylinder Nos.: All values A1–1–1–1–1–1, B1–1–1–1–1–1

Sheets: 25 (5×5)

Quantities sold: 9p 294,437; 13p 321,276; 29p 231,422; 31p 171,528; 34p 162,429

Withdrawn: 18.3.86

A **23** Royal Engineers, 1890

A **24** Duke of Albany's Own Highlanders (72nd Highland Regt), 1856

A **25** Royal Artillery, 1855

A **26** South Hampshire Regiment, 1810

A **27** Royal Irish Regiment, 1782

Regiments of the Alderney Garrison

(Des E. Stemp. Litho Harrison)

1985 (24 SEPT). *Perf* 14½ (C)

A23	A **23**	9p multicoloured	. . . .	45	45
A24	A **24**	14p multicoloured	. . . .	1·00	1·00
A25	A **25**	29p multicoloured	. . . .	1·50	1·50
A26	A **26**	31p multicoloured	. . . .	1·75	1·75
A27	A **27**	34p multicoloured	. . . .	2·00	2·00
A23/7		*Set of 5*	. . . .	6·00	6·00
		First Day Cover			8·00
		Presentation Pack	10·00	
		Set of 5 Gutter Pairs	12·00	

No. A24 shows the tartan and insignia of the 78th Highland Regiment in error.

Plate Nos.: All values 1A, 1B, 1C, 1D (each ×5)

Sheets: 50 (2 panes 5×5)

Imprint: Central, left-hand margin of each pane

Quantities sold: 9p 286,572; 14p 283,493; 29p 224,196; 31p 151,94? 34p 145,422

Withdrawn: 23.9.86

A **28** Fort Grosnez

A **29** Fort Tourgis

A **30** Fort Clonque

A **31** Fort Albert

Alderney Forts

(Des R. Reed. Litho Cartor)

1986 (23 SEPT). *Perf* 13×13½ (C)

A28	A **28**	10p multicoloured	. . . .	1·10	1·?
A29	A **29**	14p multicoloured	. . . .	1·75	1·?
A30	A **30**	31p multicoloured	. . . .	4·00	4·?
A31	A **31**	34p multicoloured	. . . .	4·25	4·?
A28/31		*Set of 4*	. . . .	10·00	10·?
		First Day Cover			12·?
		Presentation Pack	14·00	
		Set of 4 Gutter Pairs	20·00	

Plate Nos.: All values 1A, 1B, 1C, 1D (each ×5)

Sheets: 50 (2 panes 5×5)

Imprint: Left-hand margin of left-hand pane

Quantities sold: 10p 325,706; 14p 231,891; 31p 143,423; 3? 138,556

Withdrawn: 22.9.87

A **32** *Liverpool* (full-rigged ship), 1902

A **33** *Petit Raymond* (schooner), 1906

A **34** *Maina* (yacht), 1910

A **39** Goodwin's Map of 1831

A **35** *Burton* (steamer), 1911

A **36** *Point Law* (oil tanker), 1975

A **40** General Staff Map of 1943

lderney Shipwrecks

(Des C. Jaques. Litho Questa)

A **41** Ordnance Survey Map of 1988

1987 (5 MAY). *Perf* 14×14½ (C)

?2	A **32**	11p multicoloured	2·00	1·75
?3	A **33**	15p multicoloured	2·25	2·00
?4	A **34**	29p multicoloured	5·50	5·25
?5	A **35**	31p multicoloured	6·00	5·75
?6	A **36**	34p multicoloured	6·50	6·25
?2/6		*Set of* 5	20·00	19·00
		First Day Cover		19·00
		Presentation Pack	24·00	
		Set of 5 *Gutter Pairs*	40·00	

Plate Nos. All values 1A, 1B, 1C, 1D (each ×4)

Sheets: 50 (2 panes 5×5)

Imprint: Bottom, right-hand margin of each pane

Quantities sold: 11p 228,998; 15p 233,861; 29p 139,453; 31p 148,572; 34p 145,641

Withdrawn: 4.5.88

250th Anniversary of Bastide's Survey of Alderney

(Des J. Cooter. Litho Enschedé)

1989 (7 JULY). *Perf* 13½×14 (C)

A37	A **37**	12p multicoloured	45	45
A38	A **38**	18p blk, greenish blue & orge-brn	60	60
A39	A **39**	27p black, greenish blue and dull yellow-green	1·25	1·25
A40	A **40**	32p black, greenish blue & brt rose-red	1·40	1·40
A41	A **41**	35p multicoloured	1·60	1·60
A37/41		*Set of* 5	4·75	4·75
		First Day Cover		6·00
		Presentation Pack	6·50	
		Set of 5 *Gutter Pairs*	9·50	

Plate Nos.: 12p 1–1–1–1; 18p, 27p, 32p 1–1–1; 35p 1–1–1–1–1

Sheets: 50 (2 panes 5×5)

Imprint: Central, both side margins of each pane

Quantities sold: 12p 169,993; 18p 194,667; 27p 148,621; 32p 158,600; 35p 153,544

Withdrawn: 6.7.90

A **37** Moll's Map of 1724

A **38** Bastide's Survey of 1739

A **42** H.M.S. *Alderney* (bomb ketch), 1738

A **43** H.M.S. *Alderney* (frigate), 1742

91

A **44** H.M.S. *Alderney* (sloop), 1755

A **45** H.M.S. *Alderney* (submarine), 1945

A **51** Trinity House Vessel *Patricia* and Arms

A **46** H.M.S. *Alderney* (patrol vessel), 1979

Royal Navy Ships named after Alderney

(Des A. Theobald. Litho B.D.T.)

1990 (3 MAY). *Perf* 13½ (C)

A42	A **42**	14p black and olive-bistre	45	45
A43	A **43**	20p black and orange-brown . .	65	65
A44	A **44**	29p black and cinnamon	1·25	1·25
A45	A **45**	34p black & pale turquoise-blue	1·25	1·25
A46	A **46**	37p black and cobalt	1·40	1·40
A42/6		Set of 5	4·50	4·50
		First Day Cover		6·50
		Presentation Pack	5·50	
		Set of 5 Gutter Pairs	9·00	

Plate Nos.: 14p, 20p, 29p, 34p 1A–1A, 1B–1B; 37p 1A–1A, 1B–1B, 1C–1C, 1D–1D

Sheets: 50 (2 panes 5×5)

Imprint: Central, side margins of each pane

Quantities sold: 14p 290,801; 20p 291,996; 29p 142,011; 34p 146,711; 37p 151,711

Withdrawn: 4.5.91

A **47** Wreck of H.M.S. *Victory*, 1744

A **48** Lighthouse Keeper's Daughter rowing back to the Casquets

A **49** MBB-Bolkow Bo 105D Helicopter leaving pad on St. Thomas Tower

A **50** Migrating Birds over Lighthouse

Automation of the Casquets Lighthouse

(Des A. Theobald. Litho Cartor)

1991 (30 APR). *Perf* 14×13½ (C)

A47	A **47**	21p multicoloured	1·60	2·00
A48	A **48**	26p multicoloured	2·00	2·25
A49	A **49**	31p multicoloured	2·50	2·75
A50	A **50**	37p multicoloured	3·50	3·75
A51	A **51**	50p multicoloured	6·00	5·00
A47/51		Set of 5	14·00	14·00
		First Day Cover		14·00
		Presentation Pack	17·00	
		Set of 5 Gutter Pairs	28·00	

Plate Nos.: All values 1A, 1B, 1C, 1D (each ×4)

Sheets: 50 (2 panes 5×5)

Imprint: Central, side margins

Quantities sold: 21p 280,555; 26p 164,155; 31p 158,465; 37p 158,375; 50p 238,825

Withdrawn: 29.4.92

A **52** Two French Warships on Fire

A **53** Crews leaving burning Ships

A **54** French Warship sinking

A **55** "The Battle of La Hogue"

100th Anniversary of Battle of La Hogue

(Des C. Abbott. Litho B.D.T.)

1992 (18 SEPT). *Perf* 14×15 (50p) *or* 13½ *(others), both comb*

52	A **52**	23p multicoloured	....	2·00	2·00
53	A **53**	28p multicoloured	....	2·75	2·75
54	A **54**	33p multicoloured	....	3·00	3·00
55	A **55**	50p multicoloured	....	4·50	4·50
52/5		Set of 4	....	11·00	11·00
		First Day Cover	....		12·00
		Presentation Pack	....	12·00	
		Set of 4 Gutter Pairs	......	22·00	

Nos. A52/4 show details of the painting on the 50p value.

Plate Nos.: All values 1A, 1B (each ×5)

Sheets: 50 (2 panes 5×5)

Imprint: Central, right-hand margin (50p) or central, side margins (others)

Quantities sold: 23p 238,820; 28p 188,685; 33p 172,565; 50p 186,096

Withdrawn: 17.9.93

56 Spiny Lobster

A **57** Plumose Anemone

58 Starfish

A **59** Sea Urchin

Endangered Species. Marine Life

(Des A. Peck. Litho Questa)

1993 (2 NOV). *Perf* 14½ (C)

56	A **56**	24p multicoloured	....	90	90
		a. Horiz strip of 4. Nos. A56/9		4·25	
57	A **57**	28p multicoloured	....	1·00	1·00
58	A **58**	33p multicoloured	....	1·25	1·25
59	A **59**	39p multicoloured	....	1·60	1·60
56/9		Set of 4	....	4·25	4·25
		First Day Cover	....		5·75
		Presentation Pack	....	5·75	

Plate Nos.: All values 1A, 1B (each ×5)

Sheets: 16 (4×4). Nos. A56/9 were printed together, *se-tenant*, in horizontal strips of 4 throughout the sheet

Imprint: Central, right-hand margin

Quantity sold: 216,788 strips

Withdrawn: 1.11.94

A **60** Blue-tailed Damselfly, Dark Hair Water Crowfoot and Branched Bur-reed

A **61** White-toothed Shrew and Flax-leaved St. John's Wort

A **62** Fulmar and Kaffir Fig

A **63** Clouded Yellow (butterfly) and Red Clover

A **64** Bumble Bee, Prostrate Broom and Giant Broomrape

A **65** Dartford Warbler and Lesser Dodder

A **66** Peacock (butterfly) and Stemless Thistle

A **67** Mole and Bluebell

A **68** Great Green
Grasshopper and
Common Gorse

A **69** Six-spot Burnet
(moth) and
Viper's Bugloss

A **73** Puffin and English
Stonecrop

A **74** Emperor (moth)
and Bramble

A **70** Common Blue
(butterfly) and
Pyramidal Orchid

A **70**a Small Tortoiseshell
and Buddleia

A **75** Pale-spined
Hedgehog and
Pink Oxalis

A **76** Common Tern and
Bermuda Grass

A **71** Common Rabbit
and Creeping
Buttercup

A **72** Great Black-backed
Gull and Sand
Crocus

A **77** Northern Gannet and
Fucus vesiculosus
(seaweed)

Flora and Fauna

(Des Wendy Bramall. Litho B.D.T. (No. A71a) or Questa
(others))

1994 (5 MAY)–**98.** *Perf* 14½ (C)

A **72**a Rock Pipit and
Sea Stock

A **72**b Sand Digger Wasp
and Sea Bindweed

A60	A **60**	1p multicoloured (a)	10	1
A61	A **61**	2p multicoloured (a)	10	1
A62	A **62**	3p multicoloured (a)	10	1
A63	A **63**	4p multicoloured (a)	10	1
A64	A **64**	5p multicoloured (a)	10	1
A65	A **65**	6p multicoloured (a)	15	2
A66	A **66**	7p multicoloured (a)	15	2
A67	A **67**	8p multicoloured (a)	15	2
A68	A **68**	9p multicoloured (a)	20	2
A69	A **69**	10p multicoloured (a)	20	2
A70	A **70**	16p multicoloured (a)	30	3
		a. Perf 14×15	30	3
		ab. Booklet pane of 8	2·50	
A70b	A **70**a	18p multicoloured (c)	35	4
		ba. Perf 14×15	50	5
		bb. Booklet pane of 8	4·00	
A71	A **71**	20p multicoloured (a)	40	4
		a. Perf 14×15 (d)	40	4
		ab. Booklet pane of 8	3·25	

A72	A **72**	24p multicoloured (a)	50	55
		a. Perf 14×15	50	55
		ab. Booklet pane of 8	3·75	
A72b	A **72**a	25p multicoloured (c)	50	55
		ba. Perf 14×15	50	55
		bb. Booklet pane of 8	4·00	
A72c	A **72**b	26p multicoloured (c)	50	55
A73	A **73**	30p multicoloured (a)	60	65
A74	A **74**	40p multicoloured (a)	80	85
A75	A **75**	50p multicoloured (a)	1·00	1·10
A76	A **76**	£1 multicoloured (a)	2·00	2·10
A77	A **77**	£2 multicoloured (b)	4·00	4·25
A60/77		Set of 21	11·50	12·50
		First Day Covers (5)		17·00
		Presentation Packs (3)	14·00	
		Stamp-cards (set of 21) . .	4·50	18·00
		Set of 21 Gutter Pairs	23·00	

Nos. A70a, A70ba, A71a, A72a and A72ba were only issued in booklets with the upper and lower edges of the panes imperforate.

Printings: (a) 5.5.94; (b) 28.2.95; (c) 2.1.97; (d) 25.3.98

Plate Nos.: 1p, 3p, 5p, 7p, 9p, 16p, 18p, 20p, 25p, 26p, 40p 1A, 1B (each ×4); 2p, 4p, 6p, 8p, 10p, 24p, 30p, 50p 1C, 1D (each ×4); £1, £2 1A, 1B, 1C, 1D (each ×4)

Sheets: 50 (2 panes 5×5)

Imprint: £1, £2 Central left margin of each pane; others central left or right margin of each pane

A **78** Royal Aircraft Factory SE5A

A **79** Miles Master II and other Miles Aircraft

A **80** Miles Aerovan and Miles Monitor

A **81** Miles Falcon Six winning King's Cup Air Race, 1935

A **82** Miles Hawk Speed Six winning Manx Air Derby, 1947

A **83** Miles Falcon Six breaking U.K.–Cape Record, 1936

Birth Centenary of Tommy Rose (aviator)

(Des C. Abbott. Litho B.D.T.)

1995 (1 SEPT). Perf 14×15 (C)

A78	A **78**	35p multicoloured	85	85
		a. Horiz strip of 3. Nos. A78/80	2·50	
A79	A **79**	35p multicoloured	85	85
A80	A **80**	35p multicoloured	85	85
A81	A **81**	41p multicoloured	1·00	1·00
		a. Horiz strip of 3. Nos. A81/3	3·00	
A82	A **82**	41p multicoloured	1·00	1·00
A83	A **83**	41p multicoloured	1·00	1·00
A78/83		Set of 6	5·50	5·50
		First Day Cover		6·50
		Presentation Pack	6·50	
		Gutter Strips of 6 (2)	11·00	

Plate Nos.: Both values 1A, 1B, 1C (each ×5)

Sheets: 12 (2 panes 3×2). Nos. A78/80 and A81/3 were printed together, se-tenant, as horizontal strips of 3 throughout the sheet

Imprint: Central, bottom margin

Withdrawn: 31.8.96

RETURN OF THE ISLANDERS 15 DECEMBER 1945

A **84**a Returning Islanders
(*illustration reduced. Actual size* 93×70 *mm*)

50th Anniversary of Return of Islanders to Alderney

(Des C. Abbott. Litho B.D.T.)

1995 (16 NOV). *Sheet* 93×70 *mm. Perf* 13½ (C)
MSA84 A **84**a £1.65 multicoloured . . . . . . 4·00 4·00
First Day Cover . . . . 4·25
Presentation Pack . . . . . . 4·25

Withdrawn: 15.11.96

A **85** Signallers training on Alderney

A **86** Communications Station, Falkland Islands

A **87** Dish Aerial and Land Rover, Gulf War

A **88** Service with United Nations

25th Anniversary of Adoption of 30th Signal Regiment by Alderney

(Des A. Theobald. Litho Walsall)

1996 (24 JAN). *Perf* 14 (C)
A85 A **85** 24p multicoloured 65 65
 a. *Horiz strip of* 4. *Nos.* A85/8 5·00
A86 A **86** 41p multicoloured . . . . 1·10 1·10
A87 A **87** 60p multicoloured . . . . 1·50 1·50

A88 A **88** 75p multicoloured . . . . 1·75 1·75
A85/8 Set of 4 . . . . 5·00 5·00
First Day Cover . . . . 7·00
Presentation Pack . . . . . . 7·00
Gutter Strip of 8 . . . . 10·00

Plate Nos.: All values 1A, 1B, 1C, 1D, 1E, 1F (each ×4)
Sheets: 16 (2 panes 4×2). Nos. A85/8 were printed in *se-tenant* strips of 4 across the sheet, each strip forming a composite design
Imprint: Central, bottom margin
Withdrawn: 28.1.97

A **89** Cat with Butterfly

A **90** Blue and White on Table

A **91** Tabby Kitten grooming Blue and White Persian Kitten

A **92** Red Persian under Table

A **93** White Cat with Tortoiseshell and White in Toy Cart

A **94** Siamese playing with Wool

Cats

(Des P. le Vasseur. Litho B.D.T.)

1996 (19 JULY). *Perf* 13½ (C)
A89 A **89** 16p multicoloured 45 45
A90 A **90** 24p multicoloured 65 65
A91 A **91** 25p multicoloured 65 65
A92 A **92** 35p multicoloured 95 95

A93	A **93**	41p multicoloured	. . . .	1·10	1·10
A94	A **94**	60p multicoloured	. . . .	1·75	1·75
A89/94		Set of 6	. . . .	5·00	5·00
		First Day Cover	. . . .		6·00
		Presentation Pack	. . . . . .	6·00	
		Set of 6 Gutter Pairs	. . . .	10·00	
MSA95	144×97 mm. Nos. A89/94		. . . . . .	5·00	5·00
		First Day Cover	. . . .		6·00

Plate Nos.: All values 1A, 1B (each ×4)

Sheets: 50 (2 panes 5×5)

Imprint: Central, right-hand margin of top pane

Withdrawn: 18.7.97

A **95** Harold   A **96** John Arlott   A **97** Pelham J.
Larwood   Warner

A **98** W. G. Grace   A **99** John Wisden

150th Anniversary of Cricket on Alderney

(Des R. Ollington. Litho Walsall)

1997 (21 AUG). *Perf* 13½ (C)

A96	A **95**	18p multicoloured	. . . .	50	50
A97	A **96**	25p multicoloured	. . . .	65	65
A98	A **97**	37p multicoloured	. . . .	1·00	1·00
A99	A **98**	43p multicoloured	. . . .	1·25	1·25
A100	A **99**	63p multicoloured	. . . .	1·60	1·60
A96/100		Set of 5	. . . .	4·50	4·50
		First Day Cover	. . . .		5·50
		Presentation Pack	. . . . . .	5·50	
		Set of 5 Gutter Pairs	. . . .	9·00	
MSA101	190×75 mm. Nos. A96/100 and label			4·50	4·50
		First Day Cover	. . . .		5·50

Plate Nos.: All values 1A, 1B (each ×5)

Sheets: 50 (2 panes 5×5)

Imprint: Central, top and bottom margins

Withdrawn: 20.8.98

A **100** Railway under   A **101** *Ariadne* (paddle
Construction   steamer) at
                               Anchor

A **102** Quarrying Stone   A **103** Quarry Railway

A **104** Queen Victoria   A **105** Royal Yacht
and Prince Albert   *Victoria and*
on Alderney   *Albert* and Guard
                           of Honour

A **106** Railway Workers A **107** Royal Party in
greet Queen   Railway Wagons
Victoria

Garrison Island (1st series). 150th Anniversary of Harbour

(Des R. Carter. Litho Questa)

1997 (20 NOV)–**98**. *Perf* 14½×14 (C)

A102	A **100**	18p multicoloured	. . . .	45	45
		a. Horiz pair. Nos. A102/3. .		90	90
		b. Booklet pane. Nos. A102/5 with margins all round (10.11.98)		2·25	
		c. Booklet pane. Nos. A102/3 and A106/7 with margins all round (10.11.98)		2·25	

A103	A **101**	18p multicoloured	45	45
A104	A **102**	25p multicoloured	65	65
		a. Horiz pair. Nos. A104/5. .	1·25	1·25
		b. Booklet pane. Nos. A104/5 and A108/9 with margins all round (10.11.98)	2·75	
A105	A **103**	25p multicoloured	65	65
A106	A **104**	26p multicoloured	70	70
		a. Horiz pair. Nos. A106/7. .	1·40	1·40
		b. Booklet pane. Nos. A106/9 with margins all round (10.11.98)	3·00	
A107	A **105**	26p multicoloured	70	70
A108	A **106**	31p multicoloured	80	80
		a. Horiz pair. Nos. A108/9. .	1·60	1·60
A109	A **107**	31p multicoloured	80	80
A102/9		Set of 8	4·75	4·75
		First Day Cover		5·50
		Presentation Pack	5·50	

See also Nos. A116/23 and A132/9.

Plate Nos.: All values 1A, 1B (each ×4)

Sheets: 20 (4×5), the two designs for each value printed together, *se-tenant*, in horizontal pairs throughout the sheets, each pair forming a composite design.

Imprint: Central, side margins

Withdrawn: 19.11.98

A **108** Modern Superlite Helmet and Wreck of *Point Law* (oil tanker)

A **109** Cousteau-Gagnan Demand Valve and Wreck of *Stella* (steamer)

A **110** Heinke Closed Helmet and *Liverpool* (full-rigged ship)

A **111** Siebe Closed Helmet

A **112** Deane Open Helmet

21st Anniversary of Alderney Diving Club

(Des Victoria Kinnersly. Litho B.D.T.)

1998 (10 FEB). *Perf* 13 (C)

A110	A **108**	20p multicoloured	50	50
A111	A **109**	30p multicoloured	75	75
A112	A **110**	37p multicoloured	90	90
A113	A **111**	43p multicoloured	1·00	1·00
A114	A **112**	63p multicoloured	1·50	1·50
A110/14		Set of 5	4·25	4·25
		First Day Cover		5·00
		Presentation Pack	5·00	
		Set of 5 Gutter Pairs . .	8·50	
MSA115		190×75 mm. Nos. A110/14 and label	4·25	4·25
		First Day Cover		5·00

Plate Nos.: All values 1A, 1B (each ×5)

Sheets: 50 (2 panes 5×5)

Imprint: Central, side margins

Withdrawn: 9.2.99

A **113** Alderney Post Office

A **114** Traders in Victoria Street

A **115** Court House

A **116** Police Station and Fire Engine

A **117** St. Anne's Church

A **118** Wedding Party at Albert Gate

A **119** *Courier* (ferry) at Braye Bay

A **120** Fishermen at Quay

Garrison Island (2nd series)

(Des R. Carter. Litho Questa)

1998 (10 NOV). *Perf* 14½×14 (C)

A116	A **113**	20p multicoloured	50	50
		a. *Horiz pair. Nos.* A116/17	1·00	1·00
		b. *Booklet pane. Nos.* A116/19 *with margins all round*	2·00	
		c. *Booklet pane. Nos.* A116/17 *and* A120/1 *with margins all round* . .	2·25	
A117	A **114**	20p multicoloured	50	50
A118	A **115**	25p multicoloured	60	60
		a. *Horiz pair. Nos.* A118/19	1·25	1·25
		b. *Booklet pane. Nos.* A118/19 *and* A122/3 *with margins all round* . .	3·00	
A119	A **116**	25p multicoloured	60	60
A120	A **117**	30p multicoloured	70	70
		a. *Horiz pair. Nos.* A120/1 . .	1·40	1·40
		b. *Booklet pane. Nos.* A120/3 *with margins all round*	3·00	
A121	A **118**	30p multicoloured	70	70
A122	A **119**	37p multicoloured	85	85
		a. *Horiz pair. Nos.* A122/3 . .	1·75	1·75
A123	A **120**	37p multicoloured	85	85
A116/23		*Set of* 8	4·75	4·75
		First Day Cover		5·50
		Presentation Pack	5·50	

Plate Nos.: 20p, 30p 1A (×4); 25p, 37p 1B (×4)

Sheets: 20 (4×5), the two designs for each value were printed together, *se-tenant*, in horizontal pairs throughout the sheets, each pair forming a composite design

Imprint: Central, side margins

Withdrawn: 9.11.99

A **121***a* Stained Glass Window commemorating Mary Rogers (Chief Stewardess) (25p.); *Stella* leaving Southampton (£1.75) (*illustration reduced. Actual size* 110×90 *mm*)

Centenary of the Wreck of Stella (mail steamer)

(Des Joanna Brehaut. Litho B.D.T.)

1999 (5 FEB). *Sheet* 110×90 *mm. Perf* 14 (C)

MSA124	A **121***a*	25p, £1.75, multicoloured . .	2·00	2·25
		First Day Cover		4·75
		Presentation Pack	4·75	

A **122** Solar Eclipse at 10.15 am

A **123** At 10.51 am

A **124** At 11.14 am

A **125** At 11.16 am

A **126** At 11.17 am

A **127** At 11.36 am

Total Eclipse of the Sun on 11 August

(Des Victoria Kinnersly. Litho Enschedé)

1999 (27 APR). *Perf* 13½×13 (C)

A125	A **122**	20p multicoloured	40	45
A126	A **123**	25p multicoloured	50	55

A127	A **124**	30p multicoloured	60	65
A128	A **125**	38p multicoloured	75	80
A129	A **126**	44p multicoloured	90	95
A130	A **127**	64p multicoloured	1·25	1·40
A125/30		Set of 6	4·25	4·75
		First Day Cover		5·50
		Presentation Pack	5·50	
		Set of 6 Gutter Pairs	8·75	
MSA131		191×80 mm. Nos. A125/30 and label	4·25	4·75
		First Day Cover		5·50
		Postcard	75	

No. **MS**A131 also includes the "PHILEXFRANCE '99", Paris, and the "iBRA '99", Nuremberg, emblems on the sheet margin.

Plate Nos.: All values 1A, 1B (each ×4)

Sheets: 50 (2 panes 5×5)

Imprint: Central, side margins

A **128** Field Gun and Crew, Fort Grosnez, c 1855

A **129** Parade of 9th Bn, Royal Garrison Artillery

A **130** The Arsenal, Fort Albert, c 1862

A **131** Royal Engineers loading Wagons

A **132** 2nd Bn, Royal Scots on Parade

A **133** Garrison at Work, Fort Tourgis, c 1865

A **134** Gun Emplacement, Fort Houmet Herbé, c 1870

A **135** Royal Alderney Artillery Militia loading Cannon

Garrison Island (3rd series). Forts

(Des R. Carter. Litho Questa)

1999 (19 OCT). *Perf* 14½×14 (C)

A132	A **128**	20p multicoloured	40	45
		a. Horiz pair. Nos. A132/3	80	
		b. Booklet pane. Nos. A132/5, with margins all round	1·75	
		c. Booklet pane. Nos. A132/3 and A138/9, with margins all round	2·25	
		d. Booklet pane. Nos. A132/3 and A136/7, with margins all round	2·00	
A133	A **129**	20p multicoloured	40	45
A134	A **130**	25p multicoloured	50	55
		a. Horiz pair. Nos. A134/5	1·00	
		b. Booklet pane. Nos. A134/7, with margins all round	2·25	
		c. Booklet pane. Nos. A134/5 and A138/9, with margins all round	2·50	
A135	A **131**	25p multicoloured	50	55
A136	A **132**	30p multicoloured	60	65
		a. Horiz pair. Nos. A136/7	1·25	
		b. Booklet pane. Nos. A136/9, with margins all round	2·75	
A137	A **133**	30p multicoloured	60	65
A138	A **134**	38p multicoloured	75	80
		a. Horiz pair. Nos. A138/9	1·50	
A139	A **135**	38p multicoloured	75	80
A132/9		Set of 8	4·50	5·00
		First Day Cover		5·50
		Presentation Pack	5·50	

Plate Nos.: All values 1A, 1B (each ×4)

Sheets: 20 (4×5), the two designs for each value were printed together, *se-tenant*, in horizontal pairs throughout the sheets, each pair forming a composite design

Imprint: Central, right-hand margin

STAMP BOOKLETS

RICES given are for complete booklets.

ALDERNEY
BAILIWICK OF GUERNSEY

8 stamps
£1.28

Bailiwick rate

AB **1** Common Blue and Pyramidal Orchid
(illustration reduced. Actual size 99×60 mm)

1994 (5 MAY)–**95.** *Multicoloured covers as Type* AB **1**.
*Without barcode on the reverse. Panes attached by
selvedge*
ASB1 £1.28 booklet containing pane No. A70*ab*
(cover Type AB **1**) . . . .   2·50
    a. With barcode sticker on reverse (1995) . .   2·50
ASB2 £1.92 booklet containing pane No. A72*ab*
(cover showing Great Black-backed Gull and
Sand Crocus . . . .   3·75

1997 (2 JAN). *Multicoloured covers as Type* AB **1**. *Without
barcode on the reverse. Panes attached by selvedge*
ASB3 £1.44 booklet containing pane No. A70*bb*
(cover showing Small Tortoiseshell (butterfly)
and Buddleia) . . . .   4·00
ASB4 £2 booklet containing pane No. A72*bb* (cover
showing Rock Pipit and Sea Stock) . . . .   4·00
  Sold out: 9.99 (No. ASB3)

1998 (25 MAR). *Multicoloured cover as Type* AB **1**. *With
barcode on the reverse. Pane attached by selvedge*
ASB5 £1.60 booklet containing pane No. A71*ab*
(*cover showing Common Rabbit and Creeping
Buttercup*) . . . .   3·25

AB **2** Map of Alderney
(*illustration reduced. Actual size 164×98 mm*)

Garrison Island (1st and 2nd series)

1998 (10 NOV). *Multicoloured cover as Type* AB **2** *containing
text and illustrations on panes and interleaving pages. With
barcode on the reverse. Stitched*
ASB6 £8.48 booklet containing panes Nos. A102*b*/*c*,
A104*b*, A106*b*, A116*b*/*c*, A118*b* and A120*b* . .   20·00

  Withdrawn: 9.11.99

Garrison Island (3rd series). Forts

1999 (19 OCT). *Multicoloured cover as Type* AB **2** *containing
text and illustrations on panes and interleaving pages. With
barcode on reverse. Stitched*
ASB7 £6.78, booklet containing panes Nos.
A132*b*/*d*, A134*b*/*c* and A136*b* (cover shows
view of fortified coastline) . . . .   13·00

Isle of Man

REGIONAL ISSUES

Although specifically issued for regional use, these issues were initially valid for use throughout the U.K. Regional issues ceased to be valid in the Isle of Man from 5 July, 1973 when the island established its own independent postal administration and introduced its own stamps.

DATES OF ISSUE. Conflicting dates of issue have been announced for some of the regional issues, partly explained by the stamps being released on different dates by the Philatelic Bureau in Edinburgh or the Philatelic Counter in London and in the regions. We have adopted the practice of giving the earliest known dates, since once released the stamps could have been used anywhere in the U.K.

INVALIDATION. Nos. 1/7 were invalidated as from 1 March, 1972 in common with other British 'fsd' stamps. Nos. 8/11 were invalidated for use in the Isle of Man on 5 July, 1973, but, together with other British stamps, were accepted for the prepayment of postage on letters from the island until 5 August, 1973. The Manx Regionals remained valid for use in the rest of the United Kingdom and were withdrawn from sale at the British Post Office Philatelic Sales counters on 4 July, 1974.

1 Multiple Crowns

2

3

(Des J. Nicholson. Portrait by Dorothy Wilding Ltd. Photo Harrison)

1958–68. *Wmk Type* **1.** *Perf* 15×14 (C)

1	**2**	2½d carmine-red (8.6.64)	50	1·25
2	**3**	3d deep lilac (18.8.58)	30	20
		a. *Chalk-surfaced paper* (17.5.63)	12·00	10·00
		p. *One centre phosphor band* (27.6.68)	30	50
3		4d ultramarine (7.2.66)	1·50	1·50
		p. *Two phosphor bands* (5.7.67)	30	30
1/3p		*Set of 3*	1·00	1·60
1		*First Day Cover*		40·00
2		*First Day Cover*		30·00
3		*First Day Cover*		10·00

Cylinder Nos.: 2½d 1; 3d (ord and phos) 1; 4d (ord and phos) 1

Sheets: 240 (12×20)

Quantities sold (ordinary only): 2½d 4,298,160; 3d 35,959,420 (up to 31.3.68 and including 1,080,000 on chalky paper); 4d 4,353,840

Withdrawn: 31.8.66 2½d

Sold out: 11.67 4d ordinary; 12.68 3d ordinary, 4d phosphor; 4.69 3d phosphor

1968–69. *No wmk. Chalk-surfaced paper. One centre phosphor band (Nos. 5/6) or two phosphor bands (others). Perf* 15×14 (C)

4	**3**	4d blue (24.6.68)	25	30
5		4d olive-sepia (4.9.68)	25	40
6		4d bright vermilion (26.2.69)	45	75
7		5d royal blue (4.9.68)	45	75
4/7		*Set of 4*	1·25	2·00
5,7		*First Day Cover*		4·00

Cylinder Nos.: 4d (blue) 1; 4d (olive-sepia) 1; 4d (bright vermilion) 1; 5d 1

Sheets: 240 (12×20)

Sold out: 16.7.69 4d blue

Withdrawn: 14.3.71 (locally), 25.11.71 (British Philatelic Counters) 4d

4

Decimal Currency

(Des J. Matthews. Portrait after plaster cast by Arnold Machin. Photo Harrison)

1971 (7 JULY). *Chalk-surfaced paper. One centre phosphor band (2½p) or two phosphor bands (others). Perf* 15×14 (C)

8	**4**	2½p bright magenta	20	15
9		3p ultramarine	20	15
10		5p reddish violet	40	50
11		7½p chestnut	40	65
8/11		*Set of 4*	1·25	1·25
		First Day Cover		3·00
		Presentation Pack	2·50	

All values were originally issued on ordinary cream paper, but the 2½p and 3p later appeared on white fluorescent paper.

Cylinder Nos.: (dot and no dot): 2½p 3, phos 5; 3p 1, phos 4; 5p 4, phos 12; 7½p 4, phos 10

Sheets: 200 (10×20)

Withdrawn: 4.7.73 (locally), 4.7.74 (British Philatelic Counters)

INDEPENDENT POSTAL ADMINISTRATION

The Isle of Man established an independent postal administration on 5 July, 1973 and introduced its own stamps.

NO WATERMARK. All the following issues are on unwatermarked paper *unless otherwise stated.*

5 Castletown

6 Port Erin

7 Snaefell

8 Laxey

9 Tynwald Hill

10 Douglas Promenade

11 Port St. Mary

12 Fairy Bridge

13 Peel

14 Cregneish

15 Ramsey Bay

16 Douglas Bay

17 Manx Cat

20 Manx Loaghtyn Ram

18 Monk's Bridge, Ballasalla

19 Derbyhaven

21 Manx Shearwater

22 Viking Longship

(Des J. Nicholson. Photo Courvoisier)

1973 (5 JULY)–**75.** *Granite paper. Perf* 11½ (C)

12	**5**	½p multicoloured (*ab*)	10	10
13	**6**	1p multicoloured (*ae*)	10	10
14	**7**	1½p multicoloured (*ak*)	10	10
15	**8**	2p multicoloured (*aj*)	10	10
16	**9**	2½p multicoloured (*a*)	10	10
17	**10**	3p mult (*sage-green border*) (*ac*)	10	10
		a. *Error. Olive-bistre border* †	£150	£125
18	**11**	3½p mult (*olive-brown border*) (*ad*)	15	15
		a. *Error. Grey-brown border* † . .	£150	£125
19	**12**	4p multicoloured (*a*)	15	15
20	**9**	4½p multicoloured (*f*)	20	20
21	**13**	5p multicoloured (*ah*)	20	20
22	**10**	5½p multicoloured (*g*)	25	25
23	**14**	6p multicoloured (*al*)	25	25
24	**8**	7p multicoloured (*g*)	30	30
25	**15**	7½p multicoloured (*a*)	25	25
26		8p multicoloured (*f*)	35	35

27	**16**	9p multicoloured (*an*).........		30	35
28	**17**	10p multicoloured (*an*).........		40	35
29	**18**	11p multicoloured (*i*)		30	30
30	**19**	13p multicoloured (*i*)		40	40
31	**20**	20p multicoloured (*an*).........		50	50
32	**21**	50p multicoloured (*an*).........		1·50	1·25
33	**22**	£1 multicoloured (*am*)		3·00	2·50
12/33		Set of 22		8·00	7·50
		First Day Covers (7)			9·00
		Presentation Packs (6)	10·00		

†These errors occur on printings (*c*) and (*d*). That on the 3p resembles the border colour of the ½p and that on the 3½p the 2p.

Printings: (*a*) 5.7.73; (*b*) 1.11.73; (*c*) 16.4.74; (*d*) 29.7.74; (*e*) 2.9.74; (*f*) 8.1.75; (*g*) 28.5.75; (*h*) 16.6.75; (*i*) 29.10.75; (*j*) 1.12.75; (*k*) 2.2.76; (*l*) 20.9.76; (*m*) 16.2.77; (*n*) 7.7.77

Printings (*a*) and (*i*) have thick shiny gum, but all the other printings have matt, almost invisible gum. Printings (*f*), (*g*) and (*i*) are inscribed "1975". The remainder are inscribed "1973".

Sheets: 50 (5×10) ½p to 9p, 11p, 13p; (10×5) 10p, 20p to £1

Withdrawn: 31.12.78 (except ½p, 3p and 3½p values in booklets withdrawn 15.5.79. In addition 2p and 3½p values were kept available for use on postal orders after 31.12.78 until finally withdrawn on 30.6.83 (2p) or 31.12.85 (3½p))

23 Landing of the Vikings on Man, A.D. 938

Inauguration of Postal Independence

(Des J. Nicholson. Photo Harrison)

1973 (5 JULY). *Perf* 14 (C)

34	**23**	15p multicoloured		60	60
		First Day Cover			1·75
		Presentation Pack..........	3·00		

For 15p inscr 'POST OFFICE DECENNIUM 1983' see No. 256

Cylinder Nos.: 1A (×4)

Sheets: 50 (10×5)

Quantity sold: 350,000

Sold out: Soon after issue

24 No. 1 *Sutherland*, 1873

25 No. 4 *Caledonia*, 1885

26 No. 13 *Kissack*, 1910

27 No. 3 *Pender*, 1873

Steam Railway Centenary

(Des J. Nicholson. Photo Harrison)

1973 (4 AUG). *Perf* 15×14 (C)

35	**24**	2½p multicoloured		20	2
36	**25**	3p multicoloured		20	2
37	**26**	7½p multicoloured		80	9
38	**27**	9p multicoloured		1·00	9
35/8		Set of 4		2·00	2·0
		First Day Cover			2·5
		Presentation Pack..........	3·00		

Cylinder Nos. All values 1A (×5)

Sheets: 50 (5×10)

Quantities sold: 2½p 617,122; 3p 808,173; 7½p 331,695; 9p 324,414

Withdrawn: 3.8.74

28 Leonard Randles, First Winner, 1923

29 Alan Holmes, Double Winner, 1957

Golden Jubilee of Manx Grand Prix

(Des J. Nicholson. Litho John Waddington)

1973 (4 SEPT). *Perf* 14 (C)

39	**28**	3p multicoloured		30	2(
40	**29**	3½p multicoloured		30	2(
39/40		Set of 2		60	4(
		First Day Cover			1·0(
		Presentation Pack..........	1·00		
		Set of 2 Gutter Pairs........	2·00		

Plate Nos.: Both values 1A, 1B, 1C, 1D (each ×4)

Sheets: 50 (2 panes 5×5)

Imprint: Central, bottom margin

Quantities sold: 3p 550,347; 3½p 653,355

Withdrawn: 3.9.74

30 Princess Anne and
Capt. Mark Philips

oyal Wedding

(Des A. Larkins. Recess and litho De La Rue)

973 (14 NOV). *Perf* 13½ (C)

1	30	25p multicoloured	1·00	1·00
		First Day Cover		1·50
		Presentation Pack	1·75	
		Gutter Pair	2·25	

Plate Nos.: 1A, 1B (each ×4)

Sheets: 50 (2 panes 5×5)

Imprint: Right-hand corner, bottom margin

Quantity sold: 400,813

Withdrawn: 13.11.74

1 Badge, Citation and Sir
William Hillary (founder)

32 Wreck of *St. George*,
1830

33 *Manchester & Salford*,
1868–87

34 *Osman Gabriel*

150th Anniversary of Royal National Lifeboat Institution

(Des J. Nicholson. Photo Courvoisier)

1974 (4 MAR). *Granite paper. Perf* 11½ (C)

42	31	3p multicoloured	10	10
43	32	3½p multicoloured	15	15
44	33	8p multicoloured	40	40
45	34	10p multicoloured	45	45
42/5		Set of 4	1·00	1·00
		First Day Cover		1·50
		Presentation Pack	1·60	

Sheets: 100 (10×10)

Quantities sold: 3p 674,984; 3½p 849,990; 8p 374,941; 10p 375,043

Withdrawn: 3.3.75

35 Stanley Woods, 1935

36 Freddy Frith, 1937

37 Max Deubel and Emil
Horner, 1961

38 Mike Hailwood, 1961

Tourist Trophy Motor Cycle Races (1st issue)

(Des J. Nicholson. Litho De La Rue)

1974 (29 MAY). *Perf* 13×13½ (C)

46	35	3p multicoloured	10	10
47	36	3½p multicoloured	10	10
48	37	8p multicoloured	45	45
49	38	10p multicoloured	60	45
46/9		Set of 4	1·10	1·00
		First Day Cover		1·40
		Presentation Pack	1·25	
		Set of 4 Gutter Pairs	2·25	

See also Nos. 63/6

Plate Nos.: All values 1A, 1B, 1C, 1D (each ×6); 3p also 1A
(×4)–2A–2A, 1B (×4)–2B–2B, 1C (×4)–2C–2C, 1D (×4)–2D–2D; 8p
also 1A–1A–2A–1A (×3), 1B–1B–2B–1B (×3), 1C–1C–2C–1C (×3),
1D–1D–2D–1D (×3)

Sheets: 50 (2 panes 5×5)

Imprint: Right-hand corner, bottom margin

Quantities sold: 3p 578,045; 3½p 816,235; 8p 334,760; 10p 403,177

Withdrawn: 28.5.75

39 Rushen Abbey and Arms

40 Magnus Haraldson rows King Edgar on the Dee

41 King Magnus and Norse Fleet

42 Bridge at Avignon and Bishop's Mitre

Historical Anniversaries. Events described on stamps

(Des J. Nicholson, from ideas by G. Kneale. Litho Questa (3½p, 10p) or John Waddington (others))

1974 (18 SEPT). *Perf* 14 (C)

50	**39**	3½p multicoloured	10	10
51	**40**	4½p multicoloured	10	10
52	**41**	8p multicoloured	40	40
53	**42**	10p multicoloured	50	50
50/3		*Set of 4*	1·00	1·00
		First Day Cover		1·00
		Presentation Pack	1·40	
		Set of 4 Gutter Pairs	2·10	

Plate Nos.: All values 1A, 1B, 1C, 1D (each ×4)

Sheets: 50 (2 panes 5×5)

Imprint: Right-hand corner, bottom margin and left-hand corner, top margin

Quantities sold: 3½p 931,610; 4½p 1,025,044; 8p 450,418; 10p 425,305

Withdrawn: 17.9.75

43 Churchill and Bugler Dunne at Colenso, 1899

44 Churchill and Government Buildings, Douglas

45 Churchill and Manx A.A. Gun Crew

46 Churchill as Freeman of Douglas

Birth Centenary of Sir Winston Churchill

(Des G. Kneale. Photo Courvoisier)

1974 (22 NOV). *Granite paper. Perf* 11½ (C)

54	**43**	3½p multicoloured	10	10
55	**44**	4½p multicoloured	10	10
56	**45**	8p multicoloured	25	35
57	**46**	20p multicoloured	75	55
54/7		*Set of 4*	1·10	1·00
		First Day Cover		1·40
		Presentation Pack	1·40	
MS58	121×91 mm. Nos. 54/7		1·10	1·00
		First Day Cover		1·75

No. **MS**58 is inscribed '30th NOV. 1974'.

Sheets: 25 (5×5)

Quantities sold: 3½p 916,748; 4½p 853,537; 8p 424,691; 20p 429,586; miniature sheet 362,089

Withdrawn: 21.11.75

47 Cabin School and Names of Pioneers

48 Terminal Tower Building, John Gill and Robert Carran

49 Robert and Margaret Clague, and Clague House Museum

50 *William T. Graves* and Thomas Quayle

Manx Pioneers in Cleveland, Ohio

(Des J. Nicholson. Photo Courvoisier)

1975 (14 MAR). *Granite paper. Perf 11½* (C)

59	**47**	4½p multicoloured	....	10	10
60	**48**	5½p multicoloured	....	15	10
61	**49**	8p multicoloured	....	35	40
62	**50**	10p multicoloured	....	50	50
59/62		*Set of 4*	....	1·00	1·00
		First Day Cover	....		1·10
		Presentation Pack	....	1·40	

Sheets: 50 (5×10)

Quantities sold: 4½p 473,352; 5½p 999,802; 8p 433,352; 10p 447,945

Withdrawn: 13.3.76 (5½p sold out 12.75)

51 Tom Sheard, 1923

52 Walter Handley, 1925

53 Geoff Duke, 1955

54 Peter Williams, 1973

Tourist Trophy Motor Cycle Races (2nd issue)

(Des J. Nicholson. Litho John Waddington)

1975 (28 MAY). *Perf 13½* (C)

63	**51**	5½p multicoloured	....	20	15
64	**52**	7p multicoloured	....	30	20
65	**53**	10p multicoloured	....	50	30
66	**54**	12p multicoloured	....	50	45
63/6		*Set of 4*	....	1·25	1·00
		First Day Cover	....		1·75
		Presentation Pack	....	1·50	
		Set of 4 Gutter Pairs	....	2·50	

Plate Nos.: 5½p, 7p 1B, 1D (each ×5); 10p 1A, 1B, 1C (each ×5); 12p 1A, 1C (each ×5)

Sheets: 50 (2 panes 5×5)

Imprint: Right-hand corner, bottom margin

Quantities sold: 5½p 633,250; 7p 520,285; 10p 399,710; 12p 440,208

Withdrawn: 27.5.76

55 Goldie and the Nunnery, Douglas

56 Goldie and Map of Africa

57 Goldie and Royal Geographical Society Emblem

58 River Scene on the Niger

50th Death Anniversary of Sir George Goldie

(Des G. Kneale. Photo Courvoisier)

1975 (9 SEPT). *Granite paper. Perf 11½* (C)

67	**55**	5½p multicoloured	....	10	15
68	**56**	7p multicoloured	....	20	20
69	**57**	10p multicoloured	....	40	30
70	**58**	12p multicoloured	....	40	45
67/70		*Set of 4*	....	1·00	1·00
		First Day Cover	....		1·25
		Presentation Pack	....	1·40	

Sheets: 50 (10×5) 7p, 10p; (5×10) others

Quantities sold: 5½p 488,317; 7p 426,849; 10p 373,771; 12p 439,843

Withdrawn: 8.9.76

59 Title Page of Manx Bible

60 Rev. Philip Moore and Ballaugh Old Church

61 Bishop Hildesley and Bishops Court

62 John Kelly saving Bible Manuscript

Christmas and Bicentenary of Manx Bible

(Des J. Nicholson. Litho Questa)

1975 (29 OCT). *Perf* 14 (C)

71	**59**	5½p multicoloured	15	15
72	**60**	7p multicoloured	20	20
73	**61**	11p multicoloured	35	35
74	**62**	13p multicoloured	40	40
71/4		*Set of 4*	1·00	1·00
		First Day Cover		1·10
		Presentation Pack	1·25	
		Set of 4 Gutter Pairs	2·00	

Plate Nos. 13p 1C, 1D (each ×4); others 1A, 1B (each ×4)

Sheets: 50 (2 panes 5×5)

Quantities sold: 5½p 738,774; 7p 607,377; 11p 405,126; 13p 402,463

63 William Christian listening to Patrick Henry

64 Conveying the Fincastle Resolutions

65 Patrick Henry and William Christian

66 Christian as an Indian Fighter

Bicentenary of American Revolution and Col. William Christian Commemoration

(Des and litho John Waddington)

1976 (12 MAR). *Perf* 13½ (C)

75	**63**	5½p multicoloured	15	15
76	**64**	7p multicoloured	20	20

77	**65**	13p multicoloured	35	35
		a. *Black* (*face value and inscr*) *printed double*		
78	**66**	20p multicoloured	50	50
75/8		*Set of 4*	1·10	1·10
		First Day Cover		1·10
		Presentation Pack	1·50	
		Set of 4 Gutter Pairs	2·25	
MS79		150×90 mm. Nos. 75/8. Perf 14 (C)	1·50	1·60
		First Day Cover		2·75
		Presentation Pack	2·25	

Plate Nos.: 5½p, 20p 1A, 1C (each ×4); others 1B, 1D (each ×4)

Sheets: 50 (2 panes 5×5)

Quantities sold: 5½p 487,310; 7p 524,144; 13p 558,348; 20p 424,728; miniature sheet 209,367

Withdrawn: 11.3.77

67 First Horse Tram, 1876

68 'Toast-rack' Tram, 1890

69 Horse-bus, 1895

70 Royal Tram, 1972

Douglas Horse Trams Centenary

(Des J. Nicholson. Photo Courvoisier)

1976 (26 MAY). *Granite paper. Perf* 11½ (C)

80	**67**	5½p multicoloured	10	15
81	**68**	7p multicoloured	15	15

82	**69**	11p multicoloured	....	45	35
83	**70**	13p multicoloured	....	50	45
80/3		*Set of 4*	....	1·10	1·00
		First Day Cover	....		1·10
		Presentation Pack.	....	1·40	

Sheets 25 (5×5)

Quantities sold: 5½p 627,083; 7p 480,417; 11p 391,871; 13p 389,604

Withdrawn: 25.5.77

71 Barroose Beaker   **72** Souvenir Teapot   **73** Laxey Jug

74 Cronk Aust Food Vessel   **75** Sansbury Bowl

76 Knox Urn

Europa. Ceramic Art

(Des J. Nicholson. Photo Courvoisier)

1976 (28 JULY). *Granite paper. Perf 11½* (C)

84	**71**	5p multicoloured	....	25	20
		a. Strip of 3. Nos. 84/6	....	70	60
85	**72**	5p multicoloured	....	25	20
86	**73**	5p multicoloured	....	25	20
87	**74**	10p multicoloured	....	40	35
		a. Strip of 3. Nos. 87/9	....	1·25	1·10
88	**75**	10p multicoloured	....	40	35
89	**76**	10p multicoloured	....	40	35
84/9		*Set of 6*	....	1·75	1·50
		First Day Cover	....		3·00
		Presentation Pack.	....	2·00	

Sheets: 9 (3×3) containing the three designs of each value horizontally and vertically *se-tenant*

Quantities sold: 5p 256,400 of each design; 10p 262,900 of each design

Sold out: 20.11.76 (5p); 12.76 (10p)

77 Diocesan Banner   **78** Onchan Banner

79 Castletown Banner   **80** Ramsey Banner

Christmas and Centenary of Mothers' Union

(Des G. Kneale. Litho Questa)

1976 (14 OCT). *Perf 14½* (C)

90	**77**	6p multicoloured	....	15	15
91	**78**	7p multicoloured	....	15	15
92	**79**	11p multicoloured	....	40	35
93	**80**	13p multicoloured	....	40	45
90/3		*Set of 4*	....	1·00	1·00
		First Day Cover	....		1·00
		Presentation Pack.	....	1·25	

Plate Nos.: 6p 1B (×5); 11p 1A (×5); others 1C (×5)

Sheets: 50 (10×5)

Imprint: Right-hand corner, bottom margin and left-hand corner, top margin

Quantities sold: 6p 905,752; 7p 890,762; 11p 397,807; 13p 390,057

Withdrawn: 13.10.77

81 Queen Elizabeth II   **82** Queen Elizabeth and Prince Philip

83 Queen Elizabeth II

Silver Jubilee

(Des A. Larkins. Litho and recess De La Rue)

1977 (1 MAR). *Perf* 14×13 (7p) *or* 13×14 (*others*), *both comb*

94	**81**	6p multicoloured	20	20
95	**82**	7p multicoloured	20	20
96	**83**	25p multicoloured	80	70
94/6		Set of 3	1·10	1·00
		First Day Cover		1·00
		Presentation Pack	1·25	
		Set of 3 Gutter Pairs	2·25	

Plate Nos.: 6p, 7p 1A (×5)–2A, 1B (×5)–2B, 1C (×5)–2C, 1D (×5)–2D; 25p 1B, 1D (each ×6)

Sheets: 50 (2 panes 5×5)

Imprint: Right-hand corner, bottom margin

Quantities sold: 6p 942,356; 7p 911,191; 25p 651,101

Withdrawn: 28.2.78

84 Carrick Bay from 'Tom-the-Dipper'

85 View from Ramsey

Europa. Landscapes

(Des J. Nicholson. Litho Questa)

1977 (26 MAY). *Perf* 13½×14 (C)

97	**84**	6p multicoloured	20	20
98	**85**	10p multicoloured	30	30
97/8		Set of 2	50	50
		First Day Cover		1·00
		Presentation Pack	1·00	
		Set of 2 Gutter Pairs	1·00	

Plate Nos.: 6p, 1A, 1B, 1C, 1D, 2A, 2B, 2C, 2D (each ×4); 10p 1A, 1B, 1C, 1D (each ×5), 2A–1A–1A–2A–1A, 2B–1B–1B–2B–1B, 2C–1C–1C–2C–1C, 2D–1D–1D–2D–1D

Sheets: 40 (2 panes 4×5)

Imprint: Right-hand corner, bottom margin and left-hand corner, top margin

Quantities sold: 6p 778,685; 10p 843,525

Withdrawn: 25.5.78

86 F. A. Applebee, 1912

87 St. John Ambulance Brigade at Governor's Bridge, *c.* 1938

88 Scouts working Scoreboard

89 John Williams, 1976

Linked Anniversaries

(Des J. Nicholson. Litho John Waddington)

1977 (26 MAY). *Perf* 13½ (C)

99	**86**	6p multicoloured	20	1
100	**87**	7p multicoloured	20	2
101	**88**	11p multicoloured	50	4
102	**89**	13p multicoloured	50	4
99/102		Set of 4	1·25	1·0
		First Day Cover		1·0
		Presentation Pack	1·50	
		Set of 4 Gutter Pairs	2·50	

The events commemorated are: 70th anniversary of Man TT; 70th anniversary of Boy Scouts; centenary of St. Joh Ambulance Brigade

Plate Nos.: 11p 1A, 1C (each ×4); others 1B, 1D (each ×4)

Sheets: 50 (2 panes 5×5)

Imprint: Right-hand corner, bottom margin

Quantities sold: 6p 525,703; 7p 875,303; 11p 431,053; 13p 440,40⁩

Withdrawn: 25.5.78

90 Old Summer House, Mount Morrison, Peel

91 Wesley preaching in Castletown Square

2 Wesley preaching outside Bradden Church

93 New Methodist Church, Douglas

Bicentenary of the First Visit of John Wesley

(Des and photo Courvoisier)

1977 (19 OCT). *Granite paper. Perf* 11½ (C)

03	**90**	6p multicoloured	15	15
04	**91**	7p multicoloured	20	20
05	**92**	11p multicoloured	35	35
06	**93**	13p multicoloured	40	40
03/6		*Set of* 4	1·00	1·00
		First Day Cover		1·00
		Presentation Pack	1·25	

Sheets: 50 (5×10)

Quantities sold: 6p 661,755; 7p 976,155; 11p 373,805; 13p 366,905

Withdrawn: 18.10.78

94 H.M.S. *Ben-My-Chree* and Short Type 184 Seaplane, 1915

95 H.M.S. *Vindex* and Bristol Scout C, 1915

96 Boulton Paul Defiant over Douglas Bay, 1941

97 Sepecat Jaguar over Ramsey, 1977

R.A.F. Diamond Jubilee

(Des A. Theobald. Litho John Waddington)

1978 (28 Feb). *Perf* 13½×14

107	**94**	6p multicoloured	....	20	15
108	**95**	7p multicoloured	....	30	20
109	**96**	11p multicoloured	....	45	35
110	**97**	13p multicoloured	....	50	40
107/10		*Set of 4*	....	1·25	1·00
		First Day Cover			1·25
		Presentation Pack		1·50	
		Set of 4 Gutter Pairs		2·50	

Plate Nos.: All values 1A, 1C (each ×4)

Sheets: 50 (2 panes 5×5)

Quantities sold: 6p 690,536; 7p 875,811; 11p 416,082; 13p 422,797

Withdrawn: 27.2.79

98 Watch Tower, Langness

99 Jurby Church

100 Government Buildings

101 Tynwald Hill

102 Milner's Tower

103 Laxey Wheel

104 Castle Rushen

105 St. Ninian's Church

106 Tower of Refuge

107 St. German's Cathedral

108 Point of Ayre Lighthouse

109 Corrin's Tower

110 Douglas Head Lighthouse

111 Fuchsia

112 Manx Cat

113 Chough

114 Viking Warrior

114a Queen Elizabeth II

(Des G. Kneale (£2), J. Nicholson (others). Litho Questa (½p to 16p), photo Courvoisier (20p to £2))

1978 (28 FEB)–**81.** (a) Perf 14 (C)

111	**98**	½p multicoloured (a)	10	10
		a. Perf 14½	20	10
112	**99**	1p multicoloured (a)	10	10
		a. Perf 14½	20	10
113	**100**	6p multicoloured (a)	30	30
114	**101**	7p multicoloured (a)	35	35
		a. Perf 14½	8·00	6·50
115	**102**	8p multicoloured (a)	25	25
		a. Perf 14½	35	35
116	**103**	9p multicoloured (a)	35	35
		a. Perf 14½	35	35
117	**104**	10p multicoloured (a)	40	40
		a. Perf 14½	35	35
118	**105**	11p multicoloured (a)	40	40
		a. Perf 14½	40	40
119	**106**	12p multicoloured (a)	50	50
		a. Perf 14½	50	40
120	**107**	13p multicoloured (a)	60	60
		a. Perf 14½	40	40
121	**108**	14p multicoloured (a)	60	60
		a. Perf 14½	50	50
122	**109**	15p multicoloured (a)	75	75
		a. Perf 14½	40	40
123	**110**	16p multicoloured (a)	90	90
		a. Perf 14½	25·00	21·00
		(b) Granite paper. Perf 11½ (C)		
124	**111**	20p multicoloured (b)	40	40
125	**112**	25p multicoloured (b)	50	50
126	**113**	50p multicoloured (b)	1·00	1·00
127	**114**	£1 multicoloured (b)	2·00	2·00
128	**114a**	£2 multicoloured (c)	4·25	4·25
111/28		Set of 18 (cheapest)	11·50	11·50
		First Day Covers* (5)		12·50
		Presentation Packs (4)	15·00	

*The most common versions of the three low and medium value first day covers prepared by the Philatelic Bureau were franked with Nos. 111a, 112/15, 116a, 117/18, 119a, 120, 121a, 122 and 123a. Some examples can be found with the ½p as No. 111, the 11p as No. 118a or the 13p as No. 120a. First day covers prepared by dealers or collectors on the island were franked with Nos. 111/18, 119a/20a, 121, 122a and 123.

ings: (a) 28.2.78; (b) 18.10.78; (c) 29.9.81

though both perforations of Nos. 111/23 were printed at the same
, some did not appear in use until some time after 28 February,
. Earliest dates for these are as follows: 1p (112a) 8.79, 7p (114a)
, 8p (115a) 6.80, 10p (117a) 8.79, 12p (119) 9.80.

e Nos.: ½, 6, 8, 9, 10, 11, 12, 13, 14, 15, 16p 1A, 1B, 1C, 1D (each
4); 1p 1A, 1B, 1C, 1D (each ×4) (No. 112), 1A–1A–2A–1A,
–1B–2B–1B, 1C–1C–2C–1C, 1D–1D–2D–1D; 7p 1A, 1B, 1C, 1D
ach ×4) (No. 114); 2A, 2B, 2C, 2D (each ×4) (No. 114a); £2
1–1–1–1, B1–1–1–1, others none

ets: 25 (5 x 5) (£2); 50 (1, 7, 10, 12, 13, 14, 15, 16p 5×10; others
0×5)

rint: ½p to 16p left-hand corner, top margin and right-hand corner,
ottom margin; 20p to £1 none; £2 central bottom margin

hdrawn: 30.6.83 1p to 16p; 31.12.83 20p to £1; 31.12.85 ½p;
0.6.90 £2

115 Queen Elizabeth in Coronation
Regalia

th Anniversary of Coronation

(Des G. Kneale. Litho Questa)

78 (24 MAY). *Perf* 14½×14 (C)
2 **115** 25p multicoloured 75 75
First Day Cover . . . . 1·00
Presentation Pack . . . . 1·25
Gutter Pair . . . . 1·50

Plate Nos.: 1A, 1B (each ×6)

Sheets: 50 (2 panes 5×5)

mprint: Left-hand corner, top margin and right-hand corner, bottom
margin

Quantity sold: 575,996

Withdrawn: 23.5.79

6 Wheel-headed   **117** Celtic   **118** Keeil
Cross-slab   Wheelcross   Chiggyrt
Stone

119 Olaf Liotulfson   **120** Odd's and   **121** Thor
Cross   Thorleif's   Cross
Crosses

Europa. Sculpture

(Des J. Nicholson. Photo Courvoisier)

1978 (24 MAY). *Granite paper. Perf* 11½ (C)
133 **116** 6p multicoloured 20 15
a. *Strip of* 3. *Nos.* 133/5 . . . . 60 50
134 **117** 6p multicoloured 20 15
135 **118** 6p multicoloured 20 15
136 **119** 11p multicoloured 35 30
a. *Strip of* 3. *Nos.* 136/8 . . . . 1·10 90
137 **120** 11p multicoloured 35 30
138 **121** 11p multicoloured 35 30
133/8   *Set of* 6 . . . . 1·50 1·25
First Day Cover . . . . 1·25
Presentation Pack . . . . 1·60

Sheets: 9 (3×3) The three designs of each value were printed
together, *se-tenant*, in horizontal and vertical strips throughout

Quantities sold: 6p 3,821,152; 11p 3,788,667

Withdrawn: 23.5.79

122 J. K. Ward and Ward   **123** Swimmer, Cyclist and
Library, Peel   Walker

124 American Bald Eagle,   **125** Lumber Camp at Three
Manx Arms and Maple   Rivers, Quebec
Leaf

Anniversaries and Events. Events described on stamps

(Des John Waddington (7p), G. Kneale (11p), J. Nicholson (others). Litho John Waddington)

1978 (10 JUNE). *Invisible gum. Perf* 13½ (C)

139	**122**	6p multicoloured	....	15	15
140	**123**	7p multicoloured	....	20	20
141	**124**	11p multicoloured	....	35	35
142	**125**	13p multicoloured	....	40	40
139/42		Set of 4	....	1·00	1·00
		First Day Covers (3)	......		1·50
		Presentation Packs (2)	....	1·40	
		Set of 4 Gutter Pairs	......	2·25	

Plate Nos.: 6p 1A, 1B, 1C, 1D (each ×4); others 1B, 1D (each ×4)

Sheets: 50 (2 panes 5×5)

Imprint: Central, bottom margin

Quantities sold: 6p 629,041; 7p 873,067; 11p 393,907; 13p 383,048

Withdrawn: 9.6.79

126 Hunt the Wren

Christmas

(Des J. Nicholson. Litho John Waddington)

1978 (18 OCT). *Perf* 13 (C)

143	**126**	5p multicoloured	....	50	50
		First Day Cover	....		1·00
		Presentation Pack	....	1·00	
		Gutter Pair	....	1·00	

Plate Nos.: 1B, 1D (each ×4)

Sheets: 50 (2 panes 5×5)

Imprint: Central, bottom margin

Quantity sold: 1,000,000

Sold out: By 4.79 (stamp) or 8.79 (presentation pack)

127 P. M. C. Kermode (founder) and *Nassa kermodei*

128 Peregrine Falcon

129 Fulmar

130 *Epitriptus cowini* (fly)

Centenary of Natural History and Antiquarian Society

(Des J. Nicholson. Litho Questa)

1979 (27 FEB). *Perf* 14 (C)

144	**127**	6p multicoloured	....	15	1
145	**128**	7p multicoloured	....	20	2
146	**129**	11p multicoloured	....	35	3
147	**130**	13p multicoloured	....	40	4
144/7		Set of 4	....	1·00	1·0
		First Day Cover	....		1·0
		Presentation Pack	....	1·50	
		Set of 4 Gutter Pairs	......	2·10	

Plate Nos.: 6p 1A, 1B, 1C, 1D (each ×4); 13p 1A, 1B (each ×4); othe 1C, 1D (each ×4)

Sheets: 50 (2 panes 5×5)

Imprint: Left-hand corner, top margin and right-hand corner, botto margin

Quantities sold: 6p 642,126; 7p 790,515; 11p 411,863; 13p 390,45

Withdrawn: 26.2.80

131 Postman, 1859   **132** Postman, 1979

Europa. Communications

(Des A. Theobald. Litho Questa)

1979 (16 MAY). *Perf* 14½ (C)

148	**131**	6p multicoloured	....	25	
149	**132**	11p multicoloured	....	50	
148/9		Set of 2	....	75	
		First Day Cover	....		1
		Presentation Pack	....	1·00	

Plate Nos.: 6p 1A, 1B (each ×6); 11p 1A, 1B (each ×5)

Sheets: 20 (4×5)

Imprint: Right-hand corner, bottom margin

Quantities sold: 6p 1,301,039; 11p 1,290,318

Sold out: By 10.79 (stamps)

Withdrawn: 15.5.80 (presentation pack)

133 Viking Longship Emblem

134 'Three Legs of Man' Emblem

114

5 Viking Raid at Garwick

136 10th-century Meeting of Tynwald

7 Tynwald Hill and St. John's Church

138 Procession to Tynwald Hill

o types of 3p:

e I. Wrongly inscribed 'INSULAREM'. '1979' imprint date.

pe II. Inscription corrected to 'INSULARUM'. '1980' imprint date.

Millennium of Tynwald

(Des J. Nicholson. Litho Harrison (3, 4p), John Waddington (others))

79 (16 MAY)–**80**. (a) Perf 14½×14 (C)

0	**133**	3p multicoloured (Type I) (a) ..		15	15
		a. Booklet pane. Nos. 150×4, 151×2 (4p stamps at top) ..		90	
		ab. Do. (4p stamps in centre)		1·50	
		b. Type II (b)		10	10
		ba. Booklet pane. Nos. 150b×4, 151×2 (4p stamps at bottom)		75	
151	**134**	4p multicoloured (ab)		15	15
		(b) Perf 13 (C)			
152	**135**	6p multicoloured (a)		15	15
153	**136**	7p multicoloured (a)		20	20
154	**137**	11p multicoloured (a)		30	30
155	**138**	13p multicoloured (a)		45	35
150/5		Set of 6		1·25	1·10
		First Day Cover..........			1·25
		Presentation Pack........		1·60	
		Set of 6 Gutter Pairs		2·50	

See also Nos. 188/9

Printings: (a) 16.5.79; (b) 29.9.80. Inscribed '1980'

Plate Nos.: 3, 4p 1A (×6); 13p 1G (×4); others 1E (×4)

Sheets: 3, 4p 80 (10 panes 2×3, 5 panes 2×2); others 40 (2 panes 4×5). The 3 and 4p values were printed together, se-tenant, each pane of 6 containing four 3p and two 4p, the 4p being in either positions 1 and 2 or 3 and 4. The panes of 4 contain the 4p value only. For details of No. 150ba see after No. 189

Imprint: 3, 4p right-hand corner, bottom margin; others central, bottom margin

Quantities sold: 6p 381,334; 7p 465,473; 11p 341,204; 13p 241,162

Withdrawn: 15.5.80 6p to 13p; 25.3.87 3p, 4p

139 Queen and Court on Tynwald Hill

140 Queen and Procession from St. John's Church to Tynwald Hill

Royal Visit

(Des G. Kneale. Litho Questa)

1979 (5 JULY). Perf 14½ (C)

156	**139**	7p multicoloured		35	35
157	**140**	13p multicoloured		50	50
156/7		Set of 2		85	85
		First Day Cover..........			1·00
		Presentation Pack........		1·00	
		Set of 2 Gutter Pairs		1·60	

Plate Nos.: 7p 1A, 1B (each ×4); 13p 1C, 1D (each ×4)

Sheets: 50 (2 panes 5×5)

Imprint: Right-hand corner, bottom margin

Quantities sold: 7p 641,930; 13p 436,516

Withdrawn: 4.7.80

141 Odin's Raven

Voyage of Odin's Raven

(Des J. Nicholson. Litho Questa)

1979 (19 OCT). *Perf* 14×14½ (C)

158	**141**	15p multicoloured	. . . .	70	70
		First Day Cover	. . . .		1·00
		Presentation Pack	. . . .	1·00	
		Gutter Pair	. . . .	1·40	

See also No. **MS**180.

Plate Nos.: 1A, 1B, 1C, 1D (each ×4)
Sheets: 50 (2 panes 5×5)
Imprint: Right-hand corner, bottom margin
Quantity sold: 412,631
Withdrawn: 18.10.80

142 John Quilliam seized by Press Gang

143 Steering H.M.S. *Victory*, Battle of Trafalgar

144 Captain John Quilliam and H.M.S. *Spencer*

145 Captain John Quilliam (member of the House of Keys)

150th Death Anniversary of Captain John Quilliam

(Des A. Theobald. Litho Questa)

1979 (19 OCT). *Perf* 14 (C)

159	**142**	6p multicoloured	. . . .	15	15
160	**143**	8p multicoloured	. . . .	20	20
161	**144**	13p multicoloured	. . . .	35	35
162	**145**	15p multicoloured	. . . .	40	40
159/62		Set of 4	. . . .	1·00	1·00
		First Day Cover	. . . .		1·50
		Presentation Pack	. . . .	1·60	
		Set of 4 Gutter Pairs	. . . . . .	2·00	

Plate Nos.: 6p 1C, 1D (each ×4); others 1A, 1B (each ×4)
Sheets: 50 (2 panes 5×5)
Imprint: Right-hand corner, bottom margin
Quantities sold: 6p 608,876; 8p 858,665; 13p 360,821; 15p 360,400
Withdrawn: 18.10.80

146 Young Girl with Teddybear and Cat

147 Father Christmas with Young Children

Christmas and International Year of the Child

(Des Mrs. E. Moore. Litho John Waddington)

1979 (19 OCT). *Perf* 13 (C)

163	**146**	5p multicoloured	25	
164	**147**	7p multicoloured	35	
163/4		Set of 2	60	
		First Day Cover		1
		Presentation Pack	1·00	
		Set of 2 Gutter Pairs	1·25	

Plate Nos. Both values 1A, 1B, 1C, 1D (each ×4)
Sheets: 50 (2 panes 5×5)
Imprint: Central, left-hand margin
Quantities sold: 5p 1,036,495; 7p 1,087,734
Withdrawn: 18.10.80

148 Conglomerate Arch, Langness

149 Braaid Circle

150 Cashtal-yn-Ard

151 Volcanic Rocks at Scarlett

152 Sugar-loaf Rock

0th Anniversary of Royal Geographical Society

(Des J. Nicholson. Litho Questa)

30 (5 FEB). *Perf* 14½ (C)

5	**148**	7p multicoloured	20	20
5	**149**	8p multicoloured	20	20
7	**150**	12p multicoloured	25	25
3	**151**	13p multicoloured	35	35
3	**152**	15p multicoloured	40	40
5/9		Set of 5	1·25	1·25
		First Day Cover		1·60
		Presentation Pack	1·60	
		Set of 5 Gutter Pairs	2·50	

ate Nos.: 12p 1A, 1B, 1C, 1D (each ×4); 15p 1C, 1D (each ×4); others 1A, 1B (each ×4)

heets: 50 (2 panes 5×5)

nprint: Right-hand corner, bottom margin

uantities sold: 7p 842,859; 8p 837,710; 12p 361,362; 13p 360,261; 15p 360,310

Withdrawn: 4.2.81

153 *Mona's Isle I*

154 *Douglas I*

155 H.M.S. *Mona's Queen II* sinking U-boat

156 H.M.S. *King Orry III* at Surrender of German Fleet

157 *Ben-My-Chree IV*

158 *Lady of Mann II*

150th Anniversary of Isle of Man Steam Packet Company

(Des J. Nicholson. Photo Courvoisier)

1980 (6 MAY). *Granite paper. Perf* 11½ (C)

170	**153**	7p multicoloured	20	20
171	**154**	8p multicoloured	20	20
172	**155**	11½p multicoloured	30	30
173	**156**	12p multicoloured	30	30
174	**157**	13p multicoloured	40	35
175	**158**	15p multicoloured	50	40
170/5		Set of 6	1·75	1·60
		First Day Cover		1·75
		Presentation Pack	1·90	
		Set of 6 Gutter Pairs	3·50	
MS176		180×125 mm. Nos. 170/5	1·75	1·75
		First Day Cover		2·75

No. **MS**176 was issued to commemorate the 'London 1980' International Stamp Exhibition.

Cylinder Nos.: All values A1–1–1–1, B1–1–1–1, C1–1–1–1, D1–1–1–1

Sheets: 40 (2 panes 5×4)

Imprint: Central, bottom margin

Quantities sold: 7p 512,449; 8p 624,090; 11½p 381,466; 12p 367,943; 13p 368,138; 15p 376,596; miniature sheet 300,678

Withdrawn: 5.5.81

159 Stained Glass Window, T. E. Brown Room, Manx Museum

160 Clifton College, Bristol

Europa. Personalities. Thomas Edward Brown (poet and scholar) Commemoration

(Des G. Kneale. Photo Courvoisier)

1980 (6 MAY). *Granite paper. Perf* 11½ (C)

177	**159**	7p multicoloured	20	20
178	**160**	13½p multicoloured	40	40
177/8		Set of 2	60	60
		First Day Cover		1·00
		Presentation Pack	1·10	
		Set of 2 Gutter Pairs	1·25	

Cylinder Nos.: Both values A1–1–1–1–1, B1–1–1–1–1, C1–1–1–1–1, D1–1–1–1–1

Sheets: 20 (2 panes 2×5)

Imprint: Bottom margin at right-hand corner of left-hand pane

Quantities sold: 7p 1,726,009; 13½p 1,708,590

Withdrawn: 5.5.81

161 King Olav V and *Norge* (Norwegian royal yacht)

Visit of King Olav V of Norway, August 1979

(Des J. Nicholson. Litho Questa)

1980 (13 JUNE). *Perf* 14×14½ (C)

179	**161**	12p multicoloured	50	50
		First Day Cover		1·00
		Presentation Pack	1·00	
		Gutter Pair	1·00	
MS180		125×157 mm. Nos. 158 and 179	1·00	1·00
		First Day Cover		1·50

No. **MS**180 also commemorates the "NORWEX 80" stamp exhibition, Oslo.

Plate Nos.: 1C, 1D (each ×4)

Sheets: 40 (2 panes 5×4)

Imprint: Right-hand corner, bottom margin

Quantities sold: 12p 449,267; miniature sheet 401,424

Withdrawn: 12.6.81

162 Winter Wren and View of Calf of Man

163 European Robin and View of Port Erin Marine Biological Station

Christmas and Wildlife Conservation Year

(Des J. Nicholson. Litho John Waddington)

1980 (29 SEPT). *Perf* 13½×14 (C)

181	**162**	6p multicoloured	20	
182	**163**	8p multicoloured	30	
181/2		*Set of 2*	50	
		First Day Cover		1·
		Presentation Pack	1·00	
		Set of 2 Gutter Pairs	1·00	

Plate Nos.: 6p 1B, 1D (each ×4); 8p 1A, 1C (each ×4)

Sheets: 40 (2 panes 4×5)

Imprint: Right-hand corner, bottom margin

Quantities sold: 6p 967,976; 8p 942,323

Withdrawn: 28.9.81

164 William Kermode and Brig *Robert Quayle*, 1819

165 'Mona Vale', Van Diemen's Land, 1834

166 Ross Bridge, Tasmania

167 'Mona Vale', Tasmania (completed 1868)

168 Robert Q. Kermode and Parliament Buildings, Tasmania

Kermode Family in Tasmania Commemoration

(Des A. Theobald. Litho Questa)

1980 (29 SEPT). *Perf* 14½ (C)

183	**164**	7p multicoloured	20	
184	**165**	9p multicoloured	25	
185	**166**	13½p multicoloured	40	
186	**167**	15p multicoloured	45	
187	**168**	17½p multicoloured	50	
183/7		*Set of 5*	1·60	1
		First Day Cover		1
		Presentation Pack	2·00	
		Set of 5 Gutter Pairs	3·25	

ate Nos.: All values 1C, 1D (each ×4)

eets: 40 (2 panes 5×4)

print: Right-hand corner, bottom margin

antities sold: 7p 416,487; 9p 498,880; 13½p 318,353; 15p 314,837; 17½p 315,107

thdrawn: 28.9.81

Peregrine Falcon   **170** Loaghtyn Ram

oklet stamps

(Des J. Nicholson. Litho Harrison)

0 (29 SEPT). *Perf* 14½×14 (C)

	169	1p multicoloured	40	40
		a. *Booklet pane. Nos.* 151, 188 *and* 189, *each* ×2	75	
	170	5p multicoloured	40	40
3/9		*Set of 2*	80	80
		First Day Cover (*Nos.* 150b ×2, 151×2, 188 *and* 189) . .		1·10
		Presentation Pack (*Nos.* 150b ×2, 151×2, 188 *and* 189) . .	1·25	

n addition to Booklets SB11/12 Nos. 188/9 also come from cial booklet sheets of 60. These sheets contain No. ba×5 and No. 188a×5.

ate Nos.: 1A (×7)

ithdrawn: 25.3.87

1 Luggers passing Red Pier, Douglas

172 Peel Lugger *Wanderer* rescuing survivors from the *Lusitania*

3 Nickeys leaving Port St. Mary Harbour

174 Nobby entering Ramsey Harbour

175 Nickeys *Sunbeam* and *Zebra* at Port Erin

Centenary of Royal National Mission to Deep Sea Fishermen

(Des J. Nicholson. Litho Questa)

1981 (24 FEB). *Perf* 14 (C)

190	**171**	8p multicoloured	. . . .	25	25
191	**172**	9p multicoloured	. . . .	30	30
192	**173**	18p multicoloured	. . . .	45	45
193	**174**	20p multicoloured	. . . .	50	50
194	**175**	22p multicoloured	. . . .	50	50
190/4		*Set of 5*	. . . .	1·75	1·75
		First Day Cover			2·00
		Presentation Pack	2·00	
		Set of 5 Gutter Pairs	3·50	

Plate Nos.: 8p 1E, 1F (each ×4); 9p 1G, 1H (each ×4); 22p 1A, 1B (each ×4); others 1C, 1D (each ×4)

Sheets: 40 (2 panes 5×4)

Imprint: Right-hand corner, bottom margin

Quantities sold: 8p 566,522; 9p 583,358; 18p 334,765; 20p 315,511; 22p 324,607

Withdrawn: 23.2.82

176 'Crosh Cuirn' Superstition

177 'Bollan Cross' Superstition

Europa. Folklore

(Des J. Nicholson. Litho Questa)

1981 (22 MAY). *Perf* 14½ (C)

195	**176**	8p multicoloured	. . . .	25	25
196	**177**	18p multicoloured	. . . .	75	75
195/6		*Set of 2*	. . . .	1·00	1·00
		First Day Cover			1·00
		Presentation Pack	1·25	
		Set of 2 Gutter Pairs	2·00	

Plate Nos.: 1A, 1B (each ×4)

Sheets: 24 (2 panes 3×4)

Imprint: Right-hand corner, bottom margin

Quantities sold: 8p 1,261,267; 18p 1,243,459

Withdrawn: 21.5.82

178 Lt. Mark Wilks (Royal Manx Fencibles) and Peel Castle

179 Ensign Mark Wilks and Fort St. George, Madras

180 Governor Mark Wilks and Napoleon, St. Helena

181 Col. Mark Wilks (Speaker of the House of Keys) and Estate, Kirby

150th Death Anniversary of Colonel Mark Wilks

(Des A. Theobald. Litho Questa)

1981 (22 MAY). *Perf* 14 (C)

197	**178**	8p multicoloured	. . . .	25	25
198	**179**	20p multicoloured	. . . .	50	50
199	**180**	22p multicoloured	. . . .	70	55
200	**181**	25p multicoloured	. . . .	80	80
197/200		*Set* of 4	. . . .	2·00	1·90
		First Day Cover			2·00
		Presentation Pack		2·50	
		Set of 4 *Gutter Pairs*		4·00	

Plate Nos.: 8, 20p 1A, 1B (each ×5); others 1A, 1B (each ×4)

Sheets: 40 (2 panes 5×4)

Imprint: 22p none; others right-hand corner, bottom margin

Quantities sold: 8p 371,280; 20p 278,840; 22p 294,480; 25p 272,640

Withdrawn: 21.5.82

182 Miss Emmeline Goulden (Mrs. Pankhurst) and Mrs. Sophia Jane Goulden

Centenary of Manx Women's Suffrage

(Des A. Theobald. Litho Questa)

1981 (22 MAY). *Perf* 14 (C)

201	**182**	9p black, olive-grey and stone . .		50	50
		First Day Cover			1·00
		Presentation Pack		1·00	
		Gutter Pair		1·00	

Plate Nos.: 1C, 1D (each ×3)

Sheets: 40 (2 panes 5×4)

Imprint: Right-hand corner, bottom margin

Quantity sold: 659,760

Withdrawn: 21.5.82

183 Prince Charles and Lady Diana Spencer

Royal Wedding

(Des. G Kneale. Litho Harrison)

1981 (29 JULY). *Perf* 14 (C)

202	**183**	9p black, bright blue & pale blue		50	5
203		25p black, bright blue and pink . .		1·50	1·5
202/3		*Set* of 2		2·00	2·0
		First Day Cover			3·5
		Presentation Pack		3·00	
		Set of 2 *Gutter Pairs*		4·00	
MS204		130×183 mm. Nos. 202/3×2		4·50	4·5
		First Day Cover			5·0

Plate Nos.: 9p 1C, 1D (each ×3); 25p 1A, 1B (each ×3)

Sheets: 50 (2 panes 5×5)

Imprint: Central, bottom margin

Quantities sold: 9p 668,864; 25p 474,364; miniature sheet 327,094

Withdrawn: 28.7.82

184 Douglas War Memorial, Poppies and Inscription

185 Major Robert Cain (war hero)

120

186 Festival of Remembrance, Royal Albert Hall

187 T.S.S. *Tynwald* at Dunkirk, May, 1940

th Anniversary of The Royal British Legion

(Des A. Theobald. Photo Courvoisier)

81 (29 SEPT). *Granite paper. Perf* 11½ (C)

5	**184**	8p multicoloured	. . . .	25	25
6	**185**	10p multicoloured	. . . .	30	35
7	**186**	18p multicoloured	. . . .	65	65
8	**187**	20p multicoloured	. . . .	75	75
5/8		Set of 4	. . . .	1·75	1·75
		First Day Cover	. . . .		1·90
		Presentation Pack	. . . .	2·00	
		Set of 4 Gutter Pairs	. . . . . .	3·50	

Cylinder Nos.: 8p A1–1–1–1, B1–1–1–1; others A1–1–1–1–1, B1–1–1–1–1

Sheets: 40 (2 panes 4×5)

mprint: Central, bottom margin

Quantities sold: 8p 314,794; 10p 799,326; 18p 284,059; 20p 261,194

Withdrawn: 28.9.82

8 Nativity Scene (stained glass window, St. George's Church)

189 Children from Special School performing Nativity Play

Christmas

(Des John Waddington (7p), G. Kneale (9p). Litho John Waddington)

1981 (29 SEPT). *Perf* 14 (C)

209	**188**	7p multicoloured	. . . .	25	25
210	**189**	9p multicoloured	. . . .	35	35
209/10		Set of 2	. . . .	60	60
		First Day Cover	. . . .		1·00
		Presentation Pack	. . . .	1·00	
		Set of 2 Gutter Pairs	. . . . . .	1·25	

The 7p value also commemorates the bicentenary of St. George's Church, Douglas and the 9p the International Year for Disabled Persons.

Plate Nos.: 7p 1A, 1B (each ×6); 9p 1A, 1B, 1C, 1D (each ×6)

Sheets: 40 (2 panes 2×10)

Imprint: Right-hand corner, bottom margin

Quantities sold: 7p 855,407; 9p 862,892

Withdrawn: 28.9.82

190 Joseph and William Cunningham (founders of Manx Boy Scout Movement) and Cunningham House Headquarters

191 Baden-Powell visiting Isle of Man, 1911

192 Baden-Powell and Scout Emblem

193 Scouts and Baden-Powell's Last Message

194 Scout Salute, Handshake, Emblem and Globe

121

75th Anniversary of Boy Scout Movement and 125th Birth Anniversary of Lord Baden-Powell

(Des G. Kneale. Litho Questa)

1982 (23 FEB). *Perf* 14×14½ (19½p) *or* 13½×14 (*others*), *all comb*

211	**190**	9p multicoloured	30	30
212	**191**	10p multicoloured	30	30
213	**192**	19½p multicoloured	60	60
214	**193**	24p multicoloured	70	70
215	**194**	29p multicoloured	90	90
211/15		*Set of* 5	2·50	2·50
		First Day Cover		2·75
		Presentation Pack	3·00	
		Set of 5 *Gutter Pairs*	5·00	

Plate Nos.: 9p 1A, 1B (each ×4); 29p 1A, 1B (each ×5); others 1C, 1D (each ×4)

Sheets: 40 (2 panes 5×4)

Imprint: Right-hand corner, bottom margin

Quantities sold: 9p 748,353; 10p 868,401; 19½p 364,487; 24p 368,346; 29p 370,466

Withdrawn: 22.2.83

195 *The Principals and Duties of Christianity (first book printed in Manx, 1707), and Bishop T. Wilson*

196 Landing at Derbyhaven (visit of Thomas, 2nd Earl of Derby, 1507)

Europa. Historic Events

(Des A. Theobald. Photo Courvoisier)

1982 (1 JUNE). *Granite paper. Perf* 12×12½ (C)

216	**195**	9p multicoloured	25	25
217	**196**	19½p multicoloured	50	50
216/17		*Set of* 2	75	75
		First Day Cover		1·00
		Presentation Pack	1·00	
		Set of 2 *Gutter Pairs*	1·50	

Cylinder Nos.: Both values A1–1–1–1–1, B1–1–1–1–1

Sheets: 24 (2 panes 3×4)

Imprint: Right-hand corner, bottom margin

Quantities sold: 9p 1,120,457; 19½p 1,129,315

Withdrawn: 31.5.83

197 Charlie Collier (first TT race (single cylinder) winner) and Tourist Trophy Race, 1907

198 Freddie Dixon (Sidecar and Junior TT winner) and Junior TT race, 19

199 Jimmie Simpson (TT winner and first to lap at 60, 70 and 80 mph) and Senior TT, 1932

200 Mike Hailwood (winne fourteen TTs) and Seni TT, 1961

201 Jock Taylor (Sidecar TT winner, 1978, 1980 and 1981) and Sidecar TT (w Benga Johansson), 198(

75th Anniversary of Tourist Trophy Motorcycle Races

(Des J. Nicholson. Litho Questa)

1982 (1 JUNE). *Perf* 14 (C)

218	**197**	9p multicoloured	20	
219	**198**	10p multicoloured	25	
220	**199**	24p multicoloured	80	
221	**200**	26p multicoloured	85	
222	**201**	29p multicoloured	1·00	
218/22		*Set of* 5	2·75	2
		First Day Cover		3
		Presentation Pack	3·00	
		Stamp Cards (*set of* 5)	1·25	4
		Set of 5 *Gutter Pairs*	5·50	

Plate Nos.: All values 1B, 1C, 1D (each ×4)

Sheets: 40 (2 panes 5×4)

Imprint: Right-hand corner, bottom margin

Quantities sold: 9p 837,930; 10p 866,223; 24p 351,406; 26p 361,0 29p 355,690

Withdrawn: 11.6.83

202 *Mona I*

203 *Manx Maid II*

‹0th Anniversary of Isle of Man Steam Packet Company ‹ail Contract

(Des J. Nicholson. Litho Questa)

‹82 (5 OCT). *Perf* 13½ (C)

3	**202**	12p multicoloured	50	50
4	**203**	19½p multicoloured	75	75
‹3/4		Set of 2	1·25	1·25
		First Day Cover		1·75
		Presentation Pack	1·60	
		Set of 2 Gutter Pairs	2·50	

Plate Nos.: Both values 1A (×4)
Sheets: 40 (2 panes 5×4)
Imprint: Right-hand bottom margin
Quantities sold: 12p 701,044; 19½p 291,100
Withdrawn: 4.10.83

‹4 The Three Wise Men

205 Snow Scene
and Robin

‹ristmas

(Des and litho John Waddington)

‹82 (5 OCT). *Perf* 13 (C)

‹5	**204**	8p multicoloured	50	50
‹6	**205**	11p multicoloured	50	50
‹5/6		Set of 2	1·00	1·00
		First Day Cover		1·25
		Presentation Pack	1·40	
		Set of 2 Gutter Pairs	2·00	

Plate Nos. 8p 1A, 1C (each ×4), 11p 1B, 1D (each ×4)
Sheets: 40 (8p 2 panes 5×4), (11p 2 panes 4×5)
Imprint: Right-hand corner, bottom margin (8p); Top right-hand margin (11p)
Quantities sold: 8p 740,651; 11p 787,552
Withdrawn: 4.10.83

206 Princess Diana with Prince William

21st Birthday of the Princess of Wales and Birth of Prince William

(Des G. Kneale. Litho Questa)

1982 (12 OCT). *Sheet* 100×83 *mm. Perf* 14½×14 (C)

MS227	**206**	50p multicoloured	3·50	3·50
		First Day Cover		4·50
		Presentation Pack	3·75	

Quantity sold: 218,759
Withdrawn: 11.10.83

207 Opening of Salvation
Army Citadel, and
T. H. Cannell, J.P.

208 Early Meeting-place,
and Gen. William
Booth

209 Salvation Army Band

210 Treating Lepers, and Lt.-Col. Thomas Bridson

Centenary of Salvation Army in Isle of Man

(Des A. Theobald. Photo Courvoisier)

1983 (15 FEB). *Granite paper. Perf* 11½ (C)

228	**207**	10p multicoloured	. . . .	30	30
229	**208**	12p multicoloured	. . . .	40	40
230	**209**	19½p multicoloured	. . . .	60	60
231	**210**	26p multicoloured	. . . .	90	90
228/31		*Set of* 4	. . . .	2·00	2·00
		First Day Cover	. . . .		3·00
		Presentation Pack	. . . . . .	2·50	
		Set of 4 *Gutter Pairs*	. . . .	4·00	

Cylinder Nos.: All values B1–1–1–1–1

Sheets: 40 (2 panes 4×5)

Imprint: Central, bottom margin

Quantities sold: 10p 467,665; 12p 567,863; 19½p 267,929; 26p 288,069

Withdrawn: 14.2.84

211 Atlantic Puffins

212 Northern Gannets

213 Lesser Black-backed Gulls

214 Common Cormorants

215 Kittiwakes

216 Shags

217 Grey Herons

218 Herring-gulls

219 Razorbills

220 Great Black-backed Gulls

221 Common Shelducks

222 Oystercatchers

223 Arctic Terns

224 Common Guillemots

225 Redshanks

226 Mute Swans

227 'Queen Elizabeth II' (Ricardo Macarron)

Sea Birds and Queen's Portrait (£5)

(Des Colleen Corlett (£5), J. Nicholson (others). Litho Questa)

1983 (15 FEB)–**85**. *Perf* 14 (20p to £1), 14×13½ (£5) *or* 14½ *(others), all comb*

32	**211**	1p multicoloured (*a*)	. . . .	30	30
33	**212**	2p multicoloured (*a*)	. . . .	30	30
34	**213**	5p multicoloured (*a*)	. . . .	60	40
35	**214**	8p multicoloured (*a*)	. . . .	60	40
36	**215**	10p multicoloured (*a*)	. . . .	60	35
37	**216**	11p multicoloured (*a*)	. . . .	60	35
38	**217**	12p multicoloured (*a*)	. . . .	70	40
39	**218**	13p multicoloured (*a*)	. . . .	70	40
40	**219**	14p multicoloured (*a*)	. . . .	70	40
41	**220**	15p multicoloured (*a*)	. . . .	80	50
42	**221**	16p multicoloured (*a*)	. . . . . .	80	50
43	**222**	18p multicoloured (*a*)	. . . .	80	60
44	**223**	20p multicoloured (*b*)	. . . .	90	1·00
45	**224**	25p multicoloured (*b*)	. . . .	1·00	1·00
46	**225**	50p multicoloured (*b*)	. . . .	1·75	1·75
47	**226**	£1 multicoloured (*b*)	. . . .	3·25	3·00
48	**227**	£5 multicoloured (*c*)	. . . .	12·00	12·00
32/48		Set of 17	. . . .	24·00	21·00
		First Day Covers (4)			26·00
		Presentation Packs (4)	. . . .	26·00	

Printings: (*a*) 15.2.83; (*b*) 14.9.83; (*c*) 31.1.85

Plate Nos. 1p to £1 1A, 1B, 1C, 1D (each x 4); £5 1A, 1B (each ×4)

Sheets: 10 (5×2) £5; 50 (5×10) others

Imprint: £5 Right-hand margin; others right-hand corner, bottom margin

Withdrawn: 30.6.88 1p to 18p; 31.12.88 20p to £1; 4.7.94 £5

28 Design Drawings by Robert Casement for the Great Laxey Wheel

29 Robert Casement and the Great Laxey Wheel

Europa. The Great Laxey Wheel

(Des J. Nicholson. Litho Questa)

1983 (18 MAY). *Perf* 14 (C)

249	**228**	10p black, azure and buff	. . . .	40	35
250	**229**	20½p multicoloured	. . . .	60	70
249/50		Set of 2	. . . .	1·00	1·00
		First Day Cover	. . . .		1·75
		Presentation Pack		1·75	
		Set of 2 Gutter Pairs	. . . .	2·00	

Plate Nos.: 10p 1A, 1B (each ×3); 20½p 1A, 1B (each ×4)

Sheets: 12 (2 panes 2×3)

Imprint: Right-hand corner, bottom margin

Quantities sold: 10p 653,743; 20½p 686,084

Withdrawn 17.5.84

230 Nick Keig (international yachtsrnan) and Trimaran *Three Legs of Man III*

231 King William's College, Castletown

232 Sir William Bragg (winner of Nobel Prize for Physics) and Spectrometer

233 General Sir George White V.C. and Action at Charasiah

150th Anniversary of King William's College

(Des J. Nicholson (10p, 31p), Colleen Corlett (12p, 28p). Photo Courvoisier)

1983 (18 MAY). *Granite paper. Perf* 11½ (C)

251	**230**	10p multicoloured	. . . .	20	20
252	**231**	12p multicoloured	. . . .	30	30
253	**232**	28p multicoloured	. . . .	80	80
254	**233**	31p multicoloured	. . . .	1·00	1·00
251/4		Set of 4	. . . .	2·00	2·00
		First Day Cover	. . . .		3·00
		Presentation Pack	. . . .	2·50	
		Set of 4 Gutter Pairs	. . . . . .	4·25	

Cylinder Nos.: 10p C1–1–1–1, D1–1–1–1; 12p C1–1–1–1, D1–1–1–1; 28p A1–1–1–1, B1–1–1–1; 31p A1–1–1–1, B1–1–1–1

Sheets: 40 (2 panes 5×4)

Imprint: Central bottom margin

Quantities sold: 10p 552,573; 12p 693,004; 28p 263,814; 31p 242,393

Withdrawn: 17.5.84

234 New Post Office Headquarters, Douglas

235 Landing of the Vikings on Man, AD 938

World Communications Year and 10th Anniversary of Isle of Man Post Office Authority.

(Des Colleen Corlett (10p), J. Nicholson (15p). Litho Questa)

1983 (5 JULY). *Perf* 14½ (C)

255	**234**	10p multicoloured	40	40
256	**235**	15p multicoloured	60	60
255/6		Set of 2	1·00	1·00
		First Day Cover		1·60
		Presentation Pack	1·60	
		Stamp Cards (set of 2)	75	1·50
		Set of 2 Gutter Pairs	2·00	

Plate Nos.: Both values 1A, 1B, 1C, 1D (each ×5)

Sheets: 40 (2 panes 4×5)

Imprint: Central, right-hand margin

Quantities sold: 10p 269,843; 15p 222,013

Withdrawn: 4.7.84

236 Shepherds

237 Three Kings

Christmas

(Des Colleen Corlett. Litho John Waddington)

1983 (14 SEPT). *Perf* 13 (C)

257	**236**	9p multicoloured	50	50
258	**237**	12p multicoloured	50	50
257/8		Set of 2	1·00	1·00
		First Day Cover		1·50
		Presentation Pack	1·25	
		Set of 2 Gutter Pairs	2·00	

Plate Nos.: Both values 1A, 1B, 1C, 1D (each ×5)

Sheets: 40 (2 panes 5×4)

Imprint: Right-hand corner, bottom margin

Quantities sold: 9p 642,763; 12p 656,060

Withdrawn: 13.9.84

238 *Manx King* (full-rigged ship)

239 *Hope* (barque)

240 *Rio Grande* (brig)

241 *Lady Elizabeth* (barque)

242 *Sumatra* (barque)

243 Wreck of *Lady Elizabe* as shown on Falkland Islands Stamp

The Karran Fleet

(Des J. Nicholson (10p to 31p); Colleen Corlett, J. Nicholso and J. Smith (miniature sheet). Litho Questa)

1984 (14 FEB). *Perf* 14 (C)

259	**238**	10p multicoloured	40	
260	**239**	13p multicoloured	55	
261	**240**	20½p multicoloured	85	
262	**241**	28p multicoloured	1·00	1·
263	**242**	31p multicoloured	1·10	1·
259/63		Set of 5	3·50	3·
		First Day Cover		4·
		Presentation Pack	4·00	
		Set of 5 Gutter Pairs	7·00	

MS264 103×94 mm. 28p Type **241**; 31p Type **243** (sold at 60p) . . . . 3·00 3·

	First Day Cover	4·
	Presentation Pack	3·50

No. **MS**264 was issued to commemorate links between t Isle of Man and the Falkland Islands.

126

Plate Nos.: All values 1A, 1B (each ×4)

Sheets: 40 (2 panes 5×4)

Imprint: Right-hand corner, bottom margin

Quantities sold: 10p 389,278; 13p 417,637; 20½p 253,949; 28p 238,292; 31p 236,196; miniature sheet 137,031

Withdrawn: 13.2.85

244 C.E.P.T. 25th Anniversary Logo

Europa

(Des J. Larrivière, adapted Colleen Corlett. Photo Courvoisier)

1984 (27 APR). *Granite paper. Perf* 12×11½ (C)

265	**244**	10p dull orange, deep reddish brown and pale orange....	35	35
266		20½p lt blue, dp blue & pale blue	70	70
		Set of 2	1·00	1·00
		First Day Cover		2·00
		Presentation Pack	1·60	

Cylinder Nos.: 10p B1–1–1; 20½p A1–1–1

Sheets: 20 (4×5)

Imprint: Central, right-hand margin

Quantities sold: 10p 705,410; 20½p 715,479

Withdrawn: 26.4.85

245 Railway Air Services De Havilland D.H.84 Dragon Mk 2

246 West Coast Air Services De Havilland D.H.86A Dragon Express *Ronaldsway*

247 B.E.A. Douglas DC-3

248 B.E.A. Vickers Viscount 800

249 Telair Britten Norman Islander

50th Anniversary of First Official Airmail to the Isle of Man and 40th Anniversary of International Civil Aviation Organization

(Des A. Theobald. Litho Questa)

1984 (27 APR). *Perf* 14 (C)

267	**245**	11p multicoloured	....	45	45
268	**246**	13p multicoloured	....	55	55
269	**247**	26p multicoloured	....	1·00	1·00
270	**248**	28p multicoloured	....	1·10	1·10
271	**249**	31p multicoloured	....	1·40	1·40
267/71		*Set of 5*	....	4·00	4·00
		First Day Cover	....		4·50
		Presentation Pack	......	4·50	
		Set of 5 Gutter Pairs	....	8·00	

Plate Nos. All values 1C, 1D (each ×4)

Sheets: 40 (2 panes 5×4)

Imprint: Right-hand corner, bottom margin

Quantities sold: 11p 399,155; 13p 440,623; 26p 234,165; 28p 173,841; 31p 171,890

Withdrawn: 26.4.85

Year Pack 1983

1984. *Comprises Nos.* 228/47, 249/58

	Year Pack	....	20·00

Withdrawn: 31.3.85

250 Window from Glencrutchey House, Douglas

251 Window from Lonan Old Church

Christmas. Stained-glass Windows

(Des D. Swinton. Litho John Waddington)

1984 (21 SEPT). *Perf* 14 (C)

272	**250**	10p multicoloured	....	50	50
273	**251**	13p multicoloured	....	50	50
272/3		*Set of 2*	....	1·00	1·00
		First Day Cover	....		1·40
		Presentation Pack	....	1·40	
		Set of 2 Gutter Pairs	......	2·00	

Plate Nos.: Both values 1A, 1C (each ×6)

Sheets: 40 (2 panes 4×5)

Imprint: Top right-hand margin

Quantities sold: 10p 652,870; 13p 668,084

Withdrawn: 20.9.85

252 William Cain's Birthplace, Ballasalla

253 The *Anna* leaving Liverpool, 1852

254 Early Australian Railway

255 William Cain as Mayor of Melbourne, and Town Hall

256 Royal Exhibition Buildings, Melbourne

William Cain (civic leader, Victoria) Commemoration

(Des J. Nicholson. Litho Questa)

1984 (21 SEPT). *Perf* 14½×14 (C)

274	**252**	11p multicoloured	. . . .	35	35
275	**253**	22p multicoloured	. . . .	75	75
276	**254**	28p multicoloured	. . . .	1·00	1·00
277	**255**	30p multicoloured	. . . .	1·10	1·10
278	**256**	33p multicoloured	. . . .	1·25	1·25
274/8		Set of 5	. . . .	4·00	4·00
		First Day Cover	. . . .		4·25
		Presentation Pack	. . . .	4·50	
		Set of 5 Gutter Pairs	. . . . . .	8·00	

Plate Nos.: All values 1B (×4)

Sheets: 40 (2 panes 5×4)

Imprint: Right-hand corner, bottom margin

Quantities sold: 11p 393,219; 22p 280,598; 28p 223,515; 30p 220,913; 33p 213,933

Withdrawn: 20.9.85

257 Queen Elizabeth II and Commonwealth Parliamentary Association Badge

258 Queen Elizabeth II and Manx Emblem

Links with the Commonwealth. 30th Commonwealth Parliamentary Association Conference

(Des and litho John Waddington)

1984 (21 SEPT). *Perf* 14 (C)

279	**257**	14p multicoloured	. . . .	50	50
280	**258**	33p multicoloured	. . . .	1·10	1·10
279/80		Set of 2	. . . .	1·60	1·60
		First Day Cover	. . . .		2·25
		Presentation Pack	. . . .	2·00	
		Set of 2 Gutter Pairs	. . . . . .	3·25	

Plate Nos.: Both values 1A, 1C (each ×7)

Sheets: 40 (2 panes 5×4)

Imprint: Right-hand corner, bottom margin

Quantities sold: 14p 373,204; 33p 231,073

Withdrawn: 20.9.85

Year Pack 1984

1985 (1 JAN). *Comprises Nos.* 259/80

	Year Pack	19·00

Withdrawn: 31.12.85

259 Cunningham House Headquarters, and Mrs. Willie Cunningham and Mrs. Joseph Cunningham (former Commissioners)

260 Princess Margaret, Isle of Man Standard and Guides

261 Lady Olave Baden-Powell opening Guide Headquarters, 1955

128

262 Guide Uniforms from 1910 to 1985

263 Guide Handclasp, Salute and Early Badge

75th Anniversary of Girl Guide Movement

(Des Colleen Corlett. Photo Courvoisier)

1985 (31 JAN). *Granite paper. Perf 11½ (C)*

281	**259**	11p multicoloured	45	45
282	**260**	14p multicoloured	75	75
283	**261**	29p multicoloured	1·10	1·10
284	**262**	31p multicoloured	1·40	1·40
285	**263**	34p multicoloured	1·60	1·60
281/5		Set of 5	4·75	4·75
		First Day Cover		5·50
		Presentation Pack	5·00	
		Set of 5 Gutter Pairs	9·50	

Cylinder Nos.: 11p, 34p A1–1–1–1–1, B1–1–1–1–1; others A1–1–1–1–1, B1–1–1–1–1

Sheets: 40 (2 panes 4×5)

Imprint: Central bottom margin of each pane

Withdrawn: 30.1.86

264 Score of Manx National Anthem

265 William H. Gill (lyricist)

266 Score of Hymn 'Crofton'

267 Dr. John Clague (composer)

Europa. European Music Year

(Des D. Swinton. Photo Courvoisier)

1985 (24 APR). *Granite paper. Perf 11½ (C)*

286	**264**	12p black, orange-brn & chestnut	50	45
		a. Horiz pair. Nos. 286/7	1·00	90
287	**265**	12p black, orange-brn & chestnut	50	45
288	**266**	22p black, brt new blue & new bl	1·00	95
		a. Horiz pair. Nos. 288/9	2·10	1·90
289	**267**	22p black, brt new blue & new bl	1·00	95
286/9		Set of 4	2·75	2·50
		First Day Cover		3·50
		Presentation Pack	3·00	

Cylinder Nos.: Both values A1–1–1, B1–1–1

Sheets: 20 (4×5). The two designs for each value printed together, *se-tenant*, in horizontal pairs throughout the sheets

Imprint: Central, bottom margin

Withdrawn: 23.4.86

268 Charles Rolls in 20 h.p. Rolls-Royce (1906 Tourist Trophy Race)

269 W. Bentley in 3 litre Bentley (1922 Tourist Trophy Race)

270 F. Gerrard in E.R.A. (1950 British Empire Trophy Race)

271 Brian Lewis in Alfa Romeo (1934 Mannin Moar Race)

272 Jaguar 'XJ-SC' ('Roads Open' Car, 1984 Motor-cycle T.T. Races)

273 Tony Pond and Mike Nicholson in Vauxhall 'Chevette' (1981 Rothmans International Rally)

Century of Motoring

(Des A. Theobald. Litho Questa)

1985 (25 MAY). *Perf* 14 (C)

290	**268**	12p multicoloured	. . . .	40	40
		a. Horiz pair. Nos. 290/1	. . . .	85	85
291	**269**	12p multicoloured		40	40
292	**270**	14p multicoloured	. . . .	55	55
		a. Horiz pair. Nos. 292/3	. . . .	1·10	1·10
293	**271**	14p multicoloured	. . . .	55	55
294	**272**	31p multicoloured	. . . .	1·40	1·25
		a. Horiz pair. Nos. 294/5	. . . .	2·75	2·50
295	**273**	31p multicoloured		1·40	1·25
290/5		Set of 6	. . . .	4·25	4·00
		First Day Cover	. . . .		4·75
		Presentation Pack	. . . .	4·50	
		Stamp Cards (set of 6)	. . . .	3·00	7·00
		Set of 3 Gutter Blocks of 4		8·50	

Plate Nos.: All values 1A, 1B (each ×6)

Sheets: 40 (2 panes 4×5). The two designs for each value printed together, *se-tenant*, in horizontal pairs throughout the sheets

Imprint: Right-hand corner, bottom margin of each pane

Withdrawn: 24.5.86

274 Queen Alexandra and Victorian Sergeant with Wife

275 Queen Mary and Royal Air Force Family

276 Earl Mountbatten and Royal Navy Family

277 Prince Michael of Kent and Royal Marine with Parents, 1982

Centenary of the Soldiers', Sailors' and Airmen's Families Association

(Des Colleen Corlett. Litho Questa)

1985 (4 SEPT). *Perf* 14 (C)

296	**274**	12p multicoloured	. . . .	40	40
297	**275**	15p multicoloured	. . . .	55	55
298	**276**	29p multicoloured	. . . .	1·10	1·10
299	**277**	34p multicoloured	. . . .	1·25	1·25
296/9		Set of 4	. . . .	3·00	3·00
		First Day Cover	. . . .		4·50
		Presentation Pack	. . . .	4·00	
		Set of 4 Gutter Pairs	. . . . . .	6·00	

Plate Nos. 12p, 34p 1A, 1B, 1C, 1D, 1E, 1F, 1G, 1H (each ×6); others 1A, 1B, 1C, 1D, 1E, 1F, 1G, 1H (each ×5)

Sheets: 40 (2 panes 5×4)

Imprint: Right-hand corner, bottom margin of each pane.

Withdrawn: 3.9.86

278 Kirk Maughold (Birthplace

279 Lieut.-Gen. Sir Mark Cubbon

280 Memorial Statue, Bangalore, India

Birth Bicentenary of Lieut.-Gen. Sir Mark Cubbon (Indian administrator)

(Des A. Theobald. Litho Questa)

1985 (2 OCT). *Perf* 14 (C)

300	**278**	12p multicoloured	. . . .	45	45
301	**279**	22p multicoloured	. . . .	1·10	1·10
302	**280**	45p multicoloured	. . . .	1·90	1·90
300/2		Set of 3	. . . .	3·00	3·00
		First Day Cover	. . . .		4·50
		Presentation Pack	. . . .	3·75	
		Set of 3 Gutter Pairs	. . . . . .	6·00	

Plate Nos.: All values 1A, 1B, 1C, 1D (each ×4)

Sheets: 40 (2 panes 5×4) 12p or (2 panes 4×5) others

Imprint: Right-hand corner, bottom margin of each pane

Withdrawn: 1.10.86

281 St. Peter's Church, Onchan

282 Royal Chapel of St. John, Tynwald

130

283 Bride Parish Church

Christmas. Manx Churches

(Des A. Theobald. Litho John Waddington)

1985 (2 OCT). *Perf* 13×13½ (C)

303	**281**	11p multicoloured	45	45
304	**282**	14p multicoloured	55	55
305	**283**	31p multicoloured	1·25	1·25
303/5		Set of 3	2·00	2·00
		First Day Cover		3·75
		Presentation Pack	3·00	
		Set of 3 Gutter Pairs	4·00	

Plate Nos.: All values 1A, 1B, 1C, 1D (each ×4)

Sheets: 40 (2 panes 5×4)

Imprint: Right-hand corner, bottom margin of each pane

Withdrawn: 1.10.86

Post Office Yearbook

1985 (9 DEC). *Comprises Nos.* 248 *and* 281/305 *in slipcase*

Yearbook . . . . 38·00

Withdrawn: 9.92

Year Pack 1985

1986 (1 JAN). *Comprises Nos.* 281/305 *with or without No.* 248

Year Pack with No. 248 . . . . 30·00

Year Pack without No. 248 . . 20·00

Withdrawn: 30.12.86

284 Swimming

285 Race Walking

286 Rifle-shooting

287 Cycling

Commonwealth Games, Edinburgh

(Des C. Abbott. Litho Questa)

1986 (5 FEB). *Perf* 14½ (C)

306	**284**	12p multicoloured	40	40
307	**285**	15p multicoloured	50	50
308	**286**	31p multicoloured	1·50	1·50
309	**287**	34p multicoloured	1·50	1·50
306/9		Set of 4	3·50	3·50
		First Day Cover		4·50
		Presentation Pack	4·00	
		Set of 4 Gutter Pairs	7·00	

No. 309 also commemorates the 50th anniversary of Manx International Cycling Week.

Plate Nos.: All values 1A, 1B, 1C, 1D (each ×5)

Sheets: 40 (2 panes 5×4)

Imprint: Right-hand corner, bottom margin of each pane

Withdrawn: 4.2.87

288 Viking Necklace and Peel Castle

289 Meayll Circle, Rushen

290 Skeleton of Great Deer and Manx Museum

291 Viking Longship Model

292 Open Air Museum, Cregneash

Centenary of Manx Museum

(Des J. Nicholson. Litho Questa)

1986 (5 FEB). *Perf* 14 (C)

310	**288**	12p multicoloured	. . . .	35	35
311	**289**	15p multicoloured	. . . .	45	45
312	**290**	22p multicoloured	. . . .	1·00	1·00
313	**291**	26p multicoloured	. . . .	1·25	1·25
314	**292**	29p multicoloured	. . . .	1·40	1·40
310/14		Set of 5	. . . .	4·00	4·00
		First Day Cover	. . . .		5·00
		Presentation Pack	. . . .	4·50	
		Set of 5 Gutter Pairs	. . . . . .	8·00	

Plate Nos.: All values 1A, 1B, 1C, 1D (each ×6)

Sheets: 40 (2 panes 5×4) 12p, 15p, 29p; (2 panes 4×5) others

Imprint: Right-hand corner, bottom margin (12p, 15p, 29p) or bottom left-hand margin (others)

Withdrawn: 4.2.87

293 Viking Longship

294 Celtic Cross Logo

Manx Heritage Year. Booklet stamps

(Des Colleen Corlett. Litho Harrison)

1986 (10 APR). *Perf* 14½×14 (C)

315	**293**	2p multicoloured	25	25
		a. Booklet pane. Nos. 315×2 and 316×4	3·50	
316	**294**	10p black, apple green and brownish grey	75	75
		a. Booklet pane. No. 316×3 and 3 stamp size labels	3·00	
315/16		Set of 2	1·00	1·00
		First Day Cover (Nos. 315×1 and 316×2)		1·50
		Presentation Pack (Nos. 315×1 and 316×2)	1·50	

In addition to Booklets SB14/15 Nos. 315/16 also come from special booklet sheets of 60 containing five each of Nos. 315a and 316a.

Plate Nos. 1A (×7)

Withdrawn: 25.3.87

295 Usnea articulata (lichen) and Neotinea intacta (orchid), The Ayres

296 Hen Harrier, Calf of Man

297 Manx Stoat, Eary Chuslin

298 *Stenobothus stigmaticus* (grasshopper), St. Michael's Isle

Europa. Nature and Environment Protection

(Des J. Nicholson and Nancy Corkish. Photo Courvoisier)

1986 (10 APR). *Granite paper. Perf* 11½ (C)

317	**295**	12p multicoloured	. . . .	60	6(
		a. Horiz pair. Nos. 317/18	. . . .	1·25	1·2£
318	**296**	12p multicoloured	. . . .	60	6(
319	**297**	22p multicoloured	. . . .	95	9£
		a. Horiz pair. Nos. 319/20	. . . .	1·90	1·9(
320	**298**	22p multicoloured	. . . .	95	9£
317/20		Set of 4	. . . .	2·75	2·7£
		First Day Cover	. . . .		4·0(
		Presentation Pack	. . . .	3·50	

Cylinder Nos.: Both values A1–1–1–1–1

Sheets: 20 (4×5). The two designs for each value printed together *se-tenant*, in horizontal pairs throughout the sheets

Imprint: Central, right-hand margin

Withdrawn: 9.4.87

299 Ellanbane (home of Myles Standish)

300 *Mayflower* crossing the Atlantic, 1620

301 Pilgrim Fathers landing at Plymouth, 1620

302 Captain Myles Standish

'Ameripex '86' International Stamp Exhibition, Chicago.
Captain Myles Standish of the Mayflower

(Des C. Abbott. Litho Cartor)

1986 (22 MAY). *Perf 13½* (C)

321	**299**	12p multicoloured	. . . .	35	35
322	**300**	15p multicoloured	. . . .	55	55
323	**301**	31p multicoloured	. . . .	1·40	1·40
324	**302**	34p multicoloured	. . . .	1·60	1·60
321/4		Set of 4	. . . .	3·50	3·50
		First Day Cover	. . . .		4·50
		Presentation Pack	. . . .	4·25	
MS325	100×75 mm. Nos. 323/4. Perf 12½. .			3·00	3·00
		First Day Cover	. . . .		3·75
		Presentation Pack	. . . .	3·50	

No. **MS**325 also commemorates the 75th anniversary of the World Manx Association.

Plate Nos.: All values 1A, 1B, 1C, 1D (each ×5)

Sheets: 20 (5×4)

Imprint: Right-hand corner, bottom margin

Withdrawn: 21.5.87

303 Prince Andrew in Naval Uniform and Miss Sarah Ferguson

304 Engagement Photograph

Royal Wedding

(Des Colleen Corlett. Litho B.D.T.)

1986 (23 JULY). *Perf 15×14* (C)

326	**303**	15p multicoloured	. . . .	75	75
327	**304**	40p multicoloured	. . . .	1·75	1·50
326/7		Set of 2	. . . .	2·50	2·25
		First Day Cover	. . . .		3·50
		Presentation Pack	. . . .	3·00	

Plate Nos.: Both values 1A, 1B (each ×5)

Sheets: 20 (4×5)

Imprint: Right-hand corner, bottom margin

Withdrawn: 22.7.87

305 Prince Philip

306 Queen Elizabeth II

307 Queen Elizabeth II and Prince Philip

Royal Birthdays

(Des Colleen Corlett. Photo Courvoisier)

1986 (28 AUG). *Granite paper. Perf 11½* (C)

328	**305**	15p multicoloured	. . . .	80	80
		a. Horiz pair. Nos. 328/9	. . . .	1·60	1·60
329	**306**	15p multicoloured	. . . .	80	80
330	**307**	34p multicoloured	. . . .	1·75	1·75
328/30		Set of 3	. . . .	3·00	3·00
		First Day Cover	. . . .		4·00
		Presentation Pack	. . . .	4·00	
		Souvenir Folder (complete sheets)	. . . .	16·00	

Nos. 328/30 also commemorate Stockholmia '86 and 350th anniversary of Swedish Post Office.

Cylinder Nos.: 15p A1–1–1–1–1, B1–1–1–1–1, C1–1–1–1–1, D1–1–1–1–1; 34p A1–1–1–1–1, B1–1–1–1–1, C1–1–1–1–1, D1–1–1–1–1

Sheets: 15p 12 (4×3). The two designs printed together, *se-tenant*, in horizontal pairs throughout the sheets; 34p 6 (2×3)

Imprint: Central, bottom margin

Withdrawn: 27.8.87

308 Robins on Globe and 'Peace and Goodwill' in Braille

309 Hands releasing Peace Dove

310 Clasped Hands and 'Peace' in Sign Language

133

Christmas and International Peace Year

(Des Colleen Corlett. Litho Questa)

1986 (25 SEPT). *Perf* 14 (C)

331	**308**	11p multicoloured	....	50	50
332	**309**	14p multicoloured	....	55	55
333	**310**	31p multicoloured	....	1·25	1·25
331/3		Set of 3	....	2·00	2·00
		First Day Cover	....		3·00
		Presentation Pack	....	2·50	
		Set of 3 Gutter Pairs	......	4·00	

No. 331 also commemorates the 50th anniversary of Manx Blind Welfare Society.

Plate Nos.: All values 1A, 1B, 1C, 1D (each ×5)

Sheets: 40 (2 panes 4×5)

Imprint: Right-hand corner, bottom margin of each pane

Withdrawn: 24.9.87

Year Pack 1986

1986 (25 SEPT). *Comprises Nos. 306/33*

	Year Pack	24·00

Withdrawn: 31.12.87

Post Office Yearbook

1986 (DEC). *Comprises Nos. 306/14, 315a, 316a, 317/27, 328/30 in complete sheets, and 331/3 in slipcase*

Yearbook	42·00

Sold out 9.90

311 North Quay

312 Old Fishmarket

313 The Breakwater

314 Jubilee Clock

315 Loch Promenade

316 Beach

Victorian Douglas

(Des A. Theobald. Litho Questa)

1987 (21 JAN–26 MAR). *Perf* 14×14½ (C)

334	**311**	2p multicoloured (a)		10	10
		a. Booklet pane. Nos. 334×2, 335×2 and 336×4 (2p stamps at top) (b)		4·00	
		ab. Ditto, but 2p stamps at bottom (b)..............		4·00	
		b. Booklet pane. Nos. 334/7, each ×2 (b)		3·50	
335	**312**	3p multicoloured (a)		10	10
336	**313**	10p multicoloured (a)		35	35
337	**314**	15p multicoloured (a)		50	50
338	**315**	31p multicoloured (a)		1·60	1·60
339	**316**	34p multicoloured (a)		1·90	1·90
334/9		Set of 6		4·00	4·00
		First Day Cover (Nos. 334/9)			4·50
		First Day Covers (2) (se-tenant strips)			7·00
		Presentation Pack (Nos. 334/9)		4·25	
		Set of 6 Gutter Pairs		8·00	

Printings: (a) 21.1.87; (b) 26.3.87

Plate Nos.: All values 1A, 1B, 1C, 1D (each ×4)

Sheets: 40 (2 panes 5×4). In addition to booklets SB16/17 Nos. 334/7 also come from special booklet sheets of 48 containing 6 each of Nos. 334a/b

Imprint: Right-hand corner, bottom margin of each pane

Withdrawn: 20.1.88 sheets; 15.3.88 booklets

317 'The Old Fishmarket and Harbour, Douglas'

318 'Red Sails at Douglas'

319 'The Double Corner, Peel'

320 'Peel Harbour'

Paintings by John Miller Nicholson

(Des A. Theobald. Litho Cartor)

1987 (18 FEB). *Perf* 13½ (C)

340	**317**	12p multicoloured	....	35	35
341	**318**	26p multicoloured	....	90	90

842	**319**	29p multicoloured	....	1·50	1·50
843	**320**	34p multicoloured	....	1·75	1·75
340/3		*Set of* 4	....	4·00	4·00
		First Day Cover	....		4·50
		Presentation Pack	....	4·50	
		Set of 4 *Gutter Pairs*	......	8·00	

Plate Nos.: All values 1A, 1B, 1C, 1D (each ×5)

Sheets: 40 (2 panes 5×4)

Imprint: Right-hand corner, bottom margin of each pane

Withdrawn: 17.2.88

321 Sea Terminal, Douglas

322 Tower of Refuge, Douglas

323 Gaiety Theatre, Douglas

324 Villa Marina, Douglas

Europa. Architecture

(Des R. Maddox, Litho B.D.T.)

1987 (29 APR). *Perf* 13½ (C)

344	**321**	12p multicoloured	....	60	60
		a. *Horiz pair. Nos.* 344/5	....	1·25	1·25
345	**322**	12p multicoloured	....	60	60
346	**323**	22p multicoloured	....	1·10	1·10
		a. *Horiz pair. Nos.* 346/7	....	2·10	2·10
347	**324**	22p multicoloured	....	1·10	1·10
344/7		*Set of* 4	....	3·00	3·00
		First Day Cover	....		4·25
		Presentation Pack	....	4·00	

Plate Nos.: Both values 1A, 1B (each ×5)

Sheets: 10 (2×5). The two designs for each value printed together, *se-tenant*, in horizontal pairs throughout the sheets

Imprint: Central, right-hand margin

Withdrawn: 28.4.88

325 Supercharged BMW 50cc, 1939

326 Manx 'Kneeler' Norton 350cc, 1953

327 MV Agusta 500cc 4, 1956

328 Guzzi 500cc V8, 1957

329 Honda 250cc 6, 1967

80th Anniversary of Tourist Trophy Motor-cycle Races

(Des B. Dix. Litho Cartor)

1987 (27 MAY). *Perf* 13½×13 (C)

348	**325**	12p multicoloured	....	40	40
349	**326**	15p multicoloured	....	60	60
350	**327**	29p multicoloured	....	1·00	1·00
351	**328**	31p multicoloured	....	1·10	1·10
352	**329**	34p multicoloured	....	1·40	1·40
348/52		*Set of* 5	....	4·00	4·00
		First Day Cover	....		5·25
		Presentation Pack	....	5·00	
		Stamp Cards (*Set of* 5)	....	2·25	5·50
		Set of 5 *Gutter Pairs*	......	8·00	
MS353		150×140 mm. Nos. 348/52. Perf 14×13½ (C)	....	5·00	5·00
		Souvenir Folder	....	7·00	

Nos. 348/53 also commemorate the centenary of the St. John Ambulance Brigade and the miniature sheet also carries the logo of 'Capex '87' International Stamp Exhibition, Toronto on its margin.

Plate Nos.: 12p, 15p, 29p, 31p, 34p 1A, 1B, 1C, 1D (each ×4); miniature sheet 1A (×4)

Sheets: 40 (2 panes 5×4)

Imprint: Right-hand corner, bottom margin of each pane (sheets) or bottom, right-hand margin (miniature sheet)

Withdrawn: 11.6.88

330 Fuchsia and
Wild Roses

331 Field Scabious
and Ragwort

332 Wood Anemone
and Celandine

333 Violets and
Primroses

Wild Flowers

(Des Nancy Corkish. Litho Enschedé)

1987 (9 SEPT). *Perf* 14½×13 (C)

354	**330**	16p multicoloured	. . . .	60	60
355	**331**	29p multicoloured	. . . .	1·10	1·10
356	**332**	31p multicoloured	. . . .	1·25	1·25
357	**333**	34p multicoloured	. . . .	1·50	1·50
354/7		*Set of 4*	. . . .	4·00	4·00
		First Day Cover			4·75
		Presentation Pack		4·25	

Plate Nos. All values 1A, 1B (each ×4)
Sheets: 20 (5×4)
Imprint: Right-hand corner, bottom margin
Withdrawn: 8.9.88

334 Stirring the
Christmas
Pudding

335 Bringing
Home the
Christmas
Tree

336 Decorating
the Christmas
Tree

Christmas. Victorian Scenes

(Des Colleen Corlett. Litho Questa)

1987 (16 OCT). *Perf* 14 (C)

358	**334**	12p multicoloured	. . . .	50	50
359	**335**	15p multicoloured	. . . .	75	75
360	**336**	31p multicoloured	. . . .	1·25	1·25
358/60		*Set of 3*	. . . .	2·25	2·25
		First Day Cover			3·50
		Presentation Pack		3·00	
		Set of 3 Gutter Pairs		4·50	

Plate Nos.: All values 1A, 1B, 1C, 1D (each ×4)
Sheets: 40 (2 panes 4×5)
Imprint: Right-hand corner, bottom margin of each pane
Withdrawn: 15.10.88

Year Pack 1987

1987 (16 OCT). *Comprises Nos. 334/52 and* 354/60
Year Pack . . . . 22·00

Withdrawn: 31.12.88

Post Office Yearbook

1987 (DEC). *Comprises Nos. 334/43, 344/7 in complete
sheets, and* **MS**353/60 *in slipcase*
Yearbook . . . . 35·00

Sold out: 5.91

337 Russell
Brookes in
Vauxhall Opel
(Manx Rally
winner, 1985)

338 Ari Vatanen in
Ford 'Escort'
(Manx Rally
winner, 1976)

339 Terry Smith in
Repco 'March
761' (Hill
Climb winner,
1980)

340 Nigel Mansell
in Williams/
Honda (British
Grand Prix
winner, 1986
& 1987)

Motor Sport

(Des C. Abbott. Litho Enschedé)

1988 (10 FEB). *Perf* 13½×14½ (C)

361	**337**	13p multicoloured	....	75	70
362	**338**	26p multicoloured	....	1·25	1·10
363	**339**	31p multicoloured	....	1·40	1·25
364	**340**	34p multicoloured	....	1·60	1·40
361/4		*Set of 4*	....	4·50	4·00
		First Day Cover	....		4·50
		Presentation Pack	....	4·75	

Plate Nos.: All values 1A, 1B (each ×4)

Sheets: 10 (2×5)

Imprint: Central, right-hand margin

Withdrawn: 9.2.89

341 Horse Tram Terminus, Douglas Bay Tramway

342 Snaefell Mountain Railway

343 Marine Drive Tramway

343*a* Douglas Cable Tramway

344 Douglas Head Incline Railway

345 Douglas and Laxey Coast Electric Tramway Car at Maughold Head

346 Douglas Cable Tramway

347 Manx Northern Railway, No. 4, *Caledonia*, at Gob-y-Deigan

348 Laxey Mine Railway Lewin Locomotive *Ant*

349 Port Erin Breakwater Tramway Locomotive *Henry B. Loch*

350 Ramsey Harbour Tramway

351 Locomotive No. 7, *Tynwald*, on Foxdale Line

351*a* T.P.O. Special leaving Douglas, 3 July 1991

352 Baldwin Reservoir Tramway Steam Locomotive No. 1, *Injebreck*

353 I.M.R. No. 13, *Kissack*, near St. Johns

353*a* Manx Northern Railway No. 4, *Caledonia*, at Gob-y-Deigan

353*b* Double-deck Horse Tram, Douglas

354 I.M.R. No. 12, *Hutchinson*, leaving Douglas

355 Groudle Glen Railway Locomotive *Polar Bear*

356 I.M.R. No. 11, *Maitland*, pulling Royal Train, 1963

356*a* Queen Elizabeth II taking Salute at Trooping the Colour

Manx Railways and Tramways, and Queen's Portrait (£2)

(Des Colleen Corlett (£2), A. Theobald (others). Litho B.D.T. (1p to 19p, 21p, 23p), Questa (20p, 25p to £1))

1988 (10 FEB)–**92.** Perf 13 (1*p* to 19p, 21*p*, 23*p*), 14½×15 (20*p*, 25*p* to £1) or 14½ (£2), all comb

365	**341**	1p multicoloured (*a*)	10	10
366	**342**	2p multicoloured (*a*)	10	10
367	**343**	3p multicoloured (*a*)	10	10
		a. Booklet pane. Nos. 367×2, 370 and 373×2 (*b*)	4·00	
		b. Booklet pane. Nos. 367×2, 371×2 and 374 (*d*)	3·00	
367*c*	**343***a*	4p multicoloured (*g*)	10	10
		ca. Booklet pane. Nos. 367*c*×3, 374 and 377*a*	4·50	
		cb. Booklet pane. Nos. 367*c*×3, 374×4 and 377*a*	6·25	
368	**344**	5p multicoloured (*a*)	20	20
369	**345**	10p multicoloured (*a*)	30	30
370	**346**	13p multicoloured (*a*)	50	50
		a. Booklet pane. Nos. 370×4 and 373×6 (*b*)	5·50	
371	**347**	14p multicoloured (*a*)	50	50
		a. Booklet pane. Nos. 371×4 and 374×6 (*d*)	5·00	
372	**348**	15p multicoloured (*af*)	50	50
		a. Booklet pane. Nos. 372 and 376×2 (*e*)	3·00	
		b. Booklet pane. Nos. 372×4 and 376×6 (*e*)	8·00	
373	**349**	16p multicoloured (*a*)	50	50
374	**350**	17p multicoloured (*ag*)	50	50
375	**351**	18p multicoloured (*a*)	55	55
375*a*	**351***a*	18p multicoloured (*h*)	55	55
		ab. Booklet pane. Nos. 375*a*×3 and 377*b*×2	4·00	
		ac. Booklet pane. Nos. 375*a*×6 and 377*b*×4	8·00	
376	**352**	19p multicoloured (*af*)	60	6
377	**353**	20p multicoloured (*c*)	60	6
377*a*	**353***a*	21p multicoloured (*g*)	60	6
377*b*	**353***b*	23p multicoloured (*h*)	60	6
378	**354**	25p multicoloured (*c*)	70	7
379	**355**	50p multicoloured (*ci*)	1·50	1·5
380	**356**	£1 multicoloured (*ci*)	3·00	3·0
380*a*	**356***a*	£2 multicoloured (*e*)	6·00	6·0
365/80*a*		Set of 21	16·00	16·0
		First Day Covers (6)		19·0
		First Day Covers (se-tenant strips) (5)		16·0
		Presentation Packs (4) (*ex* 4*p*, 18*p* (No. 375*a*), 21*p*, 23*p*)	18·00	
		Stamp Cards (1*p* to £1 *ex* 4*p*, 18*p* (No. 375*a*), 21*p*, 23*p*)	8·00	22·0
		Souvenir Folder (1*p* to £1 *ex* 4*p*, 18*p* (No. 375*a*), 21*p*, 23*p*)	9·00	

Printings: (*a*) 10.2.88; (*b*) 16.3.88; (*c*) 21.9.88; (*d*) 16.10.89. Inscribe '1989'; (*e*) 14.2.90. Inscribed '1990'; (*f*) 1.3.90. Inscribed '1990'; (*9.1.91. Inscribed '1991'; (*h*) 8.1.92. Inscribed '1992'; (*i*) 16.11.9 Inscribed '1992'

Plate Nos.: 20p, 25p, 50p, £1 1A, 1B (each ×4); £2 1A, 1B (each ×5 others 1A, 1B, 1C, 1D (each ×4)

Sheets: 25 (5×5) (£2) or 50 (5×10) (others). In addition to Bookle Nos. SB18/19 and SB21/4 Nos. 367 and 370/4 also come fro special booklet sheets of 50 containing either ten examples of th strips of five or five examples of the strips of ten. No. 372*a*, a strip three, was taken from the top or bottom of the strip of ten, N 372*b*. The 4p value was only issued in Booklets Nos. SB26/7 ar special booklet sheets of 50 containing five vertical strips of N 367*cb*, from which No. 367*ca* could also be obtained, and five ext examples of both Nos. 367*c* and 377*a*. In addition to Booklets No SB29/30 No. 375*ac* was also issued in special booklet sheets of 5 from which No. 375*ab* could also be obtained.

Imprints: Left-hand margin (£2) or right-hand corner, bottom marg (others).

Withdrawn: 31.12.93 1p to £1; 11.1.94 £2

357 Laying Isle of Man–U.K. Submarine Cable

358 *Flex Service 3* (cable ship)

ISLE OF MAN 22P

359 Earth Station, Braddan

22P ISLE OF MAN

360 'INTELSAT 5' Satellite

Europa. Transport and Communications

(Des C. Abbott. Litho Cartor)

1988 (14 APR). *Perf* 14×13½ (C)

381	**357**	13p multicoloured	60	60
		a. *Horiz pair. Nos.* 381/2	1·25	1·25
382	**358**	13p multicoloured	60	60
383	**359**	22p multicoloured	1·00	1·00
		a. *Horiz pair. Nos.* 383/4	2·00	2·00
384	**360**	22p multicoloured	1·00	1·00
381/4		*Set of 4*	3·00	3·00
		First Day Cover		3·50
		Presentation Pack	3·75	

Plate Nos.: Both values 1A, 1B, 1C, 1D (each ×4)

Sheets: 16 (4×4). The two designs of each value printed together, *se-tenant*, in horizontal pairs throughout the sheets

Imprint: Central, right-hand margin

Withdrawn: 13.4.89

361 *Euterpe* (full-rigged ship) off Ramsey, 1863

362 *Vixen* (topsail schooner) leaving Peel for Australia, 1853

363 *Ramsey* (full-rigged ship) off Brisbane, 1870

364 *Star of India* (formerly *Euterpe*) (barque) off San Diego, 1976

Manx Sailing Ships

(Des J. Nicholson. Litho Questa)

1988 (11 MAY). *Perf* 14 (C)

385	**361**	16p multicoloured	50	50
386	**362**	29p multicoloured	1·10	1·10
387	**363**	31p multicoloured	1·40	1·40
388	**364**	34p multicoloured	1·50	1·50
385/8		*Set of 4*	4·00	4·00
		First Day Cover		5·00
		Presentation Pack	4·50	
MS389		110×85 mm. Nos. 385 and 388....	3·00	3·00
		First Day Cover		3·50
		Presentation Pack	3·50	

Nos. 386/7 also commemorate the Bicentenary of Australian Settlement

Plate Nos.: All values 1A, 1B (each ×5)

Sheets: 15 (3×5)

Imprint: Bottom, left-hand margin

Withdrawn: 10.5.89

365 'Magellanica'

366 'Pink Cloud'

367 'Leonora'

368 'Satellite'

369 'Preston Guild'

370 'Thalia'

50th Anniversary of British Fuchsia Society

(Des Colleen Corlett. Litho Enschedé)

1988 (21 SEPT). *Perf* 13½×14 (C)

390	**365**	13p multicoloured	50	50
391	**366**	16p multicoloured	60	60
392	**367**	22p multicoloured	80	70
393	**368**	29p multicoloured	1·00	1·00
394	**369**	31p multicoloured	1·25	1·25
395	**370**	34p multicoloured	1·40	1·40
390/5		*Set of 6*	5·00	5·00
		First Day Cover		6·00
		Presentation Pack	5·75	

Plate Nos.: All values 1A, 1B (each ×5)

Sheets: 20 (4×5)

Imprint: Right-hand margin

Withdrawn: 20.9.89

371 Long-eared Owl

372 European Robin

373 Grey Partridge

Christmas. Manx Birds

(Des Audrey North. Litho Questa)

1988 (12 OCT). *Perf* 14 (C)

396	**371**	12p multicoloured	. . . .	70	70
397	**372**	15p multicoloured	. . . .	1·00	1·00
398	**373**	31p multicoloured	. . . .	1·60	1·60
396/8		*Set of 3*	. . . .	3·00	3·00
		First Day Cover			4·00
		Presentation Pack	3·50	
		Set of 3 Gutter Pairs	6·00	

Plate Nos.: All values 1A, 1B, 1C, 1D (each ×5)

Sheets: 40 (2 panes 5×4)

Imprint: Right-hand corner, bottom margin of each pane

Withdrawn: 11.10.89

Year Pack 1988

1988 (1 NOV). *Comprises Nos.* 361/7, 368/75, 376/7, 378/80 and 381/98

	Year Pack	32·00

Withdrawn: 31.12.89

Post Office Yearbook

1988 (1 DEC). *Comprises Nos.* 361/7, 368/75, 376/7, 378/80 and 381/98 *in slipcase*

	Yearbook	38·00

Sold out: By 9.93

374 Ginger Cat

375 Black and White Cat

376 Tortoiseshell and White Cat

377 Tortoiseshell Cat

Manx Cats

(Des P. Layton. Litho Questa)

1989 (8 FEB). *Perf* 14 (C)

399	**374**	16p multicoloured	. . . .	50	5
400	**375**	27p multicoloured	. . . .	1·00	1·0
401	**376**	30p multicoloured	. . . .	1·50	1·5
402	**377**	40p multicoloured	. . . .	1·75	1·7
399/402		*Set of 4*	. . . .	4·25	4·2
		First Day Cover			5·5
		Presentation Pack	4·75	
		Stamp Cards (set of 4)	. . . .	3·00	7·5
		Set of 4 Gutter Pairs	8·50	

Plate Nos.: 16p, 27p 1C, 1D, 1G, 1H (each ×4); 30p, 40p 1A, 1B, 1E, 1F (each ×4)

Sheets: 40 (2 panes 5×4)

Imprint: Right-hand corner, bottom margin of each pane

Withdrawn: 7.2.90

378 Tudric Pewter Clock, *c.* 1903

379 'Celtic Cross' Watercolour

380 Silver Cup and Cover, 1902–03

381 Gold and Silver Brooches from Liberty's Cymric Range

382 Silver Jewel Box, 1900

125th Birth Anniversary of Archibald Knox (artist and designer)

(Des Colleen Corlett. Litho Cartor)

1989 (8 FEB). *Perf* 13 (C)

403	**378**	13p multicoloured	....	35	35
404	**379**	16p multicoloured	....	45	45
405	**380**	23p multicoloured	....	75	75
406	**381**	32p multicoloured	....	1·40	1·40
407	**382**	35p multicoloured	....	1·50	1·50
403/7		Set of 5	....	4·00	4·00
		First Day Cover	....		5·25
		Presentation Pack	....	4·75	
		Set of 5 Gutter Pairs	......	8·00	

Plate Nos.: All values 1A, 1B, 1C, 1D (each ×5)

Sheets: 40 (2 panes 4×5) 13p, 16p, 23p; (2 panes 5×4) others

Imprint: Bottom, left-hand margin of each pane (13p, 16p, 23p) or right-hand corner, bottom margin of each pane

Withdrawn: 7.2.90

383 William Bligh and Old Church, Onchan

384 Bligh and Loyal Crew cast Adrift

385 Pitcairn Islands 1989 Bicentenary 90 c. Stamp

386 Norfolk Island 1989 39 c. *Bounty* Stamp

387 Midshipman Peter Heywood and Tahiti

388 H.M.S. *Bounty* anchored off Pitcairn

389 Fletcher Christian and Pitcairn Island

Bicentenary of the Mutiny on the Bounty

(Des C. Abbott. Litho B.D.T.)

1989 (28 APR). *Perf* 14 (C)

408	**383**	13p multicoloured	....	40	40
		a. Booklet pane. Nos. 408/10 and 412/14		4·00	
		b. Booklet pane. Nos. 408/9 and 411/14		4·00	
409	**384**	16p multicoloured	....	40	40
410	**385**	23p multicoloured	....	1·25	1·25
		a. Booklet pane. Nos. 410/11, each ×3		6·00	
411	**386**	27p multicoloured	....	1·25	1·25
412	**387**	30p multicoloured	....	70	70
413	**388**	32p multicoloured	....	75	75
414	**389**	35p multicoloured	....	80	80
408/14		Set of 7	....	5·00	5·00
		First Day Cover (ex Nos. 410/11)	....		6·00
		Presentation Pack (ex Nos. 410/11)	....	5·25	
MS415		110×85 mm. Nos. 410/11 and 414		5·00	5·00
		First Day Cover	....		5·50

Plate Nos.: 13p, 16p, 30p, 32p, 35p 1A, 1B (each ×4)

Sheets: 20 (4×5) 13p, 16p, 30p, 32p, 35p. The 23p and 27p values were only issued in £5.30 booklets and in the miniature sheet. Booklet panes Nos. 408a/b and 410a each contain two vertical rows of three stamps, separated by a central gutter

Imprint: 13p, 16p, 30p, 32p, 35p Central, left-hand margin

Withdrawn: 27.4.90 13, 16, 30, 32, 35p

390 Skipping and Hopscotch

391 Wheelbarrow, Leapfrog and Piggyback

392 Building Model House and Blowing Bubbles

393 Girl with Doll and Doll's House

Europa. Children's Games

(Des Colleen Corlett. Litho Enschedé)

1989 (17 MAY). *Perf* 13½ (C)

416	**390**	13p multicoloured	....	65	65
		a. Horiz pair. Nos. 416/17	....	1·25	1·25
417	**391**	13p multicoloured	....	65	65

418	**392**	23p multicoloured	1·00	1·00
		a. Horiz pair. Nos. 418/19	2·00	2·00
419	**393**	23p multicoloured	1·00	1·00
416/19		Set of 4	3·00	3·00
		First Day Cover		4·00
		Presentation Pack	3·50	

Plate Nos.: Both values 1A, 1B (each ×4)

Sheets: 20 (4×5). The two designs for each value printed together, *se-tenant*, in horizontal pairs throughout the sheets

Imprint: Central, right-hand margin

Withdrawn: 16.5.90

394 Atlantic Puffin

395 Black Guillemot

396 Common Cormorant

397 Kittiwake

Sea Birds

(Des W. Oliver. Litho Questa)

1989 (20 SEPT). *Perf* 14 (C)

420	**394**	13p multicoloured	80	80
		a. Strip of 4. Nos. 420/3	3·00	
		ab. Black ptd double		
421	**395**	13p multicoloured	80	80
422	**396**	13p multicoloured	80	80
423	**397**	13p multicoloured	80	80
420/3		Set of 4	3·00	3·00
		First Day Cover		5·00
		Presentation Pack	4·00	

In addition to a double image of the black printing on the design some examples of No. 420ab also show three additional impressions of the imprint at the foot of each stamp.

Examples of Nos. 420/3 sold at 'World Stamp Expo '89', held at Washington D.C. between 17 November and 3 December 1989, carried a commemorative inscription on the bottom sheet margin.

Plate Nos.: 1A, 1B, 1C, 1D (each ×4)

Sheets: 16 (4×4). The four designs were printed together, *se-tenant*, in horizontal and vertical strips throughout the sheet which exists with or without perforations across the side margins

Imprint: Central, right-hand margin

Withdrawn: 19.9.90

398 Red Cross Cadets learning Resuscitation

399 Anniversary Logo

400 Signing Geneva Convention, 1864

401 Red Cross Ambulance

402 Henri Dunant (founder)

125th Anniversary of International Red Cross and Centenary of Noble's Hospital, Isle of Man

(Des A. Theobald. Litho Questa)

1989 (16 OCT). *Perf* 14 (C)

424	**398**	14p multicoloured	40	40
425	**399**	17p grey and orange-vermilion . .	65	65
426	**400**	23p multicoloured	90	90
427	**401**	30p multicoloured	1·25	1·25
428	**402**	35p multicoloured	1·50	1·50
424/8		Set of 5	4·25	4·25
		First Day Cover		5·00
		Presentation Pack	5·00	
		Set of 5 Gutter Pairs	8·50	

Plate Nos.: 14p, 30p 1A, 1B, 1C, 1D (each ×5); 17p 1A, 1B, 1C, 1D (each ×2); 23p, 35p 1A, 1B, 1C, 1D (each ×4)

Sheets: 40 (2 panes 5×4)

Imprint: Right-hand corner, bottom margin of each pane

Withdrawn: 15.10.90

403 Mother with Baby, Jane Crookall Maternity Home

404 Mother with Child

405 Madonna and Child

406 Baptism, St. Ninian's Church

Christmas. 50th Anniversary of Jane Crookall Maternity Home and 75th Anniversary of St. Ninian's Church, Douglas

(Des Colleen Corlett. Litho Questa)

1989 (16 OCT). Perf 14½ (C)

399	**403**	13p multicoloured	. . . .	55	55
400	**404**	16p multicoloured	. . . .	70	70
401	**405**	34p multicoloured	. . . .	1·25	1·25
402	**406**	37p multicoloured	. . . .	1·40	1·40
399/32		Set of 4	. . . .	3·50	3·50
		First Day Cover			4·00
		Presentation Pack		3·75	
		Set of 4 Gutter Pairs		7·00	

Plate Nos.: 13p, 34p 1A, 1B, 1C, 1D (each ×5); 16p, 37p 1A, 1B, 1C, 1D (each ×4)

Sheets: 40 (2 panes 4×5)

Imprint: Right-hand corner, bottom margin of each pane

Withdrawn: 15.10.90

Year Pack 1989

1989 (16 OCT). Comprises Nos. 399/409 and 412/32

	Year Pack	30·00

Withdrawn 31.12.90

Post Office Yearbook

1989 (NOV). Comprises Nos. 399/409, 412/19, 420/3 in complete sheet, and 424/32 in slipcase

	Yearbook	40·00

Sold out: By 9.93

407 'The Isle of Man Express going up a Gradient'

408 'A way we have in the Isle of Man'

409 'Douglas – waiting for the Male Boat'

410 'The Last Toast Rack Home, Douglas Parade'

411 'The Last Isle of Man Boat'

Isle of Man Edwardian Postcards

(Des D. Swinton. Litho B.D.T.)

1990 (14 FEB). Perf 14 (C)

433	**407**	15p multicoloured	. . . .	30	30
434	**408**	19p multicoloured	. . . .	55	55
435	**409**	32p multicoloured	. . . .	1·00	1·00
436	**410**	34p multicoloured	. . . .	1·40	1·40
437	**411**	37p multicoloured	. . . .	1·50	1·50
433/7		Set of 5	. . . .	4·25	4·25
		First Day Cover			5·00
		Presentation Pack		5·50	
		Stamp Cards (set of 5)		3·00	6·00
		Set of 5 Gutter Pairs		8·50	

Plate Nos.: All values 1A, 1B, 1C, 1D (each ×4)

Sheets: 40 (2 panes 5×4)

Imprint: Right-hand corner, bottom margin of each pane

Withdrawn: 13.2.91

412 Modern Postman

413 Ramsey Post Office, 1990

414 Postman,
1890

415 Douglas Post Office,
1890

Europa. Post Office Buildings

(Des A. Kellett. Litho Cartor)

1990 (18 APR). *Perf* 13½ (C)

438	**412**	15p multicoloured	. . . .	65	65
		a. Horiz pair. Nos. 438/9	. . . .	1·25	1·25
439	**413**	15p multicoloured	. . . .	65	65
440	**414**	24p multicoloured	. . . .	1·00	1·00
		a. Horiz pair. Nos. 440/1	. . . .	2·00	2·00
441	**415**	24p multicoloured	. . . .	1·00	1·00
438/41		Set of 4	. . . .	3·00	3·00
		First Day Cover	. . . .		3·50
		Presentation Pack	. . . .	4·00	

Plate Nos.: Both values 1A, 1B (each ×4)

Sheets: 20 (4×5). The two designs for each value printed together, *se-tenant*, in horizontal pairs throughout the sheets.

Withdrawn 17.4.91

416 Penny Black

417 Wyon Medal,
1837

418 Wyon's Stamp
Essay

419 Perkins Bacon
Engine-turned
Essay, 1839

420 Twopence
Blue, 1840

421 Marginal Block of Four
Penny Blacks

150th Anniversary of the Penny Black

(Des Colleen Corlett. Eng Inge Madle (No. **MS**447). Recess and litho (No. **MS**447) or litho (others) Enschedé)

1990 (3 MAY). *Perf* 14×13½ (C)

442	**416**	1p black, buff and gold	10	1
		a. Sheetlet. Horiz strip of 5.		
		Nos. 442/6	4·50	
		b. Sheetlet. No. 442×25	3·00	
		c. Booklet pane. No. 442×8		
		with margins all round	1·00	
443	**417**	19p gold, black and buff	65	6
		a. Booklet pane. Nos. 443/6×2		
		with margins all round	8·00	
444	**418**	32p multicoloured	1·40	1·4
445	**419**	34p multicoloured	1·40	1·4
446	**420**	37p multicoloured	1·60	1·6
442/6		Set of 5	4·50	4·5
		First Day Cover		5·0
		Presentation Pack	5·00	
MS447		100×71 mm. **421** £1 black, gold		
		and buff	4·00	4·0
		First Day Cover		5·0
		Presentation Pack	4·50	

Sheetlet No. 442*a* was reissued on 24 August 199 overprinted 'From STAMP WORLD LONDON '90 to NE\ ZEALAND 1990' for sale at the New Zealand exhibition.

The Penny Black stamps shown on Nos. 442*b/c* each hav different corner letters at foot. The sheetlet of 25 was issue in conjunction with a special postal concession which allowe hand-addressed personal mail for the island to be posted f 1p between 10 am and 12 noon on 6 May 1990.

No. **MS**447 also commemorates 'Stamp World London '9 International Stamp Exhibition, London.

Plate Nos.: No. 442*b*, 1A, 1B (each ×3)

Sheets: 5 (5×1) containing Nos. 442/6 *se-tenant*, or 25 (5×5) No. 4 only

Imprint: No. 442*a*. Bottom margin, right-hand corner. No. 442 Central, bottom margin

Withdrawn: 2.5.91

422 Queen Elizabeth the Queen Mother

0th Birthday of Queen Elizabeth the Queen Mother

(Des Colleen Corlett. Litho B.D.T.)

990 (4 AUG). *Perf* 13×13½ (C)

18	**422**	90p multicoloured	4·00	4·00
		First Day Cover..........		4·50
		Presentation Pack........	5·00	

Plate Nos.: 1A, 1B (each ×5)

Sheets: 20 (5×4) containing ten stamps and ten *se-tenant* inscribed labels

Imprint: Central, right-hand margin

Withdrawn: 3.8.91

3 Hawker Hurricane Mk I, Bristol Type 142 Blenheim Mk I and Home Defence

424 Supermarine Spitfire, Westland Lysander Mk I and Vickers Walrus with Launch

425 Rearming Hawker Hurricane Mk I Fighters

426 Ops Room and Scramble

27 Civil Defence Personnel

428 Anti-aircraft Battery

50th Anniversary of the Battle of Britain

(Des A. Theobald. Litho Questa)

1990 (5 SEPT). *Perf* 14 (C)

449	**423**	15p multicoloured	50	50
		a. *Horiz pair. Nos.* 449/50	1·00	1·00
450	**424**	15p multicoloured	50	50
451	**425**	24p multicoloured	1·00	1·00
		a. *Horiz pair. Nos.* 451/2	2·00	2·00
452	**426**	24p multicoloured	1·00	1·00
453	**427**	29p multicoloured	1·25	1·25
		a. *Horiz pair. Nos.* 453/4	2·50	2·50
454	**428**	29p multicoloured	1·25	1·25
449/54		*Set of* 6	5·00	5·00
		First Day Cover..........		6·00
		Presentation Pack........	6·00	
		Souvenir Folder (*complete sheets*)	19·00	

Plate Nos.: All values 1A, 1B (each ×4)

Sheets: 8 (2×4). The two designs of each value were printed together, *se-tenant*, in horizontal pairs throughout the sheet, each showing composite panel at foot of Dover cliffs (15p), Weald landscape (24p) or London skyline (29p)

Withdrawn: 4.9.91

429 Churchill with Freedom of Douglas Casket

430 Churchill and London Blitz

431 Churchill and Searchlights over Westminster

432 Churchill with Hawker Hurricane Mk I Fighters

25th Death Anniversary of Sir Winston Churchill

(Des C. Abbott. Litho Cartor)

1990 (5 SEPT). *Perf* 13½ (C)

455	**429**	19p multicoloured	60	60
456	**430**	32p multicoloured	1·10	1·10
457	**431**	34p multicoloured	1·40	1·40
458	**432**	37p multicoloured	1·40	1·40
455/8		*Set of* 4	4·25	4·25
		First Day Cover..........		5·25
		Presentation Pack........	5·00	
		Set of 4 *Gutter Pairs*	8·50	

Plate Nos.: All values 1A, 1B, 1C, 1D (each ×5)

Sheets: 40 (2 panes 5×4)

Imprint: Right-hand corner, bottom margin of each pane

Withdrawn: 4.9.91

433 Boy on Toboggan and Girl posting Letter

434 Girl on Toboggan and Skaters

435 Boy with Snowman

436 Children throwing Snowballs

Christmas

(Des C. Abbott. Litho B.D.T.)

1990 (10 OCT). *Perf* 13×13½ (C)

459	**433**	14p multicoloured	40	40
460	**434**	18p multicoloured	60	60
461	**435**	34p multicoloured	1·25	1·25
462	**436**	37p multicoloured	1·40	1·40
459/62		*Set of* 4	3·50	3·50
		First Day Cover		4·00
		Presentation Pack	4·00	
		Set of 4 *Gutter Pairs*	7·00	

MS463 123×55 mm. As Nos. 459/62 but face values in black . . . . 4·00   4·00

    a. Blue (*inscriptions*) *omitted* . . £600

    First Day Cover . . . . 4·50

    Presentation Pack . . . . 4·50

Plate Nos.: 18p 1A, 1B, 1C, 1D (each ×5); others 1A, 1B, 1C, 1D (each ×6)

Sheets: 40 (2 panes 4×5)

Imprint: Right-hand corner, bottom margin of each pane

Withdrawn: 9.10.91

Year Pack 1990

1990 (10 OCT). *Comprises Nos.* 380a and 433/63

              Year Pack . . . . 38·00

Withdrawn: 31.12.91

Post Office Yearbook

1990 (DEC). *Comprises Nos.* 380a, 433/41, 442a/b, **MS44** and 448/63 *in slipcase*

              Yearbook . . . . 45·00

Sold out: By 9.93

437 Henry Bloom Noble and Orphans (Marshall Wane)

438 Douglas (Frederick Frith)

439 Studio Portrait of Three Children (Hilda Newby)

440 Cashtal yn Ard (Christopher Killip)

441 Peel Castle (Colleen Corlett)

Manx Photography

(Des Colleen Corlett. Litho Walsall)

1991 (9 JAN). *Perf* 14 (C)

464	**437**	17p blackish brn, pale brownish grey and black	45	4
465	**438**	21p deep brown and ochre	60	6
466	**439**	26p blackish brown, stone and brownish black	90	9
467	**440**	31p agate, pale grey-brown & blk	1·25	1·2
468	**441**	40p multicoloured	1·50	1·5
464/8		*Set of* 5	4·25	4·2
		First Day Cover		5·0
		Presentation Pack	5·00	

Plate Nos: 21p 1A–1A, 1B–1B, 40p 1A, 1B (each ×4); others 1A, 1 (each ×3)

Sheets: 20 (4×5)

Imprint: Central, right-hand margin

Withdrawn 8.1.92

Lifeboat *Sir William Hillary*, Douglas

443 *Osman Gabriel*, Port Erin

Ann and James Ritchie, Ramsey

445 *The Gough Ritchie*, Port St. Mary

446 *John Batstone*, Peel

447 'Intelsat' Communications Satellite

448 'Ariane' Rocket Launch and Fishing Boats in Douglas Harbour

449 Weather Satelite and Space Station

450 Ronaldsway Airport, Manx Radio Transmitter and Space Shuttle Launch

Europa. Europe in Space

(Des D. Miller. Litho B.D.T.)

1991 (24 APR). *Perf* 14 (C)

474	**447**	17p multicoloured	80	80
		a. *Vert pair. Nos.* 474/5	1·60	1·60
475	**448**	17p multicoloured	80	80
476	**449**	26p multicoloured	1·10	1·10
		a. *Vert pair. Nos.* 476/7	2·25	2·25
477	**450**	26p multicoloured	1·10	1·10
474/7		*Set of 4*	3·50	3·50
		First Day Cover		4·00
		Presentation Pack	4·00	

Plate Nos: Both values 1A,1B (each ×4)

Sheets: 20 (5×4). The two designs for each value printed together, *se-tenant*, in vertical pairs throughout the sheets, each pair forming a composite design

Imprint: Central, right-hand margin

Withdrawn: 23.4.92

nx Lifeboats

(Des A. Peck. Litho Questa)

1 (13 FEB). *Perf* 14 (C)

	442	17p multicoloured	45	45
	443	21p multicoloured	60	60
		a. *Black ptg double*		
	444	26p multicoloured	90	90
	445	31p multicoloured	1·25	1·25
	446	37p multicoloured	1·50	1·50
/73		*Set of 5*	4·25	4·25
		First Day Cover		5·00
		Presentation Pack	5·00	
		Set of 5 Gutter Pairs	8·50	

o. 469 is inscribed "HILARY" and No. 471 "JAMES & ANN CHIE", both in error.

ate Nos.: All values 1A, 1B, 1C, 1D (each ×4)

heets: 40 (2 panes 5×4)

print: Right-hand corner, bottom margin of each pane

ithdrawn: 12.2.92

451 Oliver Godfrey with Indian 500cc at Start, 1911

452 Freddie Dixon on Douglas 'Banking' Sidecar, 1923

453 Bill Ivy on Yamaha
125cc, 1968

454 Giacomo Agostini on
MV Agusta 500cc,
1972

455 Joey Dunlop on RVF Honda
750cc, 1985

456 Laxey Hand-cart,
1920

457 Horse-drawn Steamer,
Douglas, 1909

458 Merryweather
'Hatfield' Pump,
1936

459 Dennis 'F8' Pumping
Appliance, Peel, 1953

460 Volvo Turntable Ladder,
Douglas, 1989

80th Anniversary of Tourist Trophy Mountain Course

(Des A. Theobald. Litho Enschedé)

1991 (30 MAY). *Perf* 14½×13 (C)

478	**451**	17p multicoloured	40	40
479	**452**	21p multicoloured	60	60
480	**453**	26p multicoloured	85	85
481	**454**	31p multicoloured	1·25	1·25
482	**455**	37p multicoloured	1·40	1·40
478/82		*Set of* 5	4·00	4·00
		First Day Cover		5·25
		Presentation Pack	5·00	
		Stamp Cards (*set of* 5)	2·75	5·50
		Set of 5 *Gutter Pairs*	8·00	
MS483		149×144 mm. Nos. 478/82	4·25	4·25
		First Day Cover		6·00
		Souvenir Folder	5·00	

No. **MS**483 was reissued on 16 November 1991 overprinted for the Phila Nippon exhibition, Japan.

Plate Nos: All values 1A, 1B, 1C, 1D (each ×4)

Sheets: 40 (2 panes 5×4)

Imprint: Right-hand corner, bottom margin of each pane

Withdrawn: 29.5.92

Ninth Conference of Commonwealth Postal Administrations, Douglas

(Des Colleen Corlett. Litho B.D.T.)

1991 (1 JULY). *Perf* 13 (C)
MS484 119×77 mm. Nos. 367*c* and 377*a*,

each ×2	2·00	2·00
First Day Cover		3·00
Presentation Pack	3·00	

Withdrawn: 30.6.92

Fire Engines

(Des C. Abbott. Litho Questa)

1991 (18 SEPT). *Perf* 14½ (C)

485	**456**	17p multicoloured		40
486	**457**	21p multicoloured		60
487	**458**	30p multicoloured		85
488	**459**	33p multicoloured		1·25
489	**460**	37p multicoloured		1·40
485/9		*Set of* 5		4·00
		First Day Cover		
		Presentation Pack		5·25
		Set of 5 *Gutter Pairs*		8·00

Plate Nos: All values 1A, 1B, 1C, 1D (each ×5)

Sheets: 40 (2 panes 4×5)

Imprint: Central, gutter margin

Withdrawn: 17.9.92

461 Mute Swans, Douglas
Harbour

462 Black Swans, Curraghs
Wildlife Park

Whooper Swans,
Bishop's Dub,
Ballaugh

464 Whistling ('Bewick's')
Swans, Eairy Dam,
Foxdale

5 Coscoroba Swans,
Curraghs Wildlife Park

466 Whooper ('Trumpeter')
Swans, Curraghs
Wildlife Park

ans

(Des Colleen Corlett. Litho Cartor)

1 (18 SEPT). *Perf* 13 (C)

	461	17p multicoloured	. . . .	55	55
		a. Horiz pair. Nos. 490/1	. . . .	1·10	1·10
	462	17p multicoloured	. . . .	55	55
	463	26p multicoloured	. . . .	1·10	1·10
		a. Horiz pair. Nos. 492/3	. . . .	2·25	2·25
	464	26p multicoloured	. . . .	1·10	1·10
	465	37p multicoloured	. . . .	1·40	1·40
		a. Horiz pair. Nos. 494/5	. . . .	2·75	2·75
		ab. Black ptg double	. . . .		
	466	37p multicoloured	. . . .	1·40	1·40
/5		Set of 6	. . . .	5·50	5·50
		First Day Cover			6·00
		Presentation Pack		6·00	

ate Nos: All values 1A, 1B (each ×4)

heets: 20 (4×5). The two designs of each value were printed
together, *se-tenant*, in horizontal pairs throughout the sheet, with
the backgrounds forming composite designs

print: Central, bottom margin

ithdrawn: 17.9.92

7 The Three Kings

468 Mary With
Manger

469 Shepherds with
Sheep

470 Choir of Angels

Christmas. Paper Sculptures

(Des D. Swinton. Litho Walsall)

1991 (14 OCT). (*a*) *Sheet stamps. Perf* 14×14½ (C)

496	**467**	16p multicoloured	. . . .	50	40
497	**468**	20p multicoloured	. . . .	75	80
498	**469**	26p multicoloured	. . . .	95	95
499	**470**	37p multicoloured	. . . .	1·25	1·25
496/9		Set of 4	. . . .	3·00	3·00
		First Day Cover			4·00
		Presentation Pack		3·50	

Plate Nos: All values 1A, 1B, 1C, 1D (each ×4)

Sheets: 40 (2 panes 4×5)

Imprint: Central, gutter margin

Withdrawn: 13.10.92

(*b*) *Booklet stamps. Self-adhesive. Stamps die-cut*

500	**467**	16p multicoloured	. . . .	1·00	1·00
		a. Booklet pane. Nos. 500×8			
		and 501×4	. . . .	12·00	
501	**468**	20p multicoloured	. . . .	1·50	1·50

Year Pack 1991

1991 (14 OCT). *Comprises Nos.* 367c, 377a, 464/82 *and*
MS484/99

	Year Pack	35·00

Withdrawn: 31.12.92

Post Office Yearbook

1991 (14 OCT). *Comprises Nos.* 367c, 377a, 464/82 *and*
MS484/99

	Yearbook	40·00

Withdrawn: 30.11.94

471 North African and Italian
Campaigns, 1942–43

472 D-Day, 1944

473 Arnhem, 1944

474 Rhine Crossing, 1945

475 Operations in Near, Middle and Far East, 1945–68

476 Liberation of Falkland Islands, 1982

50th Anniversary of Parachute Regiment

(Des A. Theobald. Litho Questa)

1992 (6 FEB). *Perf* 14 (C)

502	**471**	23p multicoloured	80	80
		a. Horiz pair. Nos. 502/3	1·60	1·60
503	**472**	23p multicoloured	80	80
504	**473**	28p multicoloured	90	90
		a. Horiz pair. Nos. 504/5	1·75	1·75
505	**474**	28p multicoloured	90	90
506	**475**	39p multicoloured	1·40	1·40
		a. Horiz pair. Nos. 506/7	2·75	2·75
507	**476**	39p multicoloured	1·40	1·40
502/7		*Set of* 6	5·50	5·50
		First Day Cover		6·50
		Presentation Pack	6·00	
		Souvenir Folder (complete sheets)	21·00	

Plate Nos: All values 1A, 1B (each ×5)

Sheets: 8 (2×4). The two designs of each value were printed together, *se-tenant*, in horizontal pairs throughout the sheet

Imprint: Top, left-hand margin

Withdrawn: 5.2.93

477 Queen Elizabeth II at Coronation, 1953

478 Queen visiting Isle of Man, 1979

479 Queen in Evening Dress

480 Queen visiting Isle of Man, 1989

481 Queen arriving for Film Premiere, 1990

40th Anniversary of Accession

(Des D. Miller. Litho B.D.T.)

1992 (6 FEB). *Perf* 14 (C)

508	**477**	18p multicoloured	50	
509	**478**	23p multicoloured	70	
510	**479**	28p multicoloured	80	
511	**480**	33p multicoloured	1·40	1
512	**481**	39p multicoloured	1·50	1
508/12		*Set of* 5	4·50	4
		First Day Cover		5
		Presentation Pack	5·25	

Plate Nos: All values 1A, 1B (each ×5)

Sheets: 20 (5×4)

Imprint: Central, bottom margin

Withdrawn: 5.2.93

482 Brittle-stars

483 Phytoplankton

484 Atlantic Herring

485 Great Scallop

486 Dahlia Anemone and Delesseria

Centenary of Port Erin Marine Laboratory

(Des Jennifer Toombs. Litho Questa)

1992 (16 APR). *Perf* 14×14½ (C)

3	**482**	18p multicoloured	50	50
4	**483**	23p multicoloured	60	60
5	**484**	28p multicoloured	80	80
6	**485**	33p multicoloured	1·40	1·40
7	**486**	39p multicoloured	1·50	1·50
3/17		*Set of* 5	4·25	4·25
		First Day Cover		5·00
		Presentation Pack	4·75	
		Set of 5 *Gutter Pairs*	8·50	

Plate Nos: All values 1A, 1B, 1C, 1D (each ×4)
Sheets: 40 (2 panes 5×4)
Imprint: Top right-hand side, gutter margin
Withdrawn: 15.4.93

487 The Pilgrim Fathers embarking at Delfshaven

488 *Speedwell* leaving Delfshaven

489 'Mayflower and Speedwell at Dartmouth' **490** (L. Wilcox)

Europa. 500th Anniversary of Discovery of America by Columbus

(Des C. Abbott. Litho Enschedé)

1992 (16 APR). *Perf* 14×13½ (C)

18	**487**	18p multicoloured	75	75
		a. *Horiz pair. Nos.* 518/19	1·50	1·50
19	**488**	18p multicoloured	75	75
20	**489**	28p multicoloured	1·50	1·50
		a. *Horiz pair. Nos.* 520/1	3·00	3·00

521	**490**	28p multicoloured	1·50	1·50
518/21		*Set of* 4	4·00	4·00
		First Day Cover		4·50
		Presentation Pack	5·00	

Plate Nos: Both values 1A, 1B (each ×5)
Sheets: 20 (4×5). The two designs of each value were printed together, *se-tenant*, in horizontal pairs throughout the sheet, each pair forming a composite design
Imprint: Central, bottom margin
Withdrawn: 15.4.93

491 Central Pacific Locomotive *Jupiter*, 1869

492 Union Pacific Locomotive No. 119, 1869

493 Union Pacific Locomotive No. 844, 1992

494 Union Pacific Locomotive No. 3985, 1992

495 Golden Spike Ceremony, 10 May 1869
(*Illustration reduced. Actual size* 105×73 mm)

Construction of Union Pacific Railroad, 1866–69

(Des A. Peck. Litho Enschedé)

1992 (22 MAY). *Perf* 13½×14 (C)

522	**491**	33p multicoloured	1·10	1·10
		a. *Horiz. pair. Nos.* 522/3 *plus label*	2·25	2·25
		b. *Booklet pane. Nos.* 522/5×2 *and* **MS**526	11·00	
523	**492**	33p multicoloured	1·10	1·10

151

524	**493**	39p multicoloured		1·60	1·60
		a. Horiz pair. Nos. 524/5 plus			
		label.................		3·25	3·25
525	**494**	39p multicoloured		1·60	1·60
522/5		*Set of 4*		5·00	5·00
		First Day Cover.........			5·50
		Presentation Pack........		5·50	
		Souvenir Folder (sheets of			
		10)		22·00	
		Stamp Cards (set of 4)		3·00	6·00
MS526		105×73 mm. **495** £1.50, mult		5·50	5·50
		First Day Cover.........			6·00
		Presentation Pack........		6·00	
		Stamp Card		50	

Booklet pane No. 522*b* contains two blocks of four of Nos. 522/5 with No. **MS**526 between them. Miniature sheets from the booklet show a white margin and line of roulettes at left and right. In the blocks of four each horizontal pair is separated by a half stamp-size label.

Plate Nos: Both values 1A, 1B (each ×4)

Sheets: 10 (2×5). The two designs for each value were printed together in horizontal pairs separated by a half stamp-size label showing Union Pacific emblem or portraits of Dan and Jack Casement (railroad contractors)

Imprint: Central, right-hand margin

Withdrawn: 21.5.93

496 *King Orry V* in Douglas Harbour

497 Castletown

498 Port St. Mary

499 Ramsey

Manx Harbours

(Des Colleen Corlett. Litho Walsall)

1992 (18 SEPT). *Perf* 14½×14 (C)

527	**496**	18p multicoloured		50	50
528	**497**	23p multicoloured		60	60

529	**498**	37p multicoloured		1·40	1·4
530	**499**	40p multicoloured		1·40	1·4
527/30		*Set of 4*		3·50	3·5
		First Day Cover.........			4·5
		Presentation Pack........		4·25	

Plate Nos: All values 1A, 1B (each ×4)

Sheets: 10 (2×5)

Imprint: Right-hand corner, bottom margin

Withdrawn: 17.9.93

500 *King Orry V* (ex *Saint Eloi*) in 1972 and 1992 (*illustration reduced. Actual size* 111×68 mm)

"Genova '92" International Thematic Stamp Exhibition

(Des Colleen Corlett, Litho Walsall)

1992 (18 SEPT). *Sheet* 111×68 mm. *Perf* 14½×14 (C)

MS531	**500**	18p, £1 multicoloured	4·00	4·0
		First Day Cover.........		4·5
		Presentation Pack........	4·50	

Withdrawn: 17.9.93

501 Window, St. German's Cathedral, Peel

502 Reredos, St. Matthew the Apostle, Douglas

503 Window, St. George's, Douglas

504 Reredos, St. Mary of the Isle Catholic Church, Douglas

505 Window, Trinity Methodist Church, Douglas

ristmas, Manx Churches

(Des Colleen Corlett, Litho Questa)

92 (13 OCT). *Perf* 14½ (C)

2	**501**	17p multicoloured	. . . .	50	50
3	**502**	22p multicoloured	. . . .	70	70
4	**503**	28p multicoloured	. . . .	85	85
5	**504**	37p multicoloured	. . . .	1·00	1·00
6	**505**	40p multicoloured	. . . .	1·10	1·10
		a. Gold ptg double	. . . .		
2/6		Set of 5	. . . .	3·75	3·75
		First Day Cover.			5·50
		Presentation Pack		4·00	
		Set of 5 Gutter Pairs		7·50	

Plate Nos.: 17p, 22p 1A, 1B, 1C, 1D (each ×5); others 1A, 1B (each ×5)

Sheets: 40 (2 panes 4×5)

Imprint: Right-hand corner, bottom margin of each pane

Withdrawn: 12.10.93

ear Pack 1992

92 (13 OCT). *Comprises Nos.* 502/36

Year Pack . . . . 35·00

Withdrawn: 31.12.93

st Office Yearbook

92 (13 OCT). *Comprises Nos.* 375a, 377b, 502/36 *and* D25

Yearbook . . . . 45·00

Withdrawn: 30.11.94

6 Mansell on Lap of Honour, British Grand Prix, 1992

507 Mansell in French Grand Prix, 1992

gel Mansell's Victory in Formula 1 World Motor Racing ampionship

(Des A. Theobald. Litho Walsall)

92 (8 NOV). *Perf* 13½ (C)

7	**506**	20p multicoloured	. . . .	90	90
8	**507**	24p multicoloured	. . . .	1·10	1·10
7/8		Set of 2	. . . .	2·00	2·00
		First Day Cover.			4·00
		Presentation Pack		3·00	

Plate Nos. Both values 1A, 1B (each ×4)

Sheets: 50 (5×10)

Imprint : Bottom margin

Withdrawn: 7.11.93.

508 H.M.S. *Amazon* (frigate)

509 *Fingal* (lighthouse tender)

510 *Sir Winston Churchill* (cadet schooner)

511 *Dar Mlodziezy* (full-rigged cadet ship)

512 *Tynwald I* (paddle-steamer)

513 *Ben Veg* (freighter)

514 *Waverley* (paddle-steamer)

515 Royal Yacht *Britannia*

516 *Francis Drake* (ketch)

517 *Royal Viking Sky* (liner)

518 *Lord Nelson* (cadet barque)

519 *Europa* (liner)

520 *Snaefell V* (ferry) leaving Ardrossan

520a *Seacat* (catamaran ferry)

521 *Lady of Mann I* (ferry) off Ramsey

522 *Mona's Queen II* (paddle ferry) leaving Fleetwood

523 *Queen Elizabeth 2* (liner) and *Mona's Queen V* (ferry) off Liverpool

523a Manx Red Ensign

523b Queen Elizabeth II (hologram)

Ships

(Des A. Theobald (1p to 27p), J. Nicholson (30p, 40p, 50p, £1), Colleen Corlett (£2, £5). Litho Questa (£2), Walsall (£5) (hologram by Applied Holographics), Enschedé (others))

1993 (4 JAN)–**97.** *Perf* 14½ (£2), 14½×14 (£5) *or* 13½×13 (*others*), *all comb*

539	**508**	1p multicoloured (*a*)	10	10
540	**509**	2p multicoloured (*a*)	10	10
541	**510**	4p multicoloured (*a*)	10	10
		a. Booklet pane. Nos. 541, 544 and 548 each ×2 (*g*)	2·50	
542	**511**	5p multicoloured (*a*)	10	10
543	**512**	20p multicoloured (*ae*)	45	45
		a. Booklet pane. Nos. 543×2 and 547×3	3·00	
		b. Booklet pane. Nos. 543×4 and 547×6	5·50	
544	**513**	21p multicoloured (*ag*)	50	
545	**514**	22p multicoloured (*a*)	50	
546	**515**	23p multicoloured (*a*)	55	
547	**516**	24p multicoloured (*ae*)	55	
548	**517**	25p multicoloured (*ag*)	60	
549	**518**	26p multicoloured (*a*)	65	
550	**519**	27p multicoloured (*a*)	65	
551	**520**	30p multicoloured (*b*)	75	
552	**520**a	35p multicoloured (*f*)	85	
553	**521**	40p multicoloured (*b*)	1·00	1·
554	**522**	50p multicoloured (*b*)	1·25	1·
555	**523**	£1 multicoloured (*bg*)	2·50	2·
556	**523**a	£2 multicoloured (*c*)	5·00	5·
557	**523**b	£5 multicoloured (*d*)	15·00	15·
539/57		Set of 19	27·00	27·
		First Day Covers (6)		30·
		Presentation Packs (6)	30·00	
		Stamp Cards (Nos. 539/51, 553/5)	8·00	20·
		Souvenir Folder (Nos. 539/51, 553/5)	12·00	

For 4p, 20p and 24p in similar designs, but smaller, see No 687/93.

Printings: (*a*) 4.1.93. Inscribed '1993'; (*b*) 15.9.93. Inscribed '199 (*c*) 12.1.94. Inscribed '1994'; (*d*) 5.7.94. Inscribed '1994'; (*e*) 8.2.9 Inscribed '1995'; (*f*) 11.1.1996. Inscribed '1996'; (*g*) 14.5.9 Inscribed '1997'

Plate Nos: £2, £5 1A, 1B (each ×4): others 1A, 1B, 1C, 1D (each ×

Sheets: 25 (5×5) (£2), 10 (5×2) (£5) or 50 (5×10) (others). In additi to stamp booklets Nos. 543a/b also come from a special book sheet of 50 (5×10) which provides either 10 examples of No. 54 or 5 of 543b. No. 541a comes from a special booklet sheet of 30 (5×

Imprint: Central, bottom margin (£2, £5) or right-hand corner, botto margin (others)

Withdrawn: 30.11.98 1p to £1; 12.1.99 £2; 5.7.99 £5

524 No. 1 Motor Car and No. 13 Trailer at Groudle Gle Hotel

525 No. 9 Tunne Car and No. 19 Trailer at Douglas Bay Hotel

526 No. 19 Motc Car and No. 59 Royal Trailer Speci at Douglas Bay

527 No. 33 Motor Car, No. 45 Trailer and No. 13 Van at Derby Castle

Centenary of Manx Electric Railway

(Des A. Theobald. Litho B.D.T.)

1993 (3 FEB). *Perf* 14 (C)

559	**524**	20p multicoloured	. . . .	60	60
		a. *Booklet pane. Nos.* 559/62. .		3·50	
560	**525**	24p multicoloured	. . . .	90	90
561	**526**	28p multicoloured	. . . .	1·00	1·00
562	**527**	39p multicoloured	. . . .	1·40	1·40
559/62		*Set of* 4	. . . .	3·50	3·50
		First Day Cover			4·00
		Presentation Pack		4·00	

Booklet pane No. 559*a* exists in four versions, which differ in the order of the stamps within the block of four and in the information printed on the pane margin.

Plate Nos: All values 1A, 1B (each ×4)

Sheets: 10 (2×5)

Imprint: Central, left-hand margin

Withdrawn: 2.2.94

528 'Sir Hall Caine' (statue)

529 'The Brass Bedstead' (painting)

530 Abstract Bronze Sculpture

531 'Polar Bear Skeleton' (drawing)

Europa. Contemporary Art by Bryan Kneale

(Des Colleen Corlett. Litho B.D.T.)

1993 (14 APR). *Perf* 14 (C)

563	**528**	20p multicoloured	. . . .	70	70
		a. *Horiz pair. Nos.* 563/4	. . . .	1·40	1·40
564	**529**	20p multicoloured	. . . .	70	70

565	**530**	28p multicoloured	. . . .	1·00	1·00
		a. *Horiz pair. Nos.* 565/6	. . . .	2·00	2·00
566	**531**	28p multicoloured	. . . .	1·00	1·00
563/6		*Set of* 4	. . . .	3·00	3·00
		First Day Cover			3·50
		Presentation Pack		3·50	

Plate Nos.: Both values 1A, 1B, 1C (each ×4)

Sheets: 20 (4×5). The two designs for each value printed together, *se-tenant*, in horizontal pairs throughout the sheets

Imprint: Central, right-hand margin

Withdrawn: 13.4.94

532 Graham Oates and Bill Marshall (1933 International Six Day Trial) on Ariel Square Four

533 Sergeant Geoff Duke (1947 Royal Signals Display Team) on Triumph 3T Twin

534 Denis Parkinson (1953 Senior Manx Grand Prix) on Manx Norton

535 Richard Swallow (1991 Junior Classic MGP) on Aermacchi

536 Steve Colley (1992 Scottish Six Day Trial) on Beta Zero

Manx Motor Cycling Events

(Des C. Abbott. Litho Walsall)

1993 (3 JUNE). *Perf* 13½×14 (C)

567	**532**	20p multicoloured	. . . .	50	50
568	**533**	24p multicoloured	. . . .	70	70
569	**534**	28p multicoloured	. . . .	90	90
570	**535**	33p multicoloured	. . . .	1·25	1·25

571	**536**	39p multicoloured	1·40	1·40
567/71		Set of 5	4·25	4·25
		First Day Cover		5·00
		Presentation Pack	5·00	
		Stamp Cards (set of 5)	3·00	6·00
MS572		165×120 mm. Nos. 567/71	4·50	4·50
		Souvenir Folder		5·00

Plate Nos: All values 1A. 1B. 1C. 1D (each ×4)

Sheets: 20 (4×5)

Imprint: Right-hand corner, bottom margin

Withdrawn: 2.6.94

537 *Inachis io* (Peacock)

538 *Argynnis aglaja* (Dark Green Fritillary)

539 *Cynthia cardui* (Painted Lady)

540 *Celastrina argiolus* (Holly Blue)

541 *Vanessa atalanta* (Red Admiral)

Butterflies

(Des Colleen Corlett. Litho Questa)

1993 (15 SEPT). *Perf* 14½ (C)

573	**537**	24p multicoloured	80	80
		a. Horiz strip of 5. Nos. 573/7 . .	3·50	
574	**538**	24p multicoloured	80	80
575	**539**	24p multicoloured	80	80
576	**540**	24p multicoloured	80	80
577	**541**	24p multicoloured	80	80
573/7		Set of 5	3·50	3·50
		First Day Cover		5·00
		Presentation Pack	4·50	

Examples of Nos. 573/7 sold at "PhilaKorea '94" and "Singpex '94" come with commemorative cachets on the bottom margin

Plate Nos: 1A, 1B (each ×4)

Sheets: 20 (5×4). The five designs printes together, *se-tenant*, horizontal strips throughout the sheet

Imprint: Right-hand corner, bottom margin

Withdrawn: 14.9.94

542 Children decorating Christmas Tree

543 Girl with Snowman

544 Boy opening Presents

545 Girl with Teddy Bear

546 Children with Toboggan

Christmas

(Des Christine Haworth. Litho Questa)

1993 (12 OCT). *Perf* 14 (C)

578	**542**	19p multicoloured	55	
579	**543**	23p multicoloured	65	
580	**544**	28p multicoloured	80	
581	**545**	39p multicoloured	1·25	1
582	**546**	40p multicoloured	1·25	1
578/82		Set of 5	4·00	4
		First Day Cover		4
		Presentation Pack	4·50	
		Set of 5 Gutter Pairs	8·00	

Plate Nos.: All values 1A, 1B, 1C, 1D (each ×4)
Sheets: 40 (2 panes 4×5)
Imprint: Bottom, right-hand margin of each pane
Withdrawn: 11.10.94

ear Pack 1993

993 (12 OCT). *Comprises Nos.* 539/51, 553/5, 559/71 *and* 573/82

         Year Pack . . . . 28·00

Withdrawn: 31.12.94

ost Office Yearbook

993 (12 OCT). *Comprises Nos.* 539/51, 553/5, 559/71 *and* 573/82

         Yearbook . . . . 35·00

Sold out: 8.95

47 White-throated Robin

548 Black-eared Wheatear

49 Goldcrest   **550** Northern Oriole

51 Common Kingfisher   **552** Hoopoe

53 Magpie
(*illustration reduced. Actual size* 100×71 *mm*)

Calf of Man Bird Observatory

(Des Colleen Corlett. Litho B.D.T.)

1994 (18 FEB). *Perf* 13½×13 (*No.* **MS**589) *or* 14 (*others*), *both comb*

583	**547**	20p multicoloured	. . . .	60	60
		a. Pair. Nos. 583/4	. . . .	1·25	1·25
584	**548**	20p multicoloured	. . . .	60	60
585	**549**	24p multicoloured	. . . .	90	90
		a. Pair. Nos. 585/6	. . . .	1·75	1·75
586	**550**	24p multicoloured	. . . .	90	90
587	**551**	30p multicoloured	. . . .	1·10	1·10
		a. Pair. Nos. 587/8	. . . .	2·25	2·25
588	**552**	30p multicoloured	. . . .	1·10	1·10
583/8		Set of 6	. . . .	4·75	4·75
		First Day Cover	. . . .		5·25
		Presentation Pack	. . . .	5·25	
		Souvenir Folder (complete sheets)	. . . .	20·00	
MS589		100×71 mm. **553** £1 multicoloured		3·25	3·25
		First Day Cover	. . . .		3·50
		Presentation Pack	. . . .	3·50	

No. **MS**589 also commemorates the "Hong Kong '94" philatelic exhibition.

Plate Nos.: All values 1A, 1B (each ×4)
Sheets: 10 (2×5). The two designs for each value printed together, *se-tenant*, in horizontal and vertical pairs throughout the sheets.
Imprint: Central, right-hand margin
Withdrawn: 17.2.95

554 Gaiety Theatre, Douglas

555 Sports

556 Artist at Work and Yachts racing

557 T.T. Races and British Aerospace Hawk T.1s of Red Arrows

558 Musical Instruments

559 Laxey Wheel and Manx Cat

560 Tower of Refuge, Douglas, with Bucket and Spade

561 Cyclist

562 Tynwald Day and Classic Car

563 Santa Mince Pie Train, Groudle Glen

566 Edward Forbes and Signature

567 *Solaster moretonis* (fossil starfish)

568 *Adamsia carciniopados* (anemone) on Hermit Crab

569 *Solaster endeca* (starfish)

Booklet Stamps. Manx Tourism Centenary

(Des Colleen Corlett. Litho Cartor)

1994 (18 FEB). *Perf* 13½ (C)

590	**554**	24p multicoloured	....	60	60
		a. Booklet pane. Nos. 590/9			
		with margins all round	....	5·50	
591	**555**	24p multicoloured	....	60	60
592	**556**	24p multicoloured	....	60	60
593	**557**	24p multicoloured	....	60	60
594	**558**	24p multicoloured	....	60	60
595	**559**	24p multicoloured	....	60	60
596	**560**	24p multicoloured	....	60	60
597	**561**	24p multicoloured	....	60	60
598	**562**	24p multicoloured	....	60	60
599	**563**	24p multicoloured	....	60	60
590/9		Set of 10	....	5·50	5·50
		First Day of Cover	....		6·50
		Presentation Pack	....	6·50	
		Stamp Cards (set of 3)	....	1·25	

Nos. 590/9 were only issued in £2.40 stamp booklets.

Withdrawn: 17.2.95

Europa. Discoveries of Edward Forbes (marine biologist)

(Des Jennifer Toombs. Litho Enschedé)

1994 (5 MAY). *Perf* 13×14½ (C)

600	**564**	20p multicoloured	....	60	6■
		a. Horiz strip of 3. Nos. 600/2		1·75	
601	**565**	20p multicoloured	....	60	6■
602	**566**	20p multicoloured	....	60	6
603	**567**	30p multicoloured	....	1·00	1·0■
		a. Horiz strip of 3. Nos. 603/5		3·00	
604	**568**	30p multicoloured	....	1·00	1·0■
605	**569**	30p multicoloured	....	1·00	1·0■
600/5		Set of 6	....	4·25	4·2
		First Day of Cover	....		4·5■
		Presentation Pack	....	4·50	

Plate Nos: Both values 1A, 1B (each ×4)

Sheets: 15 (3×5). The three designs for each value printed together *se-tenant*, in horizontal strips of 3 throughout the sheets

Imprint: Central, bottom margin

Withdrawn: 4.5.95

564 *Eubranchus tricolor* (sea slug)

565 *Loligo forbesii* (Common Squid)

570 Maj.-Gen. Bedell Smith and Naval Landing Force including *Ben-My-Chree IV* (ferry)

571 Admiral Ramsay and Naval Ships including *Victoria* and *Lady of Mann* (ferries)

572 Gen. Montgomery and British Landings

573 Lt.-Gen. Dempsey and 2nd Army Landings

574 Air Chief Marshal Leigh-Mallory, U.S. Paratroops and Aircraft

575 Air Chief Marshal Tedder, British Paratroops and Aircraft

576 Lt.-Gen. Bradley and U.S. 1st Army Landings

577 Gen. Eisenhower and American Landings

50th Anniversary of D-Day

(Des A. Theobald. Litho Questa)

1994 (6 JUNE). Perf 14 (C)

606	**570**	4p multicoloured	. . . .	15	15
		a. Horiz pair. Nos. 606/7	. . . .	30	30
607	**571**	4p multicoloured	. . . .	15	15
608	**572**	20p multicoloured	. . . .	70	70
		a. Horiz pair. Nos. 608/9	. . . .	1·40	1·40
609	**573**	20p multicoloured	. . . .	70	70
610	**574**	30p multicoloured	. . . .	1·00	1·00
		a. Horiz pair. Nos. 610/11	. . . .	2·00	2·00
611	**575**	30p multicoloured	. . . .	1·00	1·00
612	**576**	41p multicoloured	. . . .	1·25	1·25
		a. Horiz pair. Nos. 612/13	. . . .	2·50	2·50
613	**577**	41p multicoloured	. . . .	1·25	1·25
606/13		Set of 8	. . . .	5·50	5·50
		First Day Cover	. . . .		5·50
		Presentation Pack	. . . .	6·00	
		Souvenir Folder (complete sheets)	. . . .	25·00	

Plate Nos.: All values 1A, 1B (each ×5)

Sheets: 8 (2×4). The two designs for each value printed together, se-tenant, in horizontal pairs throughout the sheets

Imprint: Central, left-hand margin

Withdrawn: 5.6.95

578 Postman Pat, Jess and Ffinlo at Sea Terminal, Douglas

579 Laxey Wheel

580 Cregneash

581 Manx Electric Railway Trains

582 Peel Harbour

583 Douglas Promenade

584 Postman Pat, Jess, Policeman and Children at Zebra Crossing
(illustration reduced. Actual size 110×85 mm)

Postman Pat visits the Isle of Man

(Des Colleen Corlett. Litho B.D.T.)

1994 (14 SEPT). *Perf 13 (No. **MS**620) or 15×14 (others), both comb*

614	**578**	1p multicoloured	....	15	15
		a. Booklet pane of 2 with margins all round	....	50	
615	**579**	20p multicoloured	....	70	70
		a. Booklet pane of 2 with margins all round	....	1·75	
616	**580**	24p multicoloured	....	90	90
		a. Booklet pane of 2 with margins all round	....	2·25	
617	**581**	30p multicoloured	....	1·00	1·00
		a. Booklet pane of 2 with margins all round	....	2·50	
618	**582**	36p multicoloured	....	1·25	1·25
		a. Booklet pane of 2 with margins all round	....	2·75	
619	**583**	41p multicoloured	....	1·40	1·40
		a. Booklet pane of 2 with margins all round	....	3·25	
614/19		Set of 6	....	4·75	4·75
		First Day Cover	....		5·00
		Presentation Pack	....	5·00	
		Stamp Cards (set of 6)	....	3·00	7·00
MS620		110×85 mm. **584** £1 multicoloured		3·00	3·00
		First Day Cover	....		4·00
		Presentation Pack	....	4·00	

Examples of No. **MS**620 from stamp booklets show a line of roulettes at left.

Plate Nos.: All values 1A, 1B (each ×4)

Sheets: 10 (2×5)

Imprint: Right-hand corner, bottom margin

Withdrawn: 13.9.95

585 Cycling

586 Downhill Skiing

587 Swimming

588 Hurdling

589 Centenary Logo

Centenary of International Olympic Committee

(Des D. Miller. Litho Walsall)

1994 (11 OCT). *Perf 14×14½ (C)*

621	**585**	10p multicoloured	....	30	30
622	**586**	20p multicoloured	....	55	55
623	**587**	24p multicoloured	....	70	70
624	**588**	35p multicoloured	....	95	95
625	**589**	48p multicoloured	....	1·40	1·40
621/5		Set of 5	....	3·50	3·50
		First Day Cover	....		4·00
		Presentation Pack	....	4·00	

Plate Nos: 10p 1A (×4); 20p 1B (×4); 24p 1C (×4); 35p 1D (×4); 48p 1E (×4)

Sheets: 20 (5×4)

Imprint: Central, left-hand margin

Withdrawn: 10.10.95

590 Santa Train to Santon

591 Father Christmas and Postman Pat on Mini Tractor, Douglas

592 Father Christmas and Majorettes in Sleigh, Port St. Mary

Christmas. Father Christmas in the Isle of Man

(Des Colleen Corlett. Litho Cartor)

1994 (11 OCT). *Perf 13½×14 (23p) or 14×13½ (others), all comb*

626	**590**	19p multicoloured	....	60	60
627	**591**	23p multicoloured	....	80	80
628	**592**	60p multicoloured	....	2·00	2·00
626/8		Set of 3	....	3·00	3·00
		First Day Cover	....		3·50
		Presentation Pack	....	4·00	
		Set of 3 Gutter Pairs	......	6·00	

Plate Nos.: All values 1A, 1B, 1C, 1D (each ×4)

Sheets: 40 (2 panes 5×4)

Imprint: Central, side margins of each pane

Withdrawn: 10.10.95

Year Pack 1994

1994 (11 OCT). Comprises Nos. 556 and 583/628, with or without No. 557

Year Pack with No. 557	. . . .	48·00
Year Pack without No. 557	. .	40·00

Withdrawn: 31.12.95

Post Office Yearbook

1994 (NOV). Comprises Nos. 556/7 and 583/628

Yearbook	. . . .	55·00

Sold out: 3.96

593 Foden Steam Wagon, Highway Board Depot, Douglas

594 Clayton and Shuttleworth and Fowler engines pulling Dead Whale

595 Wallis and Steevens at Ramsey Harbour

596 Marshall Engine with Threshing Machine, Ballarhenny

597 Marshall Convertible Steam Roller

Steam Traction Engines

(Des A. Peck. Litho Enschedé)

1995 (8 FEB). Perf 13½×13 (C)

629	**593**	20p multicoloured	60	60
630	**594**	24p multicoloured	70	70
631	**595**	30p multicoloured	85	85
632	**596**	35p multicoloured	1·10	1·10
633	**597**	41p multicoloured	1·25	1·25
629/33		Set of 5	4·00	4·00
		First Day Cover		4·50
		Presentation Pack	5·00	

Plate Nos.: 35p 1A, 1B, 1C, 1D (each ×4); others 1A, 1B (each ×4)

Sheets: 20 (4×5)

Withdrawn: 7.2.96

598 Car No. 2 and First Train, 1895

599 Car No. 4 in Green Livery and Car No. 3 in Laxey Valley

600 Car No. 6 and Car No. 5 in 1971

601 Goods Car No. 7 and *Caledonia* Steam Locomotive pulling Construction Train

602 Passenger Car and Argus Char-a-banc at Bungalow Hotel (*illustration reduced. Actual size 110×87 mm*)

603 Peace Doves forming Wave and Tower of Refuge, Douglas Bay

604 Peace Dove breaking Barbed Wire

Centenary of Snaefell Mountain Railway

(Des A. Theobald. Litho B.D.T.)

1995 (8 FEB). *Perf* 14 (C)

634	**598**	20p multicoloured	. . . .	70	70
		a. Booklet pane. Nos. 634/7 with margins all round	. . . .	3·25	
635	**599**	24p multicoloured	. . . .	80	80
636	**600**	35p multicoloured	. . . .	1·10	1·10
637	**601**	42p multicoloured	. . . .	1·25	1·25
634/7		Set of 4	. . . .	3·50	3·50
		First Day Cover	. . . .		4·00
		Presentation Pack	. . . .	4·00	
MS638	110×87 mm.	**602** £1 multicoloured		3·25	3·25
		a. Booklet pane. As No. **MS**638 with additional margins all round showing further inscriptions at right and left	. . . .	3·25	
		First Day Cover	. . . .		3·75
		Presentation Pack	. . . .	4·00	

Booklet pane No. 634*a* exists in three versions which differ in the order of the stamps within the block of four.

Examples of No. **MS**638 from booklet No. SB39 show a white margin, description of the design and line of roulettes at left and an additional inscription, '1895. CENTENARY SNAEFELL MOUNTAIN RAILWAY. 1995', vertically in the margin at right.

Plate Nos.: All values 1A, 1B (each ×4)

Sheets: 10 (2×5)

Imprint: Central, left-hand margin

Withdrawn: 7.2.96

Europa. Peace and Freedom

(Des Colleen Corlett and M. Magleby (20p), Colleen Corlett (30p). Litho Enschedé)

1995 (28 APR). *Perf* 14×13½ (C)

639	**603**	20p multicoloured	. . . .	75	75
640	**604**	30p multicoloured	. . . .	1·00	1·00
639/40		Set of 2	. . . .	1·75	1·75
		First Day Cover	. . . .		2·25
		Presentation Pack	. . . .	2·50	

Plate Nos.: Both values 1A, 1B (each ×5)

Sheets: 10 (5×2)

Imprint: Central, bottom margin

Withdrawn: 27.4.96

605 Spitfire, Tank and Medals

606 Typhoon, Anti-aircraft Gun and Medals

607 Lancaster, Escort Carrier and Medals

608 U.S. Navy Aircraft, Jungle Patrol and Medals

09 Celebrations in Parliament Square

610 V.E. Day Bonfire

11 Street Party

612 King George VI and Queen Elizabeth on Isle of Man in July, 1945

0th Anniversary of End of Second World War

(Des A. Theobald. Litho B.D.T.)

995 (8 MAY). *Perf* 14 (C)

41	**605**	10p multicoloured	30	30
		a. *Horiz pair. Nos.* 641/2	60	60
42	**606**	10p multicoloured	30	30
43	**607**	20p multicoloured	55	55
		a. *Horiz pair. Nos.* 643/4	1·10	1·10
44	**608**	20p multicoloured	55	55
45	**609**	24p multicoloured	70	70
		a. *Horiz pair. Nos.* 645/6	1·40	1·40
46	**610**	24p multicoloured	70	70
47	**611**	40p multicoloured	1·10	1·10
		a. *Horiz pair. Nos.* 647/8	2·25	2·25
48	**612**	40p multicoloured	1·10	1·10
41/8		*Set of* 8	4·75	4·75
		First Day Cover		5·25
		Presentation Pack	5·00	
		Souvenir Folder (*complete sheets*)	19·00	

Plate Nos.: All values 1A, 1B, 1C (each ×4)

Sheets: 8 (2×4). The two designs for each value printed together, *se-tenant*, in horizontal pairs throughout the sheets

Imprint: Central, left-hand margin

Withdrawn: 7.5.96

13 Reg Parnell in Maserati '4 CLT', 1951

614 Stirling Moss in Frazer Nash, 1951

615 Richard Seaman in Delage, 1936

616 Prince Bira in ERA R2B 'Romulus', 1937

617 Kenelm Guinness in Sunbeam 1, 1914

618 Freddie Dixon in Riley, 1934

619 John Napier in Arrol Johnston, 1905
(*illustration reduced. Actual size* 103×73 mm)

90th Anniversary of Motor Racing on Isle of Man

(Des N. Sykes. Litho Questa)

1995 (8 MAY). *Perf* 14 (C)

649	**613**	20p multicoloured	60	60
650	**614**	24p multicoloured	75	75
651	**615**	30p multicoloured	85	85
652	**616**	36p multicoloured	1·00	1·00
653	**617**	41p multicoloured	1·10	1·10
654	**618**	42p multicoloured	1·10	1·10
649/54		*Set of* 6	4·75	4·75
		First Day Cover		5·25
		Presentation Pack	5·00	
MS655		103×73 mm. **619** £1 multicoloured	2·50	2·50
		First Day Cover		2·75
		Presentation Pack	2·75	

Plate Nos.: All values 1A, 1B (each ×5)

Sheets: 20 (5×4)

Imprint: Right-hand corner, bottom margin

Withdrawn: 7.5.96

620 Thomas the Tank
Engine and Bertie
Bus being Unloaded

621 Mail Train

622 Bertie and Engines at
Ballasalla

623 Viking the Diesel
Engine, Port Erin

624 Thomas and Railcar at
Snaefell Summit

625 Engines racing past
Laxey Wheel

***50th Anniversary of Thomas the Tank Engine Stories by
Revd. Awdry. 'Thomas the Tank Engine's Dream'***

(Des O. Bell. Litho B.D.T.)

1995 (15 AUG). *Perf* 14 (C)

656	**620**	20p multicoloured		60	60
		a. *Booklet pane. Nos. 656/7*			
		with margins all round		1·50	
		b. *Booklet pane. Nos. 656 and*			
		661 with margins all round. .		2·00	
657	**621**	24p multicoloured		75	75
		a. *Booklet pane. Nos. 657/8*			
		with margins all round		1·50	
658	**622**	30p multicoloured		85	85
		a. *Booklet pane. Nos. 658/9*			
		with margins all round		1·75	
659	**623**	36p multicoloured		1·00	1·00
		a. *Booklet pane. Nos. 659/60*			
		with margins all round		2·00	
660	**624**	41p multicoloured		1·10	1·10
		a. *Booklet pane. Nos. 660/1*			
		with margins all round		2·25	

661	**625**	45p multicoloured	. . . .		1·25	1·2
656/61			*Set of 6*		5·00	5·0
			First Day Cover			5·2
			Presentation Pack		5·25	
			Stamp Cards (set of 6)		3·00	8·5

Plate Nos.: All values 1A, 1B (each ×4)

Sheets: 10 (2×5)

Imprint: Central, bottom margin

Withdrawn: 14.8.96

626 *Amanita muscaria*

627 *Boletus edulis*

628 Coprinus
disseminatus

629 *Pleurotus ostreatus*

630 *Geastrum triplex*

631 Shaggy Ink Cap and Bee Orchid
(*illustration reduced. Actual size* 100×71 *mm*)

Fungi

(Des Colleen Corlett. Litho Enschedé)

1995 (1 SEPT). *Perf* 13½ (C)

662	**626**	20p multicoloured	. . . .	50	50
663	**627**	24p multicoloured	. . . .	65	65
664	**628**	30p multicoloured	. . . .	85	85
665	**629**	35p multicoloured	. . . .	95	95
666	**630**	45p multicoloured	. . . .	1·50	1·50
662/6		Set of 5	. . . .	4·00	4·00
		First Day Cover	. . . .		4·25
		Presentation Pack	. . . .	4·25	
MS667		100×71 mm. **631** £1 multicoloured		3·00	3·00
		First Day Cover	. . . .		3·00
		Presentation Pack	. . . .	3·25	

No. **MS**667 is inscribed "Singapore World Stamp Exhibition 1st–10th September 1995" on the sheet margin.

Plate Nos.: All values 1A, 1B, 1C (each ×4)
Sheets: 20 (4×5)
Imprint: Right-hand corner, bottom margin
Withdrawn: 31.8.96

632 St. Catherine's Church, Port Erin

633 Robin on Holly Branch

634 St. Peter's Church and Wild Flowers

635 Hedgehog hibernating under Farm Machinery

Christmas

(Des Colleen Corlett. Litho B.D.T.)

1995 (10 OCT). *Perf* 14 (C)

668	**632**	19p multicoloured	. . . .	50	50
669	**633**	23p multicoloured	. . . .	65	65
670	**634**	42p multicoloured	. . . .	1·25	1·25
671	**635**	50p multicoloured	. . . .	1·50	1·50
668/71		Set of 4	. . . .	3·50	3·50
		First Day Cover	. . . .		4·00
		Presentation Pack	. . . .	4·00	
		Set of 4 Gutter Pairs	. . . . . .	7·00	

Plate Nos: All values 1A, 1B, 1C (each ×4)
Sheets: 40 (2 panes 5×4)
Imprint: Right-hand corner, bottom margin
Withdrawn: 9.10.96

Year Pack 1995

1995 (10 OCT). *Comprises Nos. 629/71*

Year Pack . . . . 38·00

Withdrawn: 31.12.96

Post Office Yearbook

1995 (OCT). *Comprises Nos. 629/38, 639/40 in sheets of 10 and 641/71*

Yearbook . . . . 42·00

Sold out: By 5.97

636 Langness Lighthouse

637 Point of Ayre Lighthouse

638 Chicken Rock Lighthouse

639 Calf of Man Lighthouse

640 Douglas Head Lighthouse

641 Maughold Head Lighthouse

Lighthouses

(Des D. Swinton. Litho Questa)

1996 (24 JAN). *Perf* 14 (C)

672	**636**	20p multicoloured	....	55	55
		a. Booklet pane. No. 672×4 with margins all round	....	1·75	
673	**637**	24p multicoloured	....	65	65
		a. Booklet pane. No. 673×4 with margins all round	....	2·25	
674	**638**	30p multicoloured	....	85	85
		a. Booklet pane. Nos. 674 and 676, each ×2, with margins all round	....	3·25	
675	**639**	36p multicoloured	....	1·00	1·00
		a. Booklet pane. Nos. 675 and 677, each ×2, with margins all round	....	3·50	
676	**640**	41p multicoloured	....	1·10	1·10
677	**641**	42p multicoloured	....	1·10	1·10
672/7		Set of 6	....	4·75	4·75
		First Day Cover	....		5·25
		Presentation Pack	....	5·50	
		Set of 6 Gutter Pairs	......	9·50	

Plate Nos.: All values 1A, 1B (each ×5)

Sheets: 40 (2 panes 4×5) 20p, 30p, 41p; (2 panes 5×4) others

Imprint: Central, left-hand margin (20p, 30p, 41p) or central, bottom margin (others)

Withdrawn: 22.1.97

642 White Manx Cat and Celtic Interlaced Ribbons

643 Cat and Union Jack Ribbons

644 Cat on Rug in German Colours, Mouse and Brandenburg Gate

645 Cat, U.S.A. Flag and Statue of Liberty

646 Cat, Map of Australia and Kangaroo

647 Cat and Kittens
(*illustration reduced. Actual size* 100×71 *mm*)

Manx Cats

(Des Nancy Corkish. Litho B.D.T.)

1996 (14 MAR). *Perf* 13½×13 (*No.* **MS**683) *or* 14 (*others*), both comb

678	**642**	20p multicoloured	....	60	6
679	**643**	24p multicoloured	....	75	7
680	**644**	36p multicoloured	....	1·00	1·0
681	**645**	42p multicoloured	....	1·25	1·2
682	**646**	48p multicoloured	....	1·40	1·4
678/82		Set of 5	....	4·50	4·5
		First Day Cover	....		4·7
		Presentation Pack	....	4·75	
		Stamp Cards (set of 5)	....	2·50	6·0
MS683		100×71 mm. **647** £1·50, mult	....	4·00	4·0
		First Day Cover	....		4·0
		Presentation Pack	....	4·25	

For No. **MS**683 with 'CAPEX '96' logo see No. **MS**712.

Plate Nos.: All values 1A, 1B (each ×4)

Sheets: 10 (2×5)

Imprint: Central, left-hand margin

Withdrawn: 13.3.97

648 Douglas Borough Arms

Centenary of Douglas Borough

(Des Colleen Corlett. Litho B.D.T.)

1996 (14 MAR). *Self-adhesive. Die-cut perf* 9×10

684	**648**	(20p) multicoloured	....	60	6
		First Day Cover	....		1·5
		Presentation Pack	....	1·25	

No. 684 was printed in sheets of 40, each stamp surrounded by white backing paper divided by roulettes. The actual stamps are separated from the backing paper by die-cut perforations. It was initially sold for 20p. and was only valid for postage within the Isle of Man.

Plate Nos: 1A, 1B (each ×4)

Sheets: 40 (8×5)

Imprint: Right-hand corner, bottom margin

Withdrawn: 30.11.98

651 *Sir Winston Churchill* (cadet schooner)

653 *Tynwald I* (paddle-steamer), 1846

657 *Francis Drake* (ketch)

Ships

(Des A. Theobald. Litho Walsall)

1996 (21 APR). *As Nos. 541, 543 and 547, but smaller as T* **651/7**. *Perf* 14 (C)

687	**651**	4p multicoloured	....	15	15
		a. Booklet pane. Nos. 687, 689 and 693, each ×2	....	5·00	
689	**653**	20p multicoloured	....	65	65
693	**657**	24p multicoloured	....	85	85
687/93		Set of 3	....	1·50	1·50
		First Day Cover	....		2·25
		Presentation Pack	....	2·25	

The 20p and 24p show the positions of the face value and Queen's head reversed

Plate Nos.: All values 1A, 1B (each ×4)

Sheets: 100 (10×10)

Imprint: Right-hand corner, bottom margin

Withdrawn: 30.11.98

665 Princess Anne (President, Save the Children Fund) and Children

666 Queen Elizabeth II and People of the Commonwealth

Europa. Famous Women

(Des D. Miller. Litho B.D.T.)

1996 (21 APR). *Perf* 14 (C)

701	**665**	24p multicoloured	....	75	75
702	**666**	30p multicoloured	....	1·00	1·00
701/2		Set of 2	....	1·75	1·75
		First Day Cover	....		3·25
		Presentation Pack	....	4·00	

The background designs of Nos. 701/2 continue onto the vertical sheet margins.

Plate Nos: Both values 1A, 1B (each ×4)

Sheets: 10 (2×5)

Withdrawn: 20.4.97

667 Alec Bennett

668 Stanley Woods

669 Artie Bell

670 Joey and Robert Dunlop

671 R.A.F. Red Arrows Display Team
(*illustration reduced. Actual size 100×70 mm*)

Tourist Trophy Motorcycle Races. Irish Winners

(Des J. Dunne. Litho Questa)

1996 (30 MAY). *Perf* 14 (C)

703	**667**	20p multicoloured	. . . .	65	65
704	**668**	24p multicoloured	. . . .	80	80
705	**669**	45p multicoloured	. . . .	1·25	1·25
706	**670**	60p multicoloured	. . . .	1·75	1·75
703/6		*Set of 4*	. . . .	4·00	4·00
		First Day Cover			4·25
		Presentation Pack		4·25	
		Souvenir Folder		12·00	
		Set of 4 Gutter Pairs		8·00	
MS707		100×70 mm. **671** £1 multicoloured		2·75	2·75
		First Day Cover			4·00
		Presentation Pack		4·00	

The souvenir folder contains Nos. 703/7, together with the stamps and miniature sheet in similar designs issued by Ireland.

Plate Nos.: 20p 1A, 1B (each ×4); 24p 1A (×4); 45p 1C (×4); 60p 1D (×4)

Sheets: 40 (2 panes 2×10)

Imprint: Right-hand corner, bottom margin

Withdrawn: 29.5.97

672 National Poppy Appeal Trophy

673 Manx War Memorial, Braddan

674 Poppy Appeal Collection Box

675 Royal British Legion Badge

75th Anniversary of Royal British Legion

(Des C. Abbott. Litho B.D.T.)

1996 (8 JUNE). *Perf* 14 (C)

708	**672**	20p multicoloured	. . . .	60	60
709	**673**	24p multicoloured	. . . .	65	65
710	**674**	42p multicoloured	. . . .	1·10	1·10
711	**675**	75p multicoloured	. . . .	2·10	2·10
708/11		*Set of 4*	. . . .	4·00	4·00
		First Day Cover			4·50
		Presentation Pack		4·50	

Plate Nos.: 75p 1A, 1B, 1C (each ×4): others 1A (×4)

Sheets: 40 (8×5)

Imprint: Right-hand corner, bottom margin

Withdrawn: 7.6.97

'CAPEX '96' International Stamp Exhibition, Toronto

1996 (8 JUNE). *No.* **MS**683 *additionally inscribed with* 'CAPEX '96' *exhibition logo on sheet margin.*

MS712	100×71 mm. **647** £1.50, mult	4·00	4·00
	First Day Cover			5·00

Withdrawn: 31.7.97

676 U.N.I.C.E.F. Projects in Mexico

677 Projects in Sri Lanka

678 Projects in Colombia

679 Projects in Zambia

680 Projects in Afghanistan

681 Projects in Vietnam

50th Anniv of U.N.I.C.E.F.

(Des C. Abbott. Litho Enschedé)

1996 (18 SEPT). *Perf* 13½×14 (C)

713	**676**	24p multicoloured	. . . .	60	60
		a. Horiz pair. Nos. 713/14	1·25	1·25
714	**677**	24p multicoloured	. . . .	60	60
715	**678**	30p multicoloured	. . . .	75	75
		a. Horiz pair. Nos. 715/16	1·50	1·50
716	**679**	30p multicoloured	. . . .	75	75
717	**680**	42p multicoloured	. . . .	1·10	1·10
		a. Horiz pair. Nos. 717/18	2·25	2·25
718	**681**	42p multicoloured	. . . .	1·10	1·10
713/18		*Set of 6*	. . . .	4·50	4·50
		First Day Cover			5·00
		Presentation Pack		5·00	

Plate Nos.: All values 1A, 1B (each ×4)

Sheets: 40 (10×4). The two designs for each value printed together, *se-tenant*, in horizontal pairs throughout the sheets.

Imprint: Right-hand corner, bottom margin

Withdrawn: 17.9.97

32 Labrador

683 Border Collie

34 Dalmatian

685 Mongrel

36 English Setter

687 Alsatian

88 Dogs at Work
(*illustration reduced. Actual size* 100×71 *mm*)

Dogs

(Des Colleen Corlett. Litho Questa)

1996 (18 SEPT). *Perf* 13½×14 (*No.* **MS**725) *or* 14½ (*others*), both comb

719	**682**	20p multicoloured	55	55
		a. *Booklet pane. No.* 719×4 *with margins all round*	1·60	
720	**683**	24p multicoloured	65	65
		a. *Booklet pane. No.* 720×4 *with margins all round*	2·00	
721	**684**	31p multicoloured	90	90
		a. *Booklet pane. Nos.* 721/4 *with margins all round*	3·50	
722	**685**	38p multicoloured	1·00	1·00
723	**686**	43p multicoloured	1·25	1·25
724	**687**	63p multicoloured	1·75	1·75
719/24		Set of 6	5·50	5·50
		First Day Cover..........		6·00
		Presentation Pack........	6·00	
MS725		100×71 mm. **688** £1.20, mult	3·25	3·25
		a. *Booklet pane. As No.* **MS**725, *but with additional white margins all round separated by roulette*	3·25	
		First Day Cover..........		3·50
		Presentation Pack........	3·50	

Plate Nos: All values 1A (×4)

Sheets: 10 (2×5)

Imprint: Left-hand corner, bottom margin

Withdrawn: 17.9.97

689 'Snowman and Pine Trees' (David Bennett)

690 'Three-legged Father Christmas' (Louis White)

691 'Family around Christmas Tree' (Robyn Whelan)

692 'Father Christmas in Sleigh' (Claire Bradley)

Christmas. Children's Paintings

(Adapted Colleen Corlett. Litho Walsall)

1996 (2 NOV). *Perf* 14×14½ (C)

726	**689**	19p multicoloured	50	50
727	**690**	23p multicoloured	65	65

728	**691**	50p multicoloured	. . . .	1·40	1·40
729	**692**	75p multicoloured	. . . .	1·90	1·90
726/9		Set of 4	. . . .	4·00	4·00
		First Day Cover	. . . .		4·50
		Presentation Pack	. . . .	4·50	

Plate Nos: All values 1A, 1B (each ×4)

Sheets: 40 (5×8)

Imprint: Right-hand corner. bottom margin

Withdrawn: 1.11.97

Year Pack 1996

1996 (NOV). *Comprises Nos. 552 and 672/729*
Year Pack . . . . 39·00

Withdrawn: 30.11.98

Post Office Yearbook

1996 (NOV). *Comprises Nos. 552 and 672/729*
Yearbook . . . . 42·00

693 Primroses and Cashtyl ny Ard

694 Lochtan Sheep and Lambs

695 Daffodils, Duck and Ducklings

696 Dabchick with Young and Frog on Lily Pad

Spring in Man

(Des Colleen Corlett. Litho B.D.T.)

1997 (12 FEB). *Perf* 14 (C)

730	**693**	20p multicoloured	. . . .	50	50
731	**694**	24p multicoloured	. . . .	70	70
732	**695**	43p multicoloured	. . . .	1·10	1·10
733	**696**	63p multicoloured	. . . .	1·60	1·60
730/3		Set of 4	. . . .	3·50	3·50
		First Day Cover	. . . .		4·25
		Presentation Pack	. . . .	4·25	
		Set of 4 Gutter Pairs	. . . . . .	7·00	

Plate Nos.: All values 1A, 1B (each ×4)

Sheets: 40 (2 panes 5×4)

Imprint: Right-hand corner, bottom margin

Withdrawn: 11.2.98

697 Barn Owl

698 Short-eared Owl

699 Long-eared Owl

700 Little Owl

701 Snowy Owl

702 Tawny Owl

703a Long-eared Owl
(*illustration reduced. Actual size* 100×71 *mm*)

(Des J. Paul. Litho B.D.T.)

997 (12 FEB). *Perf* 13 (*No.* **MS**740) *or* 14 (*others*), *both comb*

34	**697**	20p multicoloured	60	60
		a. Booklet pane. No. 734×4		
		with margins all round	1·60	
35	**698**	24p multicoloured	75	75
		a. Booklet pane. No. 735×4		
		with margins all round	2·00	
36	**699**	31p multicoloured	90	90
		a. Booklet pane. Nos. 736/9		
		with margins all round	3·50	
37	**700**	36p multicoloured	1·10	1·10
38	**701**	43p multicoloured	1·25	1·25
39	**702**	56p multicoloured	1·50	1·50
34/9		Set of 6	5·50	5·50
		First Day Cover		6·00
		Presentation Pack	6·25	
		Stamp Cards (set of 6)	2·75	7·00
MS740		100×71 mm. **703a** £1·20, mult . .	4·00	4·00
		a. Booklet pane. As No.		
		MS740 but with additional		
		white margins all round and		
		with line of roulettes at left. .	4·00	
		First Day Cover		4·25
		Presentation Pack	4·25	

No. **MS**740 includes the 'HONG KONG '97' International
*t*amp Exhibition Logo on the sheet margin.

Plate Nos.: All values 1A, 1B (each ×4)

Sheets: 10 (5×2)

Imprint: Bottom, right-hand margin

Withdrawn: 11.2.98

04 Moddey Dhoo, Peel
Castle

705 Fairies in Tree and
Cottage

06 Fairies at Fairy Bridge

707 Giant Finn Macooil
and Calf of Man

708 The Buggane of St.
Trinian's

709 Fynoderee and Farm

Europa. Tales and Legends

(Des Colleen Corlett. Litho Enschedé)

1997 (24 APR). *Perf* 13½×14 (C)

741	**704**	21p multicoloured	50	50
742	**705**	25p multicoloured	60	60
743	**706**	31p multicoloured	80	80
744	**707**	36p multicoloured	1·00	1·00
745	**708**	37p multicoloured	1·00	1·00
746	**709**	43p multicoloured	1·25	1·25
741/6		Set of 6	4·50	4·50
		First Day Cover		5·00
		Presentation Pack	5·00	

Nos. 742/3 include the "EUROPA" emblem.

Plate Nos.: All values 1A, 1B, 1C, 1D (each ×4)

Sheets: 10 (2×5)

Withdrawn: 23.4.98

710 Sopwith Tabloid

711 Grumman Tiger (1996
Schneider Trophy)

712 BAe ATP (15th anniv of
Manx Airlines)

713 BAe 146-200 (15th
anniv of Manx Airlines)

714 Boeing 757 200 (largest
aircraft to land on Isle
of Man)

715 Farman Biplane (1st
Manx flight, 1911)

716 Spitfire

717 Hawker Hurricane

Manx Aircraft

(Des R. Carter. Litho Questa)

1997 (24 APR). *Perf* 14 (C)

747	**710**	21p multicoloured	50	50
		a. *Horiz pair. Nos. 747/8*	1·00	1·00
748	**711**	21p multicoloured	50	50
749	**712**	25p multicoloured	60	60
		a. *Horiz pair. Nos. 749/50*	1·25	1·25
750	**713**	25p multicoloured	60	60
751	**714**	31p multicoloured	75	75
		a. *Horiz pair. Nos. 751/2*	1·50	1·50
752	**715**	31p multicoloured	75	75
753	**716**	36p multicoloured	90	90
		a. *Horiz pair. Nos. 753/4*	1·75	1·75
754	**717**	36p multicoloured	90	90
747/54		*Set of 8*	5·00	5·00
		First Day Cover		5·50
		Presentation Pack	5·50	
		Souvenir Folder (*complete*		
		sheets)	20·00	

No. 752 is inscribed "EARMAN" in error.

Plate Nos.: All values 1A (×4)

Sheets: 8 (2×4) the two designs for each value printed together, *se-tenant*, in horizontal pairs throughout the sheets, the backgrounds forming composite designs

Withdrawn: 23.4.98

718 14th Hole, Ramsey Golf Club

719 15th Hole, King Edward Bay Golf and Country Club

720 17th Hole, Rowany Golf Club

721 8th Hole, Castletown Golf Links

722a Golf Ball
(*illustration reduced. Actual size* 100×71 *mm*)

Golf

(Des D. Swinton. Litho Questa)

1997 (29 MAY). *Perf* 14 (C)

755	**718**	21p multicoloured	50	5·
		a. *Booklet pane. No.* 755×3		
		with margins all round	1·50	
756	**719**	25p multicoloured	60	6·
		a. *Booklet pane. No.* 756×3		
		with margins all round	1·75	
757	**720**	43p multicoloured	1·10	1·1
		a. *Booklet pane. Nos.* 757/8		
		each ×2 *with margins all*		
		round	4·00	
758	**721**	50p multicoloured	1·50	1·5·
755/8		*Set of 4*	3·25	3·2
		First Day Cover		4·0·
		Presentation Pack	4·00	
		Set of 4 Gutter Pairs	6·50	
MS759		100×71 mm. **722a** £1.30, mult . .	3·00	3·0·
		a. *Booklet pane. As No.*		
		MS759, *but with additional*		
		white margins all round	3·00	
		First Day Cover		3·2·
		Presentation Pack	3·25	

No. **MS**759 includes the 'PACIFIC 97' International Stamp Exhibition logo on the sheet margin.

Plate Nos.: All values 1A, 1B (each ×4)

Sheets: 40 (2 panes 5×4)

Imprint: Right-hand corner, bottom margin of each pane

Withdrawn: 28.5.98

23a Royal Yacht *Britannia*
(*illustration reduced. Actual size* 130×90 *mm*)

Return of Hong Kong to China

(Litho Walsall)

1997 (1 JULY). *Sheet* 130×90 *mm containing stamp as No.
546 with changed imprint date. Wmk Mult Crown CA
Diagonal. Perf* 13×13½ (C)

MS760   **723a**   23p multicoloured . . . .   1·00   1·00

Withdrawn: 30.6.98

724 Steve Colley

725 Steve Saunders

726 Sammy Miller

727 Don Smith

F.I.M. 'Trial des Nations' Motorcycle Team Trials

(Des R. Organ. Litho Cartor)

1997 (17 SEPT). *Perf* 13½ (C)

761	**724**	21p multicoloured	. . . .	50	50
762	**725**	25p multicoloured	. . . .	60	60

763	**726**	37p multicoloured	. . . .	1·00	1·00
764	**727**	44p multicoloured	. . . .	1·25	1·25
761/4		*Set of* 4	. . . .	3·00	3·00
		First Day Cover.			4·00
		Presentation Pack.	4·00	
		Set of 4 *Gutter Pairs*.	6·00	

Plate Nos.: All values 1A, 1B (each ×4)
Sheets: 40 (2 panes 5×4) 21p, 44p; (2 panes 4×5) 25p, 37p
Imprint: Central, gutter margin
Withdrawn: 16.9.98

728 Angel and
Shepherd

729 Angel and
King

730 The Nativity

Christmas

(Des Jennifer Toombs. Litho B.D.T.)

1997 (3 NOV). *Perf* 14 (C)

765	**728**	20p multicoloured	. . . .	55	55
766	**729**	24p multicoloured	. . . .	70	70
767	**730**	63p multicoloured	. . . .	1·50	1·50
765/7		*Set of* 3	. . . .	2·50	2·50
		First Day Cover.			3·00
		Presentation Pack.	3·00	

Plate Nos.: 20p, 24p 1A (×5); 63p 1A, 1B (each ×5)
Sheets: 40 (8×5), 20p, 24p; 20 (4×5) 63p
Imprint: Central, left-hand margin
Withdrawn: 2.11.98

731 Engagement of Princess Elizabeth and Lieut. Philip Mountbatten, 1947

732 Wedding Photograph, 1947

733 At Ascot, 1952

734 Golden Wedding Photograph, 1997

735*a* Queen Elizabeth and Prince Philip at Peel, 1989

Golden Wedding of Queen Elizabeth and Prince Philip

(Des Colleen Corlett. Litho and die-stamped Questa)

1997 (3 NOV). *Perf* 14 (*No.* **MS**772) *or* 14×14½, *both comb*

768	**731**	50p sepia and gold	1·25	1·25
		a. Strip of 4. Nos. 768/71	4·50	
769	**732**	50p multicoloured	1·25	1·25
770	**733**	50p multicoloured	1·25	1·25
771	**734**	50p multicoloured	1·25	1·25
768/71		Set of 4	4·50	4·50
		First Day Cover		5·00
		Presentation Pack	5·00	
		Souvenir Folder (*complete* *sheet and* **MS**772)	21·00	
MS772		100×72 mm. **735***a* £1 multicoloured	3·00	3·00
		First Day Cover		3·50

Plate Nos.: 1A (×5)

Sheets: 16 (4×4). Nos. 768/71 were printed together, *se-tenant*, a horizontal or vertical strips of 4 throughout the sheets

Imprint: Right-hand corner, bottom margin

Withdrawn: 2.11.98

Year Pack 1997

1997 (3 NOV). *Comprises Nos.* 730/72

Year Pack . . . . 37·00

Withdrawn: 30.11.98

Post Office Yearbook

1997 (3 NOV). *Comprises Nos.* 730/72

Yearbook . . . . 42·00

736 Bearded Iris

737 Daisy

738 Shamrock

739 Silver Jubilee Rose

740 Oriental Poppy

741 Heath Spotted Orchid

742 Cushag

743 Gorse

744 Princess of Wales Rose

174

E OF MAN **26**

ISLE OF MAN **30**

ISLE OF MAN **50**

5 Dog Rose

746 Fuchsia 'Lady Thumb'

747 Daffodil

OF MAN £1

ISLE OF MAN £2.50

Spear Thistle

753 Queen Elizabeth II and Queen Elizabeth the Queen Mother

o Types of 4p:—

I. 'WSP' imprint aligns with 'N' of 'MAN' (sheet stamps and 1998 booklet)

II. 'WSP' ends to right of 'N' of 'MAN' (1999 booklet)

wers

Des Colleen Corlett (1p to £1). Litho Cartor (£2.50), Walsall (others))

98 (12 FEB)–**99.** *Perf 13 (1p, 2p, 10p, 20p, 30p) or 13×13½ others), both comb*

3	**736**	1p multicoloured (b)	10	10
4	**737**	2p multicoloured (b)	10	10
5	**738**	4p multicoloured (I) (a)	10	10
		a. Booklet pane. Nos. 775 and 778/9, each ×2 (a)	2·50	
		b. Type II (c)	10	10
		ba. Booklet pane. Nos. 775b×2, 780×3 and 782 (c)	2·00	
6	**739**	5p multicoloured (c)	10	15
7	**740**	10p multicoloured (b)	20	25
8	**741**	20p multicoloured (b)	40	45
9	**742**	21p multicoloured (a)	40	45
0	**743**	22p multicoloured (c)	45	50
1	**744**	25p multicoloured (a)	50	55
2	**745**	26p multicoloured (c)	50	55
3	**746**	30p multicoloured (b)	60	65
4	**747**	50p multicoloured (a)	1·00	1·10
5	**748**	£1 multicoloured (a)	2·00	2·25
0	**753**	£2.50, multicoloured (b)	5·00	5·25
3/90		Set of 14	11·00	12·00
		First Day Covers (4)		13·50
		Presentation Packs (4)	13·50	
		Souvenir Folder (Nos. 773/85)	8·00	
		Gutter Pair (No. 790)	10·00	

Printings: (a) 12.2.98. Inscribed '1998'; (b) 2.7.98. Inscribed '1998'; (c) 26.4.99. Inscribed '1999'

Plate Nos.: 4p, 21p, 25p, 50p, £1, £2.50 1A, 1B (each ×4); others 1A (×4)

Sheets: 40 (2 panes 5×4) £2.50, 50 (10×5) (others). In addition to stamp booklets Nos. 775a and 775ba also come from separate special booklet sheets of 30 (6×5), each containing five strips

Imprint: Central, bottom margin

756 Viking Figurehead

757 Viking Longship at Sea

758 Viking Longship on Beach

759 Stern of Ship

760a Viking Ship at Peel Castle
(*illustration reduced. Actual size 100×71 mm*)

Viking Longships

(Des A. Bell. Litho B.D.T.)

1998 (14 FEB). *Perf 14 (C)*

793	**756**	21p multicoloured	50	50
794	**757**	25p multicoloured	70	70
795	**758**	31p multicoloured	80	80

796	**759**	75p multicoloured	....	2·00	2·00
793/6		Set of 4	....	3·50	3·50
		First Day Cover.	....		4·25
		Presentation Pack.	....	4·25	
		Set of 4 Gutter Pairs	......	7·00	
MS797	100×71 mm.	**760a** £1 multicoloured		2·50	2·50
		First Day Cover.	....		3·25
		Presentation Pack.	....	3·25	

Plate Nos.: All values 1A, 1B (each ×4)

Sheets: 40 (2 panes 4×5)

Imprint: Central, right-hand margin

Withdrawn: 13.2.99

761 Bottle-nosed Dolphins   **762** Basking Shark

763 Front View of Basking Shark   **764** Minke Whale

765 Killer Whale and Calf

U.N.E.S.C.O. International Year of the Ocean

(Des J. Paul. Litho Questa)

1998 (14 MAR). Perf 14 (C)

798	**761**	10p multicoloured	....	30	30
		a. Booklet pane. Nos. 798/9, each ×3 and 3 labels with margins all round	....	1·90	
		b. Booklet pane. Nos. 798/9 and 800/2, each ×2, and 1 central label with margins all round	....	5·50	
799	**762**	21p multicoloured	....	50	50
800	**763**	25p multicoloured	....	70	70
801	**764**	31p multicoloured	....	80	80
802	**765**	63p multicoloured	....	1·60	1·60
798/802		Set of 5	....	3·50	3·50
		First Day Cover.	....		4·00
		Presentation Pack.	....	4·00	
		Souvenir Folder	....	25·00	
		Stamp Cards (set of 5)	....	2·50	6·00

Plate Nos.: All values 1A, 1B (each ×4)

Sheets: 10 (2×5)

Withdrawn: 13.3.99

766 Locomotive No. 12 Hutchinson   **767** Locomotive No. 10 G. H. Wood

768 Locomotive No. 11 Maitland   **769** Locomotive No. 4 Loch

770a Pillar Box and Train at Douglas Station (25p); Locomotive No. 4 Sutherland (£1) (illustration reduced. Actual size 120×54 mm)

125th Anniversary of Isle of Man Steam Railway

(Des A. Peck. Litho Questa)

1998 (2 MAY). Perf 14½×14 (C)

803	**766**	21p multicoloured	....	50	5
		a. Booklet pane. Nos. 803/6 with margins all round	....	2·75	
804	**767**	25p multicoloured	....	60	6
805	**768**	31p multicoloured	....	80	8
806	**769**	63p multicoloured	....	1·60	1·6
803/6		Set of 4	....	3·25	3·2
		First Day Cover.	....		4·0
		Presentation Pack.	....	4·00	
		Souvenir Folder	....	25·00	
MS807	199×54 mm.	**770a** 25p mult; £1 mult		3·00	3·0
		a. Booklet pane. As No. **MS**807, but with additional margins showing diagram all round	....	2·50	
		First Day Cover.	....		3·5
		Presentation Pack.	....	3·50	

Booklet pane No. 803a exists in two versions, which differ the order of the stamps within the block of four.

Plate Nos.: All values 1A (×4)

Sheets: 40 (5×8)

Imprints: Right-hand corner, bottom margin

Withdrawn: 31.5.99

Purple Helmets
Display Team

772 Joey Dunlop

3 Dave Molyneux

774 Naomi Taniguchi

775 Mike Hailwood

e of Man T.T. Races and 50th Anniversary of Honda
otorcycle manufacturer)

(Des The Agency. Litho B.D.T.)

98 (1 JUNE). *Perf* 14 (C)

3	**771**	21p multicoloured	45	45
9	**772**	25p multicoloured	55	55
0	**773**	31p multicoloured	75	75
1	**774**	43p multicoloured	1·10	1·10
2	**775**	63p multicoloured	1·60	1·60
3/12		*Set of 5*	4·00	4·00
		First Day Cover		4·50
		Presentation Pack	4·50	
		Souvenir Folder	20·00	
		Set of 5 Gutter Pairs	8·00	

Plate Nos.: All values 1A (×4)

Sheets: 40 (2 panes 5×4 with double gutter)

Withdrawn: 31.5.99

76 Princess Diana
wearing Protective
Clothing, Angola

777 Receiving Award from
United Cerebral Palsy
Charity, New York,
1995

778 With Children, South
Korea, 1992

779 Wearing Blue Jacket,
July 1993

Diana, Princess of Wales Commemoration

(Litho Cartor)

1998 (19 JUNE). *Perf* 13½×13 (C)

813	**776**	25p multicoloured	65	65
		a. *Strip of 4. Nos.* 813/16	2·25	
814	**777**	25p multicoloured	65	65
815	**778**	25p multicoloured	65	65
816	**779**	25p multicoloured	65	65
813/16		*Set of 4*	2·25	2·25
		First Day Cover		3·00
		Presentation Pack	3·00	
		Souvenir Folder	20·00	

Plate Nos.: 1A (× 4)

Sheets: 16 (4×4). Nos. 813/16 were printed together, *se-tenant*, as horizontal or vertical strips of 4 throughout the sheet

Withdrawn: 18.6.99

780 Tynwald Day
Ceremony

781 Traditional Dancers,
Tynwald Fair

Europa. Festivals

(Des M. Thompson. Litho Cartor)

1998 (2 JULY). *Perf* 13×13½ (C)

817	**780**	25p multicoloured	65	65
818	**781**	30p multicoloured	75	75
817/18		*Set of 2*	1·40	1·40
		First Day Cover		2·50
		Presentation Pack	2·50	

Plate Nos.: Both values 1A (×4)

Sheets: 10 (2×5)

Withdrawn: 30.10.99

782 Father Christmas at North Pole

783 Father Christmas checking List

784 Flying over Spring Valley Sorting Office

785 Passing through Baldrine Village

786 Father Christmas delivering Presents

787 Large Oval Pillar Box, Kirk Onchan

788 Wall Box, Ballaterson

789 King Edward VII Pillar Box, Laxey Station

790 Wall Box, Spaldrick

791 Small Oval Pillar Box, Derby Road, Douglas

792 Wall Box, Baldrine Station

Christmas. 'A Very Special Delivery'

(Des A. Bell. Litho Enschedé)

1998 (25 Sept). *Perf* 14½×14 (C)

819	**782**	20p multicoloured	50	50
820	**783**	24p multicoloured	60	60
821	**784**	30p multicoloured	90	90
822	**785**	43p multicoloured	1·10	1·10
823	**786**	63p multicoloured	1·60	1·60
819/23		Set of 5	4·25	4·25
		First Day Cover..........		5·00
		Presentation Pack........	5·00	
		Set of 5 Gutter Pairs......	8·50	

Plate Nos.: All values 1A (×4)

Sheets: 40 (2 panes 5×4)

Imprint: Right-hand corner, bottom margin

Withdrawn: 30.10.99

Year Pack 1998

1998 (25 SEPT). *Comprises Nos. 773/823*
Year Pack.............. 36·00

Sold out: 9.98

Post Office Yearbook

1998 (25 SEPT). *Comprises Nos. 773/823*
Yearbook .... 42·00

Local Post Boxes

(Des The Agency. Litho Walsall)

1999 (4 MAR). *Perf* 14 (C)

824	**787**	10p multicoloured	20	
825	**788**	20p multicoloured	40	
826	**789**	21p multicoloured	45	
827	**790**	25p multicoloured	50	
828	**791**	44p multicoloured	90	
829	**792**	63p multicoloured	1·25	1·
824/9		Set of 6	3·50	4·
		First Day Cover..........		4·
		Presentation Pack........	4·50	
		Set of 6 Gutter Pairs......	7·25	

ate Nos.: All values 1A, 1B (each ×4)
heets: 50 (2 panes (5×5)
nprint: Right-hand corner, bottom margin

Cottage,
Ballaglass
Glen

794 Glen Maye
Waterfall

ropa. Parks and Gardens

(Des Julia Ashby-Smyth. Litho B.D.T.)

9 (4 MAR). *Perf* 14 (C)

793	25p multicoloured	. . . .	50	55
794	30p multicoloured	. . . .	60	65
/1		Set of 2	1·10	1·25
		First Day Cover.		1·90
		Presentation Pack.	1·90	

ate Nos.: Both values 1A, 1B (each ×4)
heets: 10 (5×2)

Ann and James Ritchie,
Ramsey

796 *Sir William Hillary*,
Douglas

Ruby Clery, Peel

798 Inshore Lifeboat, Port
Erin

799 1974 150th Anniversary
8p Stamp

800 *Gough Ritchie II*, Port
St. Mary

801 1991 Manx Lifeboats 21p
Stamp

802*a* Sir William Hillary (founder)
(*illustration reduced. Actual size* 100×70 *mm*)

175th Anniversary of Royal National Lifeboat Institution

(Des Mainstream Media (No. **MS**839), R. Tomlinson (others).
Litho Questa)

1999 (4 MAR). *Perf* 13½×14 (*No.* **MS**839) *or* 14, *both comb*

832	**795**	21p multicoloured	45	50
		a. Booklet pane. Nos. 832/5 and 837, *plus four printed labels, with margins all round*	3·50	
		b. Booklet pane. Nos. 832/4, 836 and 838, *plus four printed labels, with margins all round*	3·50	
833	**796**	25p multicoloured	50	55
834	**797**	37p multicoloured	75	80
835	**798**	43p multicoloured	85	90
836	**799**	43p multicoloured	85	90
837	**800**	56p multicoloured	1·10	1·25
838	**801**	56p multicoloured	1·10	1·25
832/8		Set of 7	5·50	5·75
		First Day Cover (Nos. 833/5, 837)		4·50
		Presentation Pack (Nos. 833/5, 837)	4·50	
		Set of 5 Gutter Pairs	7·50	

MS839 100×70 mm. **802**a £1 multicoloured 2·00 2·10
    a. *Booklet pane. As No.*
    MS839, *but with additional*
    margins showing lifeboats
    all round . . . . 2·00
    First Day Cover. . . . . 2·75
    Presentation Pack. . . . . 2·75

Nos. 836 and 838 were only available in £4.64 stamp booklets.

No. **MS**839 includes the "Australia '99" World Stamp Exhibition emblem on the sheet margin.

Plate Nos.: All sheet values 1A (×4)

Sheets: 40 (2 panes 5×4)

Geurey   Winter

803 Winter

Arragh   Spring

804 Spring

Sourey   Summer

805 Summer

Fouyr   Autumn

806 Autumn

Centenary of Yn Cheshaght Ghailckagh (Manx Gaelic Society). The Seasons

(Des C. Alexander. Litho Walsall)

1999 (11 MAY). *Perf* 14½×14 (C)

840	**803**	22p multicoloured	45	50
841	**804**	26p multicoloured	50	55
842	**805**	50p multicoloured	1·00	1·10
843	**806**	63p multicoloured	1·25	1·40
840/3		*Set of* 4	3·25	3·50
		First Day Cover.		4·00
		Presentation Pack.	4·00	
		Set of 4 *Gutter Pairs*	6·75	

Nos. 840/3 are inscribed "Ellan Vannin", the Manx name for the Isle of Man.

Plate Nos.: All values 1A, 1B (each ×4)

Sheets: 50 (2 panes 5×5)

Imprint: Right-hand corner, bottom margin

807a Queen Victoria; King Edward VII; King George V; K* Edward VIII; King George VI; Queen Elizabeth (*illustration reduced. Actual size* 170×75 *mm*)

British Monarchs of the 20th Century

(Des Colleen Corlett. Litho Walsall)

1999 (2 JUNE). *Sheet* 170×75 *mm. Perf* 14 (C)

MS844	**807**a	26p×6, multicoloured	3·00	3
		First Day Cover.		3
		Presentation Pack.	3·75	
		Souvenir Folder (*Nos.* 824/9,		
		MS844)	25·00	

808 Tilling-Stevens Double Deck Bus, 1922

809 Thornycroft BC Single Deck, 1928

810 Cumberland ADC 416 Single Deck, 1927

811 Straker-Squire Single Deck, 1914

812 Thornycroft A2 Single Deck, 1927

813 Leyland Lion LT9 Single Deck, 1938

nx Buses

(Des P. Hearsey. Litho B.D.T.)

99 (18 JUNE). *Perf* 14 (C)

5	**808**	22p multicoloured	45	50
		a. *Booklet pane. Nos.* 845/6 *and* 847×2, *with margins all round*	2·00	
		b. *Booklet pane. Nos.* 845/6 *and* 848×2, *with margins all round*	2·40	
		c. *Booklet pane. Nos.* 845/6 *and* 849×2, *with margins all round*	2·40	
		d. *Booklet pane. Nos.* 845/6 *and* 850×2, *with margins all round*	2·50	
5	**809**	26p multicoloured	50	55
7	**810**	28p multicoloured	55	60
3	**811**	37p multicoloured	75	80
9	**812**	38p multicoloured	75	80
0	**813**	40p multicoloured	80	85
5/50		*Set of* 6	3·75	4·00
		First Day Cover.		4·50
		Presentation Pack.	4·50	
		Stamp Cards (*set of* 6)	3·00	7·50

late Nos.: All values 1A (×4)

heets: 25 (5×5)

mprint: Central, bottom margin

4 Miss Sophie Rhys-Jones

815 Leaving St. George's Chapel, Windsor

5 Prince Edward

817 Miss Sophie Rhys-Jones and Prince Edward

818 In Landau

Royal Wedding

(Des Catherine James. Litho B.D.T.)

1999 (19 JUNE–1 SEPT). *Perf* 14 (C)

851	**814**	22p multicoloured (*a*)	45	50
852	**815**	26p multicoloured (*b*)	50	55
853	**816**	39p multicoloured (*a*)	80	85
854	**817**	44p multicoloured (*a*)	90	95
855	**818**	53p multicoloured (*b*)	1·10	1·25
851/5		*Set of* 5	3·75	4·00
		First Day Covers (2)		4·50
		Presentation Pack.	4·50	

Printings: (*a*) 19.6.99; (*b*) 1.9.99

Plate Nos.: All values 1A, 1B (each ×4)

Sheets: 25 (5×5)

Imprint: Central, bottom margin

"PhilexFrance 99" International Stamp Exhibition, Paris

1999 (2 JULY). *No.* **MS**807 *additionally inscribed with "PhilexFrance" exhibition logo on sheet margin.*

MS856 119×54 mm. **770***a* 25p mult; £1 mult   2·50   2·75

819 St. Luke's Church, Baldwin

820 St. Mark's Chapel, Malew

821 St. German's Parish Church and Cathedral, Peel

822 Kirk Christ Church, Rushen

Christmas. Churches

(Des N. Sayle. Litho Cartor)

1999 (22 SEPT). *Perf* 13½ (C)

857	**819**	21p multicoloured	40	45
858	**820**	25p multicoloured	50	55
859	**821**	30p multicoloured	60	65
860	**822**	64p multicoloured	1·25	1·40
857/60		Set of 4	2·75	3·00
		First Day Cover		3·50
		Presentation Pack	3·50	
		Set of 4 Gutter Pairs	5·50	

Plate Nos.: All values 1A (×4)

Sheets: 40 (2 panes 4×5)

Imprint: Central, bottom margin

823 'Massachusetts', 1967

824 'Words', 1968

825 'I've Gotta Get a Message to You', 1968

826 'Ellan Vannin', 1998

827 'You Win Again', 1987

828 'Night Fever', 1978

829*a* 'Immortality', 1998
(*illustration reduced. Actual size* 119×108 mm)

830*a* 'Stayin' Alive', 1978
(*illustration reduced. Actual size* 119×108 mm)

Legends of Music. The Bee Gees (pop group)

(Des The Agency. Litho Cartor)

1999 (12 OCT). *Perf* 15 (*No.* **MS**867) *or* 13½, *both comb*

861	**823**	22p multicoloured	45	
862	**824**	26p multicoloured	50	
863	**825**	29p multicoloured	60	
864	**826**	37p multicoloured	75	
865	**827**	38p multicoloured	75	
866	**828**	66p multicoloured	1·25	1·
861/6		Set of 6	4·25	4·
		First Day Cover		3·
		Presentation Pack (Nos. 861/7)	3·00	
		Souvenir Folder (complete sheets)	40·00	

S867 Two sheets, each 119×108 mm. (a) **829**a 60p multicoloured, (*circular, 40 mm diam*). (b) **830**a 90p multicoloured, (*circular, 40 mm diam*)

Set of 2 sheets	3·00	3·50
First Day Cover		4·00

Sheets: 9 stamps and three labels, arranged 3×4, with the labels in the third horizontal row

ar Pack 1999

99 (12 OCT). *Comprises Nos.* 776, 780, 782 *and* 824/67

Year Pack	50·00

st Office Yearbook

99 (12 OCT). *Comprises Nos.* 776, 780, 782 *and* 824/67

Yearbook	58·00

SOUVENIR POSTAL STATIONERY POSTCARDS

The following postcards were issued by the Isle of Man Postal Authority in connection with various philatelic exhibitions and, with the exception of Nos. PC8, PC11, and PC15/16 show imprinted stamp designs.

'San Marino 82'

1982 (1 SEPT). *Card showing imprinted stamp design as No. 217. Sold at 30p*
PC1 19½p multicoloured . . . . 1·00   1·25

Withdrawn: 30.4.84

'Tembal 83', Basel

1983 (21 MAY). *Card showing imprinted stamp design as No. 250. Sold at 30p*
PC2 20½p multicoloured . . . . 1·10   1·40

Withdrawn: 20.5.84

'Espana 84', Madrid

1984 (27 APR). *Card showing imprinted stamp design as No. 266. Sold at 30p*
PC3 20½p multicoloured . . . . 1·25   1·75

Withdrawn: 26.4.85

'Ausipex 84', Melbourne

1984 (21 SEPT). *Card showing imprinted stamp design as No. 278. Sold at 40p*
PC4 33p multicoloured . . . . 2·00   3·00

Withdrawn: 20.9.85

'Italia 85', Rome

1985 (25 OCT). *Card showing imprinted stamp designs as Nos. 292/3. Sold at 40p*
PC5 14p+14p multicoloured . . . . 1·50   3·25

Withdrawn: 24.10.86

'Ameripex 86', Chicago

1986 (22 MAY). *Card showing imprinted stamp design as No. 302. Sold at 40p*
PC6 34p multicoloured . . . . 2·25   2·50

Withdrawn: 21.5.87

'Stockholmia 86', Stockholm

1986 (28 AUG). *Card showing imprinted stamp designs as Nos. 305/6. Sold at 40p*
PC7 15p+15p multicoloured . . . . 1·25   1·50

Withdrawn: 27.8.87

'Hafnia 87', Copenhagen

1987 (16 OCT). *Card with Nos. 358/9 affixed. Sold at 50p*
PC8 12p+15p multicoloured . . . . 1·25   1·50

Withdrawn: 15.10.88

'Finlandia 88', Helsinki

1988 (1 JUNE). *Card showing imprinted stamp designs Nos. 371 and 375. Sold at 50p*
PC9 14p+18p multicoloured . . . . 1·25   1·

Withdrawn: 31.5.89

'Sydpex 88', Sydney

1988 (30 JULY). *Card showing imprinted stamp designs Nos. 386/7. Sold at 60p*
PC10 29p+31p multicoloured . . . . 1·50   1·

Withdrawn: 29.7.89

'Filacept 88', The Hague

1988 (18 OCT). *Card with Nos. 383/4 affixed. Sold at 50p*
PC11 22p+22p multicoloured . . . . 1·25   1·

Withdrawn: 17.10.89

'Belgica 90', Brussels

1990 (2 JUNE). *Card showing imprinted stamp designs Nos. 442 and 446. Sold at 50p*
PC12 1p+37p multicoloured . . . . 1·25   1·

Withdrawn: 2.93

'Essen 94'. Centenary of Picture Postcards

1994 (5 MAY). *Cards showing imprinted stamp design as N 338. Sold at 80p the pair*
PC13 31p multicoloured (Douglas). . . . . 1·00   1·
PC14 31p multicoloured (Ramsey). . . . . 1·00   1·

Withdrawn: 4.5.95

'Jakarta 95'

1995 (19 AUG). *Sold at 15p*
PC15 Komodo Dragon 50

'Beijing 95'

1995 (16 SEPT). *Sold at 15p*
PC16 Great Wall of China 50

Isle of Man T.T. Races and 50th Anniversary of Honda

1998 (1 JUNE). *Card showing imprinted stamp design as M 809. Sold at 50p*
PC17 25p multicoloured . . . . 1·00   1

MANX POSTAL MUSEUM POSTCARDS

1987 (23 MAR). *Sold at 10p*
PM1 Reopening of Regent Street Post Office, Douglas 30   1·

Sold out: By 2.90

1989 (28 APR). *Sold at 15p*
PM2 Bicentenary of the Mutiny on the Bounty 40   1·

Sold out: By 1.93

90 (10 APR). *Sold at* 18*p*

M3 'CUNARD 150' Exhibition, Liverpool.
Sinking of *Lusitania* (as No. 191) .... 50 1·50

Sold out: By 2.94

OSTAGE DUE STAMPS

1   D **2**   D **3** Badge of
Post Office
Authority

(Des and litho Questa)

73 (5 JULY). *Perf* 14×13½ (C)

1	D **1**	½p red, black & bistre-yellow (*ab*)	1·75	1·50
2		1p red, black and cinnamon (*ab*)..	65	65
3		2p red, black & lt apple-green (*ab*)	15	20
		a. Positive offset of red ptg on back................		
4		3p red, black and grey (*ab*).....	25	25
5		4p red, black & carmine-rose (*ab*)	35	35
6		5p red, black and cobalt (*ab*)	40	40
7		10p red, black & light lavender (*ab*)	50	50
8		20p red, black & pale turq-grn (*ab*)	90	90
1/8		*Set of* 8	4·50	4·25
		Presentation Pack (ptg b)	6·00	

Printings: (*a*) 5.7.73; (*b*) 1.9.73. Examples of printing (*b*) are known
used from mid-August onwards

Prices quoted above are for printing (*b*), which can be identified by
the letter "A" added after "1973" at the foot of the stamp. Collectors
should beware of spurious examples with the "A" removed. Price for
set of 8 from printing (*a*) £40 unused or used

Plate Nos.: All values 1A, 1B (each ×3)

Sheets: 100 (10×10)

Imprint: Right-hand corner, bottom margin, and left-hand corner, top
margin

Sold-out: Printing (*a*) between 13.8.73 and 10.9.73. Printing (*b*) ½p by
12.74; 1p by 2.75; 2p and 3p by 5.75; others by 31.12.75

(Des and litho Questa)

75 (8 JAN). *Perf* 14×13½ (C)

3	D **2**	½p black, red & greenish yellow	10	10
10		1p black, red and flesh	10	10
11		4p black, red and rose-lilac	10	10
12		7p black, red & lt greenish blue	20	20
13		9p black, red and brownish grey	25	25
14		10p black, red and bright mauve	30	30
15		50p black, red and orange-yellow	1·25	1·25
16		£1 black, red & turquoise-green	2·50	2·50
9/16		*Set of* 8	4·00	4·00
		First Day Cover..........		5·00
		Presentation Pack	4·50	

Plate Nos.: All values 1A, 1B (each ×3)

Sheets: 100 (10×10)

Imprint: Left-hand corner, bottom margin

Withdrawn: 31.12.82 (1p to £1): 31.12.85 ½p

(Litho B.D.T.)

1982 (5 OCT). *Centres multicoloured; background colour
given. Perf* 14½×14 (C)

D17	D **3**	1p turquoise-green	10	10
D18		2p mauve	10	10
D19		5p greenish blue	10	10
D20		10p reddish lilac	20	25
D21		20p grey.................	40	45
D22		50p buff	1·00	1·10
D23		£1 salmon...............	2·00	2·10
D24		£2 bright blue	4·00	4·25
D17/24		*Set of 8*	7·75	8·25
		First Day Cover..........		11·00
		Presentation Pack........	8·25	

Plate Nos: All values 1A (×5)

Sheets: 50 (10×5)

Imprint: Right-hand corner, bottom margin

D **4**

(Des Colleen Corlett, Litho B.D.T.)

1992 (18 SEPT). *Perf* 13×13½ (C)

D25	D **4**	£5 multicoloured	10·00	10·50
		First Day Cover..........		11·00
		Presentation Pack........	11·00	

Plate Nos: 1A, 1B (each ×4)

Sheets: 50 (10×5)

Imprint: Right-hand corner, bottom margin

STAMP BOOKLETS

PRICES. Prices are given for complete booklets. All booklets to No. SB7 are stitched.

B **1** Derbyhaven

1973 (5 JULY–17 OCT). *Coloured covers as Type* B **1**, *printed in black*

Type B **1**. *Yellow cover*
SB1   10p booklet containing 2×2½p (No. 16), 2×2p (No. 15) and 2×½p (No. 12) (*ab*) . . . .   18·00

Ballaugh Church, Green cover
SB2   25p booklet containing 10×2½p (No. 16) (*ab*)   3·50

Peel Castle. Stone cover
SB3   30p booklet containing 10×3p (No. 17) (*a*)   . .   25·00
SB3*a*   As SB3 but cover in buff (*b*) . . . .   25·00

Quayside, Douglas. Lavender-grey cover
SB4   50p booklet containing 8×2½p (No. 16) and 10×3p (No. 17) (*a*) . . . .   12·00
SB4*a*   As SB4 but grey-green cover (*b*) . . . .   10·00

Nos. SB1/4 were made up from ordinary sheets, the stamps being in vertical pairs with stitching through the side margins. Stamps from both sides of the sheets were used, so that panes come either upright or inverted.

Printings: (a) 5.7.73: (b) 17.10.73

STAMP SACHETS. These are cardboard covers, with stamps loose inside, contained in clear plastic sachets. Details of these sachets are given, but they are not priced, being outside the scope of this catalogue.

B **2**

1973 (5 JULY–1 NOV). *Stamp Sachets. Covers as Type* B **2**
10p sachet containing 5×½p (No. 12) and 3×2½p (No. 16)
10p sachet containing 2×½p (No. 12) and 3×3p (No. 17) (1 Nov)

B **3** Old Laxey Bridge
   (*illustration reduced. Actual size* 89×51 *mm*)

1974 (1 APR). *Coloured covers as Type* B **3**, *printed in bla*

Type B **3**. *Buff cover*
SB5   30p booklet containing 8×½p (No. 12), 4×3p (No. 17) and 4×3½p (No. 18) . . . .   2·

Monk's Bridge, Ballasalla, Green cover
SB6   40p booklet containing 4×½p (No. 12), 8×3p (No. 17) and 4×3½p (No. 18) . . . .   2·

St. Michael's Chapel, Langness, Red cover
SB7   50p booklet containing 12×3p (No. 17) and 4×3½p (No. 18) . . . .   2·

Nos. SB5/7 contain panes of four, and were produced in t same way as Nos. SB1/4.

1974 (29 JULY). *Stamp Sachets. Cover designs as Nos.* SB5 *but inscriptions redrawn, Contents unchanged*
30p sachet Pink cover
40p sachet Green cover
50p sachet Yellow cover

1975 (25 APR–16 JUNE). *Stamp Sachets. Blue cover showi Post Office badge*
20p sachet containing 3×2p (No. 15) and 4×3½p (No. attached to cover by the selvedge
20p sachet containing 1×½p (No. 12), 2×1½p (No. 14) a 3×5½p (No. 22), loose or attached to selvedge (28 May
20p sachet containing 4×½p (No. 12), 2×1½p (No. 14) a 3×5p (No. 21), loose or attached to selvedge (16 June)

1976 (20 SEPT)–*79. Stamp Sachet. Blue cover similar to Ty* B **3**, *showing Castle Rushen and Castletown Harbour*
20p sachet containing 2×1p (No. 13) and 3×6p (No. 23)
20p sachet containing 2×1p (No. 13) and 3×6p (No. 1 (3.79)

B **4** Viking Longship
   (*illustration reduced. Actual size* 81×49 *mm*)

illenium of Tynwald

79 (16 MAY). *Folded card covers as Type B* **4**
38   20p booklet containing 4×3p and 2×4p (No.
      150*ab*) (blue cover) . . . .   1·50
39   40p booklet containing 8×3p and 4×4p (No.
      150*a*×2) (pink cover) . . . .   1·75
310   60p booklet containing 12×3p and 6×4p (No.
      150*a*×3) (yellow cover) . . . .   2·50
Examples of Nos. SB8/9 are known containing the wrong
ne.

Withdrawn: 28.9.80

80 (29 SEPT). *Folded card covers as Type B* **4**
311   40p booklet containing 2×1p, 4×3p, 4×4p
      and 2×5p (Nos. 150*ba* and 188*a*) (pink cover
      showing Manx Loaghtyn Ram) . . . .   1·50
312   80p booklet containing 4×1p, 8×3p, 8×4p
      and 4×5p (Nos. 150*ba* and 188*a* each ×2)
      (green cover showing Peregrine Falcon) . . . .   2·75

Withdrawn: 9.4.86

85 (12 JUNE). *Booklet No.* SB11 *with cover surcharged* 50p
and an additional loose 10p *stamp inside*
313   50p booklet containing Nos. 150*ba*, 188*a* and
      one 10p (No. 236) . . . .   6·00

Withdrawn: 9.4.86

B **5** Celtic Cross Logo
    (*illustration reduced.*
    Actual size
    80×48 *mm*)

anx Heritage Year

86 (10 APR). *Folded card covers as Type B* **5**
314   50p booklet containing 2×1p, 2×4p, 2×5p
      and 3×10p (Nos. 188*a* and 316*a*) (olive-green
      cover) . . . .   4·50
315   £1.14 booklet containing 2×1p, 2×2p, 4×3p,
      4×4p, 2×5p and 7×10p (Nos. 150*ba*, 188*a*,
      315*a* and 316*a*) (greenish blue cover) . . . . . .   8·50

Withdrawn: 25.3.87

B **6** Loch Promenade
    (*illustration reduced. Actual size* 82×48 *mm*)

Victorian Douglas

1987 (26 MAR). *Folded card covers as Type B* **6**
SB16 50p booklet containing either No. 334*a* or
       334*ab* (orange-brown and deep yellow-green
       cover Type B **6**) . . . .   4·00
SB17 £1.10 booklet containing either Nos. 334*a*, or
       334*ab*, and 334*b* (orange-brown and bright
       scarlet cover showing The Breakwater) . . . .   7·00

Withdrawn: 15.3.88

B **7** Baldwin Reservoir Tramway Steam Locomotive *Injebreck*
    (*illustration reduced. Actual size* 82×48 *mm*)

Manx Railways and Tramways

1988 (16 MAR). *Folded multicoloured card covers as Type B* **7**
SB18 50p booklet containing No. 367*a* (cover Type
       B **7**) . . . .   4·00
SB19 £1.99 booklet containing Nos. 367*a* and 370*a*
       (cover showing Manx Electric Railway train at
       Maughold Head) . . . .   9·50

Withdrawn: 15.10.89

B **8** 'Mutineers casting Bligh adrift' (Robert Dodd)
 (*illustration reduced. Actual size* 155×100 *mm*)

Bicentenary of The Mutiny on the Bounty

1989 (28 APR). *Multicoloured cover as Type* B **8**. *Booklet contains text and illustrations on interleaving pages. Stitched*
SB20   £5.30 booklet containing Nos. 408*a*/*b*, 410*a* and **MS**415. . . . .   14·00

Examples of No. **MS**415 from the booklet have wider margins than the normal miniature sheets.

Withdrawn: 2.92

Manx Railways and Tramways

1989 (16 OCT). *Folded multicoloured covers as Type* B **7**
SB21   50p booklet containing No. 367*b* (cover showing Port Erin Breakwater Tramway Locomotive *Henry B. Loch*) . . . .   3·00
SB22   £2.09 booklet containing Nos. 367*b* and 371*a* (cover showing Douglas Cable Tramway) . . . .   8·00

Withdrawn: 13.2.90

Manx Railways and Tramways

1990 (14 FEB). *Folded multicoloured covers as Type* B **7**
SB23   50p booklet containing No. 372*a* (cover showing Marine Drive Tramway) . . . .   3·00
SB24   £1.74 booklet containing No. 372*b* (cover showing Ramsey Harbour Tramway) . . . . . .   8·00

Withdrawn: 8.1.91

B **9** Penny Black
 (*illustration reduced. Actual size* 125×75 *mm*)

150th Anniversary of the Penny Black and 'Stamp World London 90' International Stamp Exhibition, London

1990 (3 MAY). *Black and ochre cover as Type* B **9**. *Booklet contains text and illustrations on interleaving pages. Stapled*
SB25   £3.50 booklet containing Nos. 442*c*, 443*a* and **MS**447 . . . .   9·00

Withdrawn: 23.9.93

Manx Railways and Tramways

1991 (9 JAN). *Folded multicoloured covers as Type* B **7**
SB26   50p booklet containing No. 367*ca* (cover, 80×48 mm, showing Groudle Glen Railway steam locomotive *Polar Bear*) . . . .   4·5
SB27   £1 booklet containing No. 367*cb* (cover, 56×43 mm, showing I.M.R. No. 11 *Maitland* pulling Royal Train, 1963) . . . .   6·2

Withdrawn: 7.1.92

B **10** Three Kings
 (*illustration reduced. Actual size* 150×105 *mm*)

Christmas

1991 (14 OCT). *Deep violet cover as Type* B **10**. *Stitched*
SB28   £4.16 booklet containing No. 500*a*×2 . . . . . .   21·0

Withdrawn: 23.9.93

Manx Railways and Tramways

1992 (8 JAN). *Folded multicoloured covers as Type* B **7**, *be 56×43 mm*
SB29   £1 booklet containing No. 375*ab* (cover showing double-decker horse tram, Douglas)   4·0
SB30   £2 booklet containing No. 375*ac* (cover showing T.P.O. Special) . . . .   8·0

Withdrawn: 3.1.93

£4.38

Isle of Man Post Office
Commemorative Stamp Booklet

UNION PACIFIC RAILROAD

11 Union Pacific No. 119, 1869
(*illustration reduced. Actual size* 119×74 *mm*)

onstruction of Union Pacific Railroad

992 (22 MAY). *Multicoloured cover as Type* B **11**. *Pane
attached by selvedge*
331   £4.38 booklet containing pane No. 522*b* . . . .   11·00

Withdrawn: 27.4.94

SHIPS
SLE OF
MAN

£1.10

B **12** *Francis Drake*
(ketch)

hips

993 (4 JAN). *Multicoloured covers as Type* B **12**. *Panes
attached by selvedge*
332   £1.10 booklet containing pane No. 543*a* (cover
        Type B **12**) . . . .   3·00
333   £2.20 booklet containing pane No. 543*b* (cover
        showing *Tynwald I* . . . .   5·50

Withdrawn: 20.4.96

ISLE OF MAN POST OFFICE

Contents
4 x 20·4 x 24·4 x 20·4 x 39
Price £4.44

MANX ELECTRIC RAILWAY
1893-CENTENARY-1993

13 No. 9 Tunnel Car and Crew
(*illustration reduced. Actual size* 160×98 *mm*)

Centenary of Manx Electric Railway

1993 (3 FEB). *Multicoloured cover as Type* B **13**. *Stitched*
SB34   £4.44 booklet containing pane No. 559*a*×4   12·00

Withdrawn: 27.4.94

CHRISTMAS '93

Christmas '93

ISLE OF MAN 19°

£1.90 (10 stamps)

B **14** (*illustration reduced.
Actual size* 62×95 *mm*)

Christmas

1993 (12 OCT). *Folded multicoloured covers as Type* B **14**.
Panes attached by selvedge
SB35   £1.90 booklet containing No. 578×10 (cover
        Type B **14**) . . . .   4·50
SB36   £2.30 booklet containing No. 579×10 (cover
        showing No. 579) . . . .   5·50

Withdrawn: 10.10.95

**HAPPY HOLIDAYS
IN THE ISLE OF MAN**

1894 Isle of Man Tourism Centenary 1994

£2.40
10 x 24p stamps
& 12 labels

Isle of Man Post Office Stamp Booklet

B **15** (*illustration reduced. Actual size* 134×85 *mm*)

Manx Tourism Centenary

1994 (18 FEB). *Multicoloured cover as Type* B **15**. *Pane
attached by selvedge*
SB37   £2.40 booklet containing pane No. 590*a* and
        pane of 12 (3×4) greetings labels   . . . .   5·50

Sold out: By 9.95

B **16** Postman Pat, Jess, Ferry and Aircraft
(*illustration reduced. Actual size* 152×85 *mm*)

Postman Pat visits the Isle of Man

1994 (14 SEPT). *Multicoloured cover as Type B* **16** *cut out to show stamps from first pane. Booklet contains text and illustrations on labels attached to panes. Stitched*
SB38   £4.04 booklet containing Nos. 614*a*/19*a*, **MS**620 and pane of 8 character labels . . . . . .   13·00

Withdrawn: By 2.97

B **17** Car and Passengers at Snaefell Summit
(*illustration reduced. Actual size* 162×97 *mm*)

Centenary of Snaefell Mountain Railway

1995 (8 FEB). *Black, scarlet and grey cover as Type B* **17**. *Booklet contains text and illustrations on labels attached to panes. Stitched*
SB39   £4.63 booklet containing No. 634*a*×3 and **MS**638*a* . . . .   12·00

Withdrawn: By 2.97

B **18** Thomas the Tank Engine
(*illustration reduced. Actual size* 151×80 *mm*)

50th Anniversary of Thomas the Tank Engine Stories by Revd. Awdry. "Thomas the Tank Engine's Dream"

1995 (15 AUG). *Multicoloured cover as Type B* **18** *cut out t show stamps from first pane. Stitched*
SB40   £3.92 booklet containing Nos. 656*a*/*b*, 657*a*, 658*a*, 659*a* and 660*a* . . . .   11·0

Withdrawn: By 2.97

B **19** Aerial view of Langness Lighthouse
(*illustration reduced. Actual size* 130×82 *mm*)

Lighthouses

1996 (24 JAN). *Multicoloured cover as Type B* **19**. *Bookl contains text and illustrations on interleaving page Stitched*
SB41   £4.74 booklet containing Nos. 672*a*/5*a*. . . . . .   10·C
Withdrawn: By 5.97

Ships

1996 (21 APR). *Multicoloured cover as Type B* **12**. *Pa attached by selvedge*
SB42   96p booklet containing pane No. 687*a* (cover showing *Sir Winston Churchill*) . . . .   5·C
Sold out: 5.97

B **20** (*illustration reduced. Actual size* 118×81 *mm*)
Dogs

1996 (18 SEPT). *Multicoloured cover as Type B* **20**. *Book contains text and illustrations on interleaving pag Stitched*
SB43   £4.71 booklet containing Nos. 719*a*, 720*a*, 721*a* and **MS**725*a* . . . .   10·
Withdrawn: 17.9.97

190

21 Tawny Owl
(*illustration reduced. Actual size* 152×80 *mm*)

B **23** Cushag

Owls

1997 (12 FEB). *Multicoloured cover as Type* B **21**. *Booklet contains text and illustrations on interleaving pages. Stitched*

B44   £4.62 booklet containing Nos. 734a/6a and
        MS740a . . . .   11·00

Withdrawn: 11.2.98

Ships

1997 (14 MAY). *Multicoloured cover as Type* B **12**. *Pane attached by selvedge*

B45   £1 booklet containing pane No. 541a (cover
        showing Royal Yacht *Britannia*) . . . .   2·50
        *a. With extra loose 4p stamp and optd inside
        front cover* . . . .   3·00

No. SB45a was issued from booklet machines until 1 July 1997 when the postal rates were revised. The overprint inside the front cover was applied by handstamp.

Withdrawn: 31.12.97 No. SB45a; 30.11.98 No. SB45

22 King Edward Bay Golf and Country Club
(*illustration reduced. Actual size* 160×96 *mm*)

Golf

1997 (29 MAY). *Multicoloured cover as Type* B **22**. *Booklet contains text and illustrations on panes and interleaving pages. Stitched*

B46   £4.54 booklet containing Nos. 755a/7a and
        MS759a . . . .   10·00

Withdrawn: 28.5.98

Flowers

1998 (12 FEB). *Multicoloured cover as Type* B **23**. *Pane attached by selvedge*

B47   £1 booklet containing No. 775a . . . .   2·50

Withdrawn: 31.8.99

B **24** Basking Shark
(*illustration reduced. Actual size* 157×105 *mm*)

U.N.E.S.C.O. *International Year of the Ocean*

1998 (16 MAR). *Multicoloured cover as Type* B **24**. *Booklet contains text and illustrations on interleaving pages. Stitched*

B48   £3.62 booklet containing Nos. 798a/b . . . . . .   7·00

B **25** Steam Train at Douglas Station
(*illustration reduced. Actual size* 157×105 *mm*)

125th Anniversary of Isle of Man Steam Railway

1998 (2 MAY). *Multicoloured cover as Type* B **25**. *Booklet contains text and illustrations on interleaving pages. Stitched*

B49   £4.05 booklet containing Nos. 803*a*×2 and
       MS807*a* . . . .   8·00

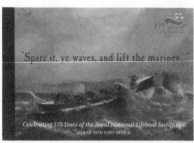

B **26** *Manchester & Salford,* 1868–1887
       (*illustration reduced. Actual size* 158×108 *mm*)

175th Anniversary of Royal National Lifeboat Institution

1999 (4 MAR). *Multicoloured cover as Type* B **26**. *Booklet contains text and illustrations on interleaving pages. Stitched*

SB50   £4.64 booklet containing Nos. 832*a*/*b* and
        MS839*a* . . . .   9·25

Flowers

1999 (26 APR). *Multicoloured cover as Type* B **23**. *Pane attached by selvedge*

SB51   £1 booklet containing pane No. 775*ba* (cover
        showing Dog Rose). . . . .   2·00

B **27** Bus Radiator and Headlights
        (*illustration reduced. Actual size* 158×100 *mm*)

Manx Buses

1999 (18 JUNE). *Multicoloured cover as Type* B **27**. *Booklet contains text and illustrations on panes and interleaving pages. Stitched*

SB52   £4.78 booklet containing panes Nos. 845*a*/*d*. .   9·50

JERSEY

THE GERMAN OCCUPATION 1940–1945

oon after the commencement of the occupation of Jersey by erman forces on 1 July, 1940 orders were given by the ierman Commandant to the Island's Postmaster for stocks of he currently available stamps to be forwarded to the Jersey rinters, J. T. Bigwood, for overprinting with a swastika and ERSEY 1940'. All values of the 1937–8 definitives from ½d to 0s, excluding the 1d, were so overprinted as were the 1940 ostal Centenary stamps, excluding the 1d, but whilst this vas in progress the Bailiff of Jersey protested to the German :ommandant who referred the matter to Berlin and was rdered to destroy the stocks. Four complete sets to 1s, and a ew singles, however, are known to exist. At the same time igwoods prepared a local 1d stamp incorporating the arms of ersey and the words 'ETATS DE JERSEY'. These were rinted in imperforate sheets of thirty (10×3) and are known vith and without a swastika and '1940' overprint. These also vere destroyed with the exception of two sheets of each vhich have been cut up for collectors and a damaged sheet vith the overprint which is complete. There is also a complete heet of the unoverprinted stamp in the National Postal Museum.

Jersey eventually issued locally printed ½d and 1d stamps, he 1d on 1 April, 1941 and the ½d on 29 January, 1942. No istinct shades exist though both values come on newsprint aper and, in addition, the 1d is known on chalk-surfaced aper.

In June 1943 a pictorial set of six stamps from ½d to 3d was ssued, the designer being the well-known Jersey artist dmund Blampied. Two values, the 1d and 2½d, are known on ewsprint paper.

Both these and the earlier issues remained on sale untill 13 pril, 1946 after which date they could no longer be used.

2

he Swastika Overprints

940. *Prepared for use but not issued. Stamps of Great Britain overprinted by J. T. Bigwood, States' Printers*

(a) On 1937–9 definitive issue

at. o.	Type No.		Unused
W1	1	½d green	£1500
W2		1½d red-brown	£1500
W3		2d orange	£1500
W4		2½d ultramarine	£1500
W5		3d violet	£1500

SW6	1	4d grey-green	£1500
SW7		5d brown	£1500
SW8		6d purple	£1500
SW9		7d emerald-green	£1500
SW10		8d bright carmine	£1500
SW11		9d deep olive-green	£1500
SW12		10d turquise-blue	£1500
SW13		1s bistre-brown	£1500

(b) On 1940 Stamp Centenary issue

SW14	2	½d green	£1500
SW15		1½d red-brown	£1500
SW16		2d orange	£1500
SW17		2½d ultramarine	£1500
SW18		3d violet	£1500

3   **4**

(Des R. W. Cutland. Typo J. T. Bigwood)

1940. *Prepared for use but not issued. No wmk. Imperforate*

SW19	3	1d scarlet	£1500
SW20	4	1d scarlet	£1500

5 Arms of Jersey

Stamps issued during the German Occupation

(Des Major N. V. L. Rybot. Typo *Jersey Evening Post*, St. Helier)

1941–43. *White paper. No wmk. Perf* 11 (L)

1	5	½d bright green (29.1.42)	4·00	3·25
		a. Imperf between (vertical pair)	£800	
		b. Imperf between (horizontal pair)	£700	
		c. Imperf (pair)	£250	
		d. On greyish paper (1.43)	5·00	5·75
2		1d scarlet (1.4.41)	4·25	3·25
		a. Imperf between (vertical pair)	£800	
		b. Imperf between (horizontal pair)	£700	
		c. Imperf (pair)	£275	
		d. On chalk-surfaced paper	40·00	38·00
		e. On greyish paper (1.43)	5·00	5·75
1		First Day Cover (plain)		7·00
2		First Day Cover (plain)		7·00

193

Sheets: 60 (6×10)

Imprint: ½d 'EVENING POST', JERSEY, JANUARY, 1942
1d 'EVENING POST', JERSEY, 17/3/41

Quantities printed: ½d 703,500; 1d 1,030,620

Withdrawn and invalidated: 13.4.46

6 Old Jersey Farm

7 Portelet Bay

8 Corbière
Lighthouse

9 Elizabeth Castle

10 Mont Orgueil
Castle

11 Gathering Vraic
(seaweed)

Pictorial Issue

(Des E. Blampied. Eng H. Cortot. Typo French Govt Printing
Works, Paris)

1943 (1 JUNE).**–44**. No wmk. Perf 13½ (C)

3	**6**	½d green	8·00	7·25
		a. Rough, grey paper (6.10.43)	8·50	8·50
4	**7**	1d scarlet	2·25	1·00
		a. On newsprint (28.2.44)	2·50	2·00
5	**8**	1½d brown (8.6.43)	4·00	4·00
6	**9**	2d orange-yellow (8.6.43)	5·25	4·00
7	**10**	2½d blue (29.6.43)	2·00	1·75
		a. On newsprint (25.2.44)	1·50	2·25
		ba. Thin paper (design shows through on reverse)	£200	
8	**11**	3d violet (29.6.43)	1·50	3·75
3/8		Set of 6	20·00	20·00
		First Day Covers (3)		70·00
		Set of 6 Gutter Pairs	60·00	

Printings: The sheets of the various printings were dated in the sheet
corners as follows:

½d 1st Printing 1/5/43
2nd Printing 3/5/43
3rd Printing 6/10/43
1d 1st Printing 7/5/43
2nd Printing 8/5/43
3rd Printing 7/10/43
4th Printing 28/2/44
1½d 1st Printing 17/5/43
2nd Printing 18/5/43
2d 1st Printing 20/5/43
2nd Printing 21/5/43
2½d 1st Printing 31/5/43
2nd Printing 25/2/44
3d 1st Printing 4/6/43
2nd Printing 5/6/43

Sheets: 60 (2 panes 3×10)

Imprint: None

Quantities printed: ½d (No. 3) 360,000; ½d (No. 3a) 120,000; 1d (No. 4)
960,000; 1d (No. 4a) 240,000; 1½d 360,000; 2d 360,000; 2½d (No. 7)
360,000; 2½d (Nos. 7a/b) 360,000; 3d 360,000

Withdrawn and invalidated: 13.4.46

REGIONAL ISSUES

Although specifically issued for regional use, these issues
were initially valid for use throughout Great Britain. However
they ceased to be valid in Jersey and Guernsey from
1 October, 1969 when these islands each established their
own independent postal administration and introduced their
own stamps.

DATES OF ISSUE. Conflicting dates of issue have been
announced for some of the regional issues, partly explained by
the stamps being released on different dates by the Philatelic
Bureau in Edinburgh or the Philatelic Counter in London and in
the regions. We have adopted the practice of giving the
earliest known dates, since once released the stamps could
have been used anywhere in the U.K.

INVALIDATION. The regional issues of Jersey were
invalidated for use in Jersey and Guernsey on 1 November
1969 (although Guernsey granted a further extension for
British and regional stamps till the end of March 1970). The
stamps continued to be valid for use in the rest of the United
Kingdom until 29 February, 1972. Those still current remained
on sale at philatelic sales counters until 30 September, 1970.

11a Multiple
Crowns

12

13

Des E. Blampied (Type **12**), W. Gardner (Type **13**). Portrait by Dorothy Wilding Ltd. Photo Harrison)

58–67. *Wmk Type* **11***a. Perf* 15×14 (C)

12	2½d carmine-red (8.6.64)	35	1·00
	a. Imperf three sides (*pair*)	£2000	
13	3d deep lilac (18.8.58)	35	30
	p. One centre phosphor band (9.6.67)	25	25
	4d ultramarine (7.2.66)	30	30
	p. Two phosphor bands (5.9.67)	25	30
1	*Set of* 3	75	1·40
	First Day Cover	30·00	
	First Day Cover	17·00	
	First Day Cover	8·00	

Cylinder Nos.: 2½d 1; 3d (ord) 1, 2; 3d (phos) 2; 4d (ord) 1; 4d (phos) 1

Sheets: 240 (12×20)

Quantities sold (ordinary only): 2½d 4,770,000; 3d 35,169,720; 4d 6,623,040

Withdrawn: 31.8.66 2½d

Sold out: 10.67 3d (ordinary); 11.67 4d (ordinary); 10.68 3d and 4d (phosphor)

68–69. *No wmk. Chalk-surfaced paper. One centre phosphor band* (4*d values*) *or two phosphor bands* (5*d*). *Perf* 15×14 (C)

13	4d olive-sepia (4.9.68)	25	30
	4d bright vermilion (26.2.69)	25	40
	5d Royal blue (4.9.68)	25	60
/14	*Set of* 3	70	1·10
, 14	*First Day Cover*	3·00	

Cylinder Nos.: 4d (olive-sepia) 1; 4d (bright vermilion) 1; 5d 1

Withdrawn: 30.9.69 (locally), 30.9.70 (British Philatelic Counters) 4d olive-sepia, 4d bright vermilion and 5d

NDEPENDENT POSTAL DMINISTRATION

ersey established their own independent postal dministration on 1 October, 1969 and introduced their own amps.

O WATERMARK. All the following issues are on nwatermarked paper.

4 Elizabeth Castle

16 Portelet Bay

17 La Corbière Lighthouse

18 Mont Orgueil Castle by Night

19 Arms and Royal Mace

20 Jersey Cow

21 Chart of the English Channel

22 Mont Orgueil Castle by Day

23 Queen Elizabeth II (after Cecil Beaton)

15 La Hougue Bie (Prehistoric Tomb)

24 Jersey Airport

25 Legislative Chamber

195

26 The Royal Court   **27** Queen Elizabeth II
(after Cecil Beaton)

(Des V. Whiteley. Photo Harrison (½d to 1s 9d), Courvoisier (others))

1969 (1 OCT)–**70**. *Granite paper* (2s 6d to £1). *Multicoloured; frame colours given. Perf 14 (½d to 1s. 9d) or 12 (others), all comb*

15	**14**	½d ochre (a)	10	70
		a. *Thick paper* (a)	1·00	1·25
16	**15**	1d brown (abc)	15	20
		a. *Booklet stamp with blank margins* * (a)	75	
		b. *Thick paper* (a)	90	1·00
17	**16**	2d claret (a)	10	15
		a. *Thinner paper* (bc)	25	25
18	**17**	3d ultramarine (a)	20	15
		a. *Thinner paper* (d)	50	60
		b. *Orange omitted*	£120	
19	**18**	4d yellow-olive (a)	15	10
		a. *Booklet stamp with blank margins* * (a)	40	
		b. *Thinner paper* (c)	40	50
20	**19**	5d bistre (a)	15	10
		a. *Thinner paper* (c)	50	70
21	**20**	6d yellow-brown (ab)........	25	30
		a. *Thinner paper* (e)	7·00	7·50
22	**21**	9d orange-brown (a)	40	75
		a. *Thinner paper* (d)	2·50	3·00
23	**22**	1s reddish lilac (a)	75	75
		a. *Thinner paper* (c)	2·00	2·00
24	**21**	1s 6d myrtle-green (a)	1·25	1·25
		a. *Thinner paper* (d)	2·75	3·00
25	**23**	1s 9d pale myrtle-green (a)	1·25	1·25
		a. *Thinner paper* (c)	12·00	12·00
26	**24**	2s 6d black and pale mauve (a) ..	2·00	1·75
27	**25**	5s black and pale blue (a)	8·00	6·00
28	**26**	10s black and pale slate-blue (a) ..	24·00	16·00
		a. *Error. Green border*†	£4500	
29	**27**	£1 pale bistre (af)††	2·00	2·00
15/29		*Set of 15*	35·00	25·00
		First Day Cover		26·00
15/29		*Presentation Packs* (3)	40·00	

*Nos. 16a and 19a are on medium paper. No. 16b on thick paper comes from 7s and 10s booklets.

†During the final printing of the 10s a sheet was printed in the colours of the 50p, No. 56, ie. green border instead of slate.

††Printing (f) is the decimal issue which can be positive distinguished by the inscriptions in the left sheet margin whic read 'Sheet value £25' at bottom and 'Value per row £5' at to instead of 'Sheet value £25 0s. 0d.' and 'Value per row £5 0s 0d.' respectively. It exists with more blue in the Queen's dres and less red in the drapery but this printing also include intermediate shades close to printing (a).

The thinner paper varieties result from a deliberate chang as the thicker paper did not adhere well; it may be furthe distinguished by the gum which is white instead of creamy.

There are a number of shades in this issue which are in pa due to the variation in the paper.

There was no postal need for the ½d value as the ½d coin ha been withdrawn prior to its issue in anticipation o decimalisation.

Printings: (a) 1.10.69; (b) 18.2.70; (c) 15.4.70; (d) 5.5.70; (e) 27.5.70 (f) 3.73

Cylinder Nos.: ½d, 1d, 2d, 4d, 1s 1A (×5); 3d 1A (×7): 5d, 6d, 9d, 1s 6d 1s 9d 1A (×6): 2s 6d to £1 None

Sheets: 60 (6×10) ½d to 1s 6d; (10×6) 1s 9d; 25 (5×5) 2s 6d to £1

Quantities sold: ½d 999,439; 1d 1,050,124; 2d 726,837; 3d 635,019 4d 7,148,849; 5d 4,886,016; 6d 550,766; 9d 954,649; 1s 577,086 1s 6d 419,872; 1s 9d 306,674; 2s 6d 244,894; 5s 206,629; 10 179,981; £1 271,194

Withdrawn: 14.2.72 (except ½d, sold out 10.69, and £1 withdraw 31.8.77)

Invalidated: 14.2.72 (except £1)

28 First Day Cover

Inauguration of Post Office

(Des R. Sellar. Photo Harrison)

1969 (1 OCT). *Multicoloured; background colours given. Pe 14 (C)*

30	**28**	4d magenta	25	2
31		5d new blue	30	3
32		1s 6d red-brown	1·00	1·1
33		1s 9d bright emerald..........	1·25	1·4
30/3		*Set of 4*	2·50	2·7
		First Day Cover		5·0
		Presentation Pack..........	3·00	

Cylinder Nos.: All values 1A (×4)

Sheets: 60 (6×10)

Quantities sold: 4d 1,483,686; 5d 742,820; 1s 6d 272,155; 1s 9 238,856

Withdrawn: 1.10.70

Invalidated: 14.2.72

'Lord Coutanche'
(Sir James Gunn)

30 'Sir Winston
Churchill'
(Van Praag)

31 'Liberation' (Edmund
Blampied)

32 S.S. *Vega* (unknown
artist)

5th Anniversary of Liberation

(Des Rosalind Dease from paintings. Photo Courvoisier)

1970 (9 MAY). *Granite paper. Perf* 11½ (C)

24	**29**	4d multicoloured	25	25
25	**30**	5d multicoloured	25	25
26	**31**	1s 6d multicoloured	1·40	1·40
27	**32**	1s 9d multicoloured	1·50	1·50
24/7		Set of 4	3·00	3·00
		First Day Cover		4·50
		Presentation Pack.	3·25	

A special Presentation Pack in gold, red and blue-green on olive was given to Jersey schoolchildren (*Price* £15). The normal Presentation Pack is printed in gold and blue-green

Sheets: 50 (10×5) 4d, 5d; (5×10) 1s 6d, 1s 9d

Quantities sold: 4d 1,617,751; 5d 1,296,678; 1s 6d 334,468; 1s 9d 319,893

Withdrawn: 9.5.71

Invalidated: 14.2.72

33 'A Tribute to Enid
Blyton'

34 'Rags to Riches'

35 'Gourmet's Delight'

36 'We're the Greatest'

'Battle of Flowers' Parade

(Des Jennifer Toombs. Photo Courvoiser)

1970 (28 JULY). *Granite paper. Perf* 11½ (C)

38	**33**	4d multicoloured	25	25
39	**34**	5d multicoloured	40	40
40	**35**	1s 6d multicoloured	5·50	2·50
41	**36**	1s 9d multicoloured	6·00	2·50
38/41		Set of 4	11·00	5·00
		First Day Cover		5·25
		Presentation Pack.	12·00	

Sheets: 50 (5×10)

Quantities sold: 4d 1,905,109; 5d 1,498,301; 1s 6d 262,072; 1s 9d 231,077

Withdrawn: 27.7.71

Invalidated: 14.2.72

37 Martello Tower,
Archirondel

Decimal Currency

(Des V. Whiteley. Photo Harrison (½ to 9p), Courvoisier (others))

1970–74. *Designs as Type* **37** *etc., but with values inscribed in decimal currency and new design (6p). Chalk-surfaced paper (4½p, 5½p, 8p), granite paper (10p, 20p, 50p)*

42	**14**	½p multicoloured (bgk)	10	10
		a. Booklet stamp with blank margins (b)	40	
43	**17**	1p multicoloured (bn)..........	10	10
		a. Orange omitted		
44	**20**	1½p multicoloured (b)	10	10
45	**18**	2p multicoloured (b)	10	10
		a. Booklet stamp with blank margins	1·25	
46	**19**	2½p multicoloured (bk)..........	10	10
		a. Booklet stamp with blank margins (b)	40	
		ab. Gold (Mace) omitted........	£375	
		ac. Gold (Mace) ptg double	£300	
47	**15**	3p multicoloured (bch)	10	10
		a. Booklet stamp with blank margins (e)	50	
48	**16**	3½p multicoloured (bh)..........	15	15
		a. Booklet stamp with blank margins (h)	50	
49	**21**	4p multicoloured (bfimo)	15	15
49a	**19**	4½p multicoloured (j)	20	20
		ab. Uncoated paper	£375	
50	**22**	5p multicoloured (blmo)........	10	15
50a	**20**	5½p multicoloured (j)	40	25
51	**37**	6p multicoloured (b)	25	30
52	**21**	7½p multicoloured (b)	30	40
52a	**18**	8p multicoloured (j)	25	25
53	**23**	9p multicoloured (b)	50	30
54	**24**	10p multicoloured (adh)	50	55
55	**25**	20p multicoloured (adh)	75	75
56	**26**	50p multicoloured (al)	1·75	1·75
42/56		Set of 18	5·00	5·00
		First Day Cover (3)		10·00
42/56, 29		Presentation Packs (4)	7·00	

Gum: From 1974 printings appeared with dextrin added to the PVA gum giving a bluish-green tinge and mottled appearance. These are on the ½, 2½, 3 and 3½p. The 4½ and 5½p only come with dextrin, and the 10, 20 and 50p only with gum arabic.

The Presentation Packs for this series exist in two different sizes, 4½ in × 5½ in of the initial supply and 8½ in × 4½ in for replacement stock.

Printings: (a) 1.10.70; (b) 15.2.71; (c) 1.8.72; (d) 15.11.72; (e) 1.12.72; (f) 1.10.73; (g) 3.12.73; (h) 1.7.74; (i) 12.8.74; (j) 31.10.74; (k) 1.11.74; (l) 28.1.75; (m) 1.4.75; (n) 21.4.75; (o) 30.10.75

Plate Nos.: ½p, 2p, 3½p, 6p, 8p 1A (×5); 1p 1A (×7), 2A–1A (×6) (n); 1½p, 2½p, 4½p, 5½p, 7½p, 9p 1A (×6); 3p 1A (×5), 1A (×4)–2A (h); 4p 1A (×6), 2A–1A (×5) (mo); 5p 1A (×5), 2A–1A (×4) (mo); 10p to 50p None

Sheets: 50 (5×10) ½p to 8p; (10×5) 9p; 25 (5×5) 10p to 50p

Quantities sold: ½p 2,247,128; 1p 1,654,860; 1½p 817,871; 2p 2,305,239; 2½p 5,096,912; 3p 4,780,836; 3½p 2,069,095; 4p 3,908,727; 4½p 349,157; 5p 3,593,226; 5½p 333,125; 6p 1,072,224; 7½p 538,810; 8p 329,361; 9p 458,977; 10p 862,524; 20p 765,524; 50p 490,675

Withdrawn: 31.1.77 (½p to 9p); 31.8.77 (others)

38 White Eared-Pheasant   **39** Thick-billed Parrot

40 Western Black and White Colobus Monkey   **41** Ring-tailed Lemur

Wildlife Preservation Trust (First Series)

(Des Jennifer Toombs. Photo Courvoisier)

1971 (12 MAR). *Granite paper. Perf 11½ (C)*

57	**38**	2p multicoloured	50	2
58	**39**	2½p multicoloured	50	2
59	**40**	7½p multicoloured	6·00	3·7
60	**41**	9p multicoloured	6·50	3·7
57/60		Set of 4	13·00	7·2
		First Day Cover		9·0
		Presentation Pack..........	16·00	

See also Nos. 73/6, 217/21, 324/9, 447/51 and 824/9.

Sheets: 50 (5×10) 2p, 9p; (10×5) others

Quantities sold: 2p 1,025,544; 2½p 1,363,427; 7½p 233,147; 9 220,710

Withdrawn: 11.3.72

42 Royal British Legion Badge   **43** Poppy Emblem and Field

Jack Counter VC, and
Victoria Cross

45 Crossed Tricolour and
Union Jack

th Anniversary of Royal British Legion

(Des G. Drummond, Litho Questa)

71 (15 JUNE). *Perf* 14 (C)

42	2p multicoloured	. . . .	25	25
43	2½p multicoloured	. . . .	25	25
44	7½p multicoloured	. . . .	2·00	2·00
45	9p multicoloured	. . . .	2·00	2·00
/4	*Set of 4*	. . . .	4·00	4·00
	First Day Cover	. . . .		5·25
	Presentation Pack.	. . . .	5·00	

Plate Nos.: 2p, 2½p 1A, 1B (each ×4); others 1A, 1B (each ×5)

Sheets: 50 (5×10)

Imprint: Right-hand corner, bottom margin

Quantities sold: 2p 1,381,873; 2½p 1,529,866; 7½p 239,477; 9p
226,407

Withdrawn: 14.6.72

6 'Tante Elizabeth'
(E. Blampied)

47 'English Fleet in the
Channel' (P. Monamy)

8 'The Boyhood of
Raleigh' (Millais)

49 'The Blind Beggar'
(W. W. Ouless)

Paintings

(Des and photo Courvoisier)

1971 (5 OCT). *Granite paper. Perf* 11½ (C)

65	**46**	2p multicoloured	15	15
66	**47**	2½p multicoloured	25	20
67	**48**	7½p multicoloured	2·75	2·25
68	**49**	9p multicoloured	3·00	2·50
65/8		*Set of 4*	5·00	4·50
		First Day Cover		5·50
		Presentation Pack.	6·00	

See also Nos. 115/18 and 213/16.

Sheets: 50 (5×10) 2p, 9p; (10×5) others

Quantities sold: 2p 1,243,198; 2½p 1,490,595; 7½p 264,532; 9p
251,770

Withdrawn: 4.10.72

50 Jersey Fern

51 Jersey Thrift

52 Jersey Orchid

53 Jersey Viper's
Bugloss

Wild Flowers of Jersey

(Des G. Drummond. Photo Courvoisier)

1972 (18 JAN). *Granite paper. Perf* 11½ (C)

69	**50**	3p multicoloured	25	15
70	**51**	5p multicoloured	60	45
71	**52**	7½p multicoloured	2·25	2·25
72	**53**	9p multicoloured	2·50	2·25
69/72		*Set of 4*	5·00	4·50
		First Day Cover		5·50
		Presentation Pack.	6·50	

Sheets: 50 (5×10)

Quantities sold: 3p 1,124,878; 5p 332,764; 7½p 202,404; 9p 196,998

Withdrawn: 17.1.73

54 Cheetah

55 Rothschild's Mynah

56 Spectacled Bear

57 Tuatara

Wildlife Preservation Trust (Second Series)

(Des Jennifer Toombs. Photo Courvoisier)

1972 (17 MAR). *Granite paper. Perf* 11½ (C)

73	**54**	2½p multicoloured	. . . .	65	20
74	**55**	3p multicoloured	. . . .	40	35
75	**56**	7½p multicoloured	. . . .	1·40	1·50
76	**57**	9p multicoloured	. . . .	2·00	1·75
73/6		Set of 4	. . . .	4·00	3·25
		First Day Cover	. . . .		5·50
		Presentation Pack.	. . . .	5·00	

Sheets: 50 (10×5) 3p; (5×10) others

Quantities sold: 2½p 1,223,916; 3p 1,631,752; 7½p 279,935; 9p 235,968

Withdrawn: 16.3.73

58 Artillery Shako

59 Shako (2nd North Regt)

60 Shako (5th South-West Regt)

61 Helmet (3rd Jersey Light Infantry)

Royal Jersey Militia

(Des and photo Courvoisier)

1972 (27 JUNE). *Granite paper. Perf* 11½ (C)

77	**58**	2½p multicoloured	. . . .	15	1
78	**59**	3p multicoloured	. . . .	20	2
79	**60**	7½p multicoloured	. . . .	85	5
80	**61**	9p multicoloured	. . . .	1·00	6
77/80		Set of 4	. . . .	2·00	1·2
		First Day Cover	. . . .		3·0
		Presentation Pack.	. . . .	3·00	

Sheets: 50 (10×5)

Quantities sold: 2½p 1,240,393; 3p 1,857,224; 7½p 300,554; 9 271,832

Withdrawn: 26.6.73

62 Princess Anne

63 Queen Elizabeth and Prince Philip

64 Prince Charles

65 The Royal Family

Royal Silver Wedding

(Des G. Drummond from photographs by D. Groves. Photo Courvoisier)

1972 (1 NOV). *Granite paper. Perf* 11½ (C)

1	**62**	2½p multicoloured	....	10	10
2	**63**	3p multicoloured	....	10	10
3	**64**	7½p multicoloured	....	40	50
4	**65**	20p multicoloured	....	60	70
1/4		Set of 4	....	1·10	1·25
		First Day Cover	....		2·00
		Presentation Pack	....	1·50	

Sheets: 25 (5×5)

Quantities sold: 2½p 1,743,240; 3p 1,638,566; 7½p 424,029; 20p 418,824

Sold out: by 23.1.73 (7½p, 20p); 16.5.73 (3p)

Withdrawn: 31.10.73 (2½p)

66 Silver Wine Cup and Christening Cup

67 Gold Torque

68 Royal Seal of Charles II

69 Armorican Bronze Coins

Centenary of La Société Jersiaise

(Des G. Drummond. Photo Courvoisier)

1973 (23 JAN). *Granite paper. Perf* 11½ (C)

5	**66**	2½p violet-blue, new blue and black	10	10
6	**67**	3p bright cerise, orange-yellow and black	....	10	10
7	**68**	7½p multicoloured	....	40	40
8	**69**	9p multicoloured	....	50	50
5/8		Set of 4	....	1·00	1·00
		First Day Cover	....		1·40
		Presentation Pack	....	1·60	

Sheets: 50 (10×5) 3p, 7½p; (5×10) others

Quantities sold: 2½p 2,008,923; 3p 2,437,421; 7½p 363,543; 9p 327,917

Sold out: by 31.10.73 (7½p)

Withdrawn: 22.1.74 (2½p, 3p, 9p)

70 Balloon *L'Armee de La Loire* and Letter, Paris, 1870

71 Astra Seaplane, 1912

72 Supermarine Sea Eagle

73 De Havilland D.H.86 Dragon Express *Giffard Bay*

Jersey Aviation History

(Des and photo Courvoisier)

1973 (16 MAY). *Granite paper. Perf* 11½ (C)

89	**70**	3p multicoloured	....	10	10
90	**71**	5p multicoloured	....	15	15
91	**72**	7½p multicoloured	....	60	60
92	**73**	9p multicoloured	....	80	80
89/92		Set of 4	....	1·50	1·50
		First Day Cover	....		1·75
		Presentation Pack	....	1·75	

Sheets: 50 (5×10)

Quantities sold: 3p 3,085,497; 5p 641,583; 7½p 368,069; 9p 356,379

Sold out: by 31.10.73 (7½p)

Withdrawn: 15.5.74 (3p, 5p, 9p)

74 *North Western*, 1870

75 *Calvados*, 1873

76 *Carteret* at Grouville Station, 1898

77 *Caesarea*, 1873, and Route Map

Centenary of Jersey Eastern Railway

(Des G. Drummond. Photo Courvoisier)

1973 (6 AUG). *Granite paper. Perf* 11½ (C)

93	**74**	2½p multicoloured	. . . .	10	10
94	**75**	3p multicoloured	. . . .	10	10
95	**76**	7½p multicoloured	. . . .	60	40
96	**77**	9p multicoloured	. . . .	85	50
93/6		*Set of 4*	. . . .	1·50	1·00
		First Day Cover	. . . .		2·00
		Presentation Pack	. . . .	1·75	

Sheets: 50 (5×10)

Quantities sold: 2½p 1,591,063; 3p 3,051,097; 7½p 396,919; 9p 365,310

Sold out: by 31.10.73 (7½p)

Withdrawn: 5.8.74 (2½p, 3p, 9p)

78 Princess Anne and Captain Mark Phillips

Royal Wedding

(Des and photo Courvoisier)

1973 (14 NOV). *Granite paper. Perf* 11½ (C)

97	**78**	3p multicoloured	. . . .	10	10
98		20p multicoloured	. . . .	90	90
97/8		*Set of 2*	. . . .	1·00	1·00
		First Day Cover	. . . .		1·00
		Presentation Pack	. . . .	1·25	

Sheets: 25 (5×5)

Quantities sold: 3p 1,988,407; 20p 522,793

Withdrawn: 30.11.74

79 Spider Crab   **80** Conger Eel

81 Lobster   **82** Tuberculate Ormer

Marine Life

(Des Jennifer Toombs. Photo Courvoisier)

1973 (15 NOV). *Granite paper. Perf* 11½ (C)

99	**79**	2½p multicoloured	. . . .	10	10
100	**80**	3p multicoloured	. . . .	10	10
101	**81**	7½p multicoloured	. . . .	50	50
102	**82**	20p multicoloured	. . . .	70	70
99/102		*Set of 4*	. . . .	1·25	1·25
		First Day Cover	. . . .		1·50
		Presentation Pack	. . . .	1·50	

Sheets: 50 (5×10)

Quantities sold: 2½p 1,596,526; 3p 1,243,541; 7½p 501,541; 20p 517,440

Sold out: by 28.2.74 (7½p)

Withdrawn: 30.11.74 (2½p, 3p, 20p)

83 Freesias   **84** Anemones

85 Carnations and Gladioli   **86** Daffodils and Iris

Spring Flowers

(Des G. Drummond. Photo Courvoisier)

1974 (13 FEB). *Granite paper. Perf* 11½ (C)

103	**83**	3p multicoloured	. . . .	10	10
104	**84**	5½p multicoloured	. . . .	20	10
105	**85**	8p multicoloured	. . . .	60	40
106	**86**	10p multicoloured	. . . .	80	50
103/6		*Set of 4*	. . . .	1·50	1·00
		First Day Cover	. . . .		1·50
		Presentation Pack	. . . .	1·75	

Sheets: 50 (10×5)

Quantities sold: 3p 1,239,968; 5½p 590,376; 8p 475,665; 10p 507,542

Withdrawn: 28.2.75

First U.K. Pillar-box and Contemporary Cover

88 Jersey Postmen, 1862 and 1969

Modern Pillar-box and Cover

90 Mail Transport, 1874 and 1974

Centenary of Universal Postal Union

(Des G. Drummond. Photo Courvoisier)

1974 (7 JUNE). *Granite paper. Perf* 11½ (C)

107	**87**	2½p multicoloured	10	10
108	**88**	3p multicoloured	10	10
109	**89**	5½p multicoloured	35	30
110	**90**	20p multicoloured	85	60
107/10		*Set of* 4	1·25	1·00
		First Day Cover		1·25
		Presentation Pack	1·50	

Sheets: 50 (5×10)

Quantities sold: 2½p 461,174; 3p 1,380,018; 5½p 421,674; 20p 386,348

Withdrawn: 30.6.75

John Wesley

92 Sir William Hillary

Canon Wace

94 Sir Winston Churchill

Anniversaries. Events described on stamps

(Des, recess and litho De La Rue)

1974 (31 JULY). *Perf* 13×14 (C)

111	**91**	3p agate and light cinnamon	10	10
112	**92**	3½p blackish violet & light azure	10	10
113	**93**	8p blue-black and pale rose-lilac	30	35
114	**94**	20p black and pale buff	70	65
		a. Pale buff (background) omitted		
111/14		*Set of 4*	1·00	1·00
		First Day Cover		1·00
		Presentation Pack	1·50	

Plate Nos.: 3p and 20p 1A–1A, 1B–1B; 3½p and 8p 1A–1A, 1B–1B, 2A–1A, 2B–1B

Sheets: 50 (10×5)

Imprint: Right-hand corner, bottom margin

Quantities sold: 3p 908,852; 3½p 2,355,391; 8p 338,397; 20p 409,291

Withdrawn: 31.7.75

95 *Catherine and Mary* (royal yachts)

96 French Two-decker

97 Dutch Vessel

98 Battle of Cap La Hague, 1692

203

Marine Paintings by Peter Monamy

(Des and photo Courvoisier)

1974 (22 NOV). *Granite paper. Perf* 11½ (C)

115	**95**	3½p multicoloured	. . . .	10	10
116	**96**	5½p multicoloured	. . . .	20	15
117	**97**	8p multicoloured	. . . .	30	35
118	**98**	25p multicoloured	. . . .	80	80
115/18		*Set of* 4	. . . .	1·25	1·25
		First Day Cover			2·50
		Presentation Pack	2·00	

Sheets: 50 (10×5) 8p; (5×10) others

Quantities sold: 3½p 1,670,994; 5½p 448,137; 8p 416,296; 25p 415,991

Withdrawn: 30.11.75

99 Potato Digger

100 Cider Crusher

101 Six-Horse Plough

102 Hay Cart

Nineteenth-Century Farming

(Des G. Drummond. Photo Courvoisier)

1975 (25 FEB). *Granite paper. Perf* 11½ (C)

119	**99**	3p multicoloured	. . . .	10	10
120	**100**	3½p multicoloured	. . . .	10	15
121	**101**	8p multicoloured	. . . .	35	35
122	**102**	10p multicoloured	. . . .	55	50
119/22		*Set of* 4	. . . .	1·00	1·00
		First Day Cover			1·00
		Presentation Pack	1·25	

Sheets: 50 (5×10)

Quantities sold: 3p 588,185; 3½p 1,025,295; 8p 432,432; 10p 457,196

Withdrawn: 28.2.76

103 H.M. Queen Elizabeth, the Queen Mother (photograph by Cecil Beaton)

Royal Visit

(Des and photo Courvoisier)

1975 (30 MAY). *Granite paper. Perf* 11½ (C)

123	**103**	20p multicoloured	. . . .	1·00	1·
		First Day Cover			2·
		Presentation Pack	1·25	

Cylinder Nos.: A1–1–1–1–1, B1–1–1–1–1

Sheets: 25 (5×5)

Quantity sold: 572,675

Withdrawn: 31.5.76

104 Nautilus Shell

105 Parasol

106 Deckchair

107 Sandcastle with flags of Jersey and the U.K.

Jersey Tourism

(Des A. Games. Photo Courvoisier)

1975 (6 JUNE). *Designs based on holiday posters. Gran paper. Perf* 11½ (C)

124	**104**	5p multicoloured	. . . .	10	
125	**105**	8p multicoloured	. . . .	15	
126	**106**	10p multicoloured	. . . .	35	
127	**107**	12p multicoloured	. . . .	60	
124/7		*Set of* 4	. . . .	1·10	1·
		First Day Cover			2·
		Presentation Pack	2·25	
MS128		147×69 mm. Nos. 124/7	. . . .	1·00	1·
		First Day Cover			2·

Cylinder Nos.: All values A1–1–1–1–1, B1–1–1–1–1

Sheets: 50 (10×5)

Quantities sold: 5p 1,377,519; 8p 368,521; 10p 467,278;12p 389,57 miniature sheet 298,689

Withdrawn: 30.6.76

3 Common Tern

109 British Storm Petrel

) Brent Geese

111 Shag

a Birds

(Des Jennifer Toombs. Photo Courvoisier)

75 (28 JULY). *Granite paper. Perf* 11½ (C)
)	**108**	4p multicoloured	....	15	15
)	**109**	5p multicoloured	....	15	15
⁴	**110**	8p multicoloured	....	50	40
2	**111**	25p multicoloured	....	85	70
⁹/32		Set of 4	....	1·50	1·25
		First Day Cover.			1·75
		Presentation Pack	1·75	

'heets: 50 (10×5)

Quantities sold: 4p 872,260; 5p 2,871,390; 8p 384,550; 25p 362,160

Vithdrawn: 31.7.76

2 Armstrong Whitworth Siskin IIIA

113 Supermarine Southampton 1 Flying Boat

4 Supermarine Spitfire Mk I

115 Folland Fo.141 Gnat T 1

50th Anniversary of Royal Air Forces Association, Jersey Branch

(Des A. Theobald. Photo Courvoisier)

1975 (30 OCT). *Granite paper. Perf* 11½ (C)
133	**112**	4p multicoloured	....	10	10
134	**113**	5p multicoloured	....	15	15
135	**114**	10p multicoloured	....	50	35
136	**115**	25p multicoloured	....	95	80
133/6		Set of 4	....	1·50	1·25
		First Day Cover.			1·75
		Presentation Pack	1·75	

Cylinder Nos.: All values A1–1–1–1–1, B1–1–1–1–1

Sheets: 50 (5×10)

Quantities sold: 4p 1,496,640; 5p 1,805,624; 10p 581,627; 25p 407,423

Withdrawn: 30.10.76

116 Map of Jersey Parishes

117 Zoological Park

118 St. Mary's Church

119 Seymour Tower

120 La Corbière Lighthouse

121 St. Saviour's Church

122 Elizabeth Castle

123 Gorey Harbour

205

124 Jersey Airport

125 Grosnez Castle

126 Bonne Nuit Harbour

127 Le Hocq Tower

128 Morel Farm

129 Parish Arms and Island Scene

130 Flag and Map

131 Postal H.Q. and Badge

132 Parliament, Royal Court and Arms

133 Lieutenant-Governor's Flag and Government House

134 Queen Elizabeth II (photograph b Alex Wilson)

Parish Arms and Views

(Des Courvoisier (£2), G. Drummond (others). Litho Questa (½p to 15p). Photo Courvoisier (others))

1976–80. Granite paper (20p to £2). Perf 14½ (½p to 15p) or 12 (others), all comb

137	**116**	½p multicoloured (af)	10	1C
138	**117**	1p multicoloured (af)	10	1C
		a. Booklet pane of 4 (No. 138×2 plus 2 se-tenant labels) (b)	1·00	
		b. Booklet pane. No. 138×4 (begh)	1·00	
139	**118**	5p multicoloured (ad)	15	1E
		a. Booklet pane of 4 (b)	50	
140	**119**	6p multicoloured (ad)	15	1E
		a. Booklet pane of 4 (eg)	60	
141	**120**	7p multicoloured (ad)	20	2C
		a. Booklet pane of 4 (bh)	60	
142	**121**	8p multicoloured (ad)	20	2C
		a. Booklet pane of 4 (eg)	80	
143	**122**	9p multicoloured (a)	25	2E
		a. Booklet pane of 4 (h)	1·00	
144	**123**	10p multicoloured (af)	25	2E
145	**124**	11p multicoloured (a)	30	2E
146	**125**	12p multicoloured (a)	30	3C
147	**126**	13p multicoloured (a)	35	3E
148	**127**	14p multicoloured (a)	35	4C
149	**128**	15p multicoloured (a)	40	4E
150	**129**	20p multicoloured (c)	50	5C
151	**130**	30p multicoloured (c)	75	7E
152	**131**	40p multicoloured (c)	1·00	1·0C
153	**132**	50p multicoloured (c)	1·25	1·0C
154	**133**	£1 multicoloured (c)	2·50	2·5C
155	**134**	£2 multicoloured (d)	4·50	4·5C
137/55		Set of 19	12·00	12·0C
		First Day Covers (4)		13·0C
		Presentation Packs (4)	13·50	

Printings: (a) 29.1.76; (b) 5.4.76; (c) 20.8.76; (d) 16.11.77; (e) 28.2.78 (f) 31.8.78; (g) 1.10.79; (h) 6.5.80

Plate or cylinder Nos.: ½p to 9p, 13p, 14p 1A, 1B, 1C, 1D (each ×4) 10p 1A, 1B, 1C, 1D (each ×4), 1B–1B–1B–2B, 2A–1A–1A–2A 2B–1B–1B–2B, 2C–1C–1C–2C, 2D–1D–1D–2D; 11p 1A, 1B, 1C, 1D (each ×5); 12p 1A, 1B, 1C, 1D (each ×4), 1A–1A–2A–2A 1B–1B–2B–2B, 1C–1C–2C–2C, 1D–1D–2D–2D; 15p 1A, 1B, 1C, 1D (each ×4), 1A–2A–1A–1A, 1B–2B–1B–1B, 1C–2C–1C–1C 1D–2D–1D–1D, 1A–2A–2A–1A, 1B–2B–2B–1B, 1C–2C–2C–1C 1D–2D–2D–1D, 1A–3A–2A–1A, 1B–3B–2B–1B, 1C–3C–2C–1C 1D–3D–2D–1D; 20p A1–1–1–1–1, B1–1–1–1–1, C1–1–1–1–1

D1–1–1–1–1; 30p, £1 A1–1–1–1–1, B1–1–1–1–1; 40p, 50p
A1–1–1–1, B1–1–1–1; £2 A1–1–1–1–1–1–1,
B1–1–1–1–1–1–1, C1–1–1–1–1–1–1, D1–1–1–1–1–1–1

Sheets: 50 (5×10) ½p to 15p; 25 (5×5) others

Imprint: Right-hand corner, bottom margin (½p to 15p); central, bottom margin (others)

Withdrawn: 27.2.82 ½p to 9p (sheets); 20.4.82 1p, 5p to 9p (booklets); 31.7.82 10p to 15p; 28.2.83 20p to £1; 31.3.92 £2

135 Sir Walter Ralegh and Map of Virginia

136 Sir George Carteret and Map of New Jersey

37 Philippe D'Auvergne and Long Island Landing

138 John Copley and Sketch

nks with America'

(Des M. Orbell. Photo Courvoisier)

76 (29 MAY). *Granite paper. Perf* 11½ (C)

0	**135**	5p multicoloured	10	10
1	**136**	7p multicoloured	15	15
2	**137**	11p multicoloured	40	50
3	**138**	13p multicoloured	45	65
0/3		Set of 4	1·10	1·25
		First Day Cover		1·50
		Presentation Pack	1·50	

Cylinder Nos.: 5p, 11p A1–1–1–1–1, B1–1–1–1–1; others A1–1–1–1, B1–1–1–1

Sheets: 25 (5×5)

Quantities sold: 5p 980,029; 7p 1,352,629; 11p 582,706; 13p 435,561

Withdrawn: 31.5.77

139 Dr. Grandin and Map of China

140 Sampan on the Yangtze

141 Overland Trek

142 Dr. Grandin at work

Birth Centenary of Dr. Lilian Grandin (medical missionary)

(Des Jennifer Toombs. Photo Courvoisier)

1976 (25 NOV). *Granite paper. Perf* 11½ (C)

164	**139**	5p multicoloured	10	10
165	**140**	7p lt yellow, yellow-brown & blk	15	15
166	**141**	11p multicoloured	50	35
167	**142**	13p multicoloured	50	50
164/7		Set of 4	1·10	1·00
		First Day Cover		1·50
		Presentation Pack	1·50	

Cylinder Nos.: 7p A1–1–1, B1–1–1; 13p A1–1–1–1, B1–1–1–1–1; others A1–1–1–1, B1–1–1–1

Sheets: 50 (5×10)

Quantities sold: 5p 757,843; 7p 1,043,198; 11p 384,436; 13p 354,096

Withdrawn: 30.11.77

143 Coronation, 1953 (photograph by Cecil Beaton)

144 Visit to Jersey, 1957

145 Queen Elizabeth II (photograph by Peter Grugeon)

Silver Jubilee

(Des G. Drummond. Photo Courvoisier)

1977 (7 FEB). *Granite paper. Perf 11½ (C)*

168	**143**	5p multicoloured	. . . .	25	15
169	**144**	7p multicoloured	. . . .	30	20
170	**145**	25p multicoloured	. . . .	90	80
168/70		*Set of 3*	. . . .	1·25	1·00
		First Day Cover			1·50
		Presentation Pack		1·50	

Cylinder Nos.: All values A1–1–1–1–1, B1–1–1–1–1
Sheets: 25 (5×5)
Imprint: Central, bottom margin
Quantities sold: 5p 1,220,986; 7p 1,212,639; 25p 681,241
Withdrawn: 28.2.78

146 Coins of 1871 and 1877

147 One-twelfth shilling, 1949

148 Silver Crown, 1966

149 £2 Piece, 1972

Centenary of Currency Reform

(Des D. Henley. Litho Questa)

1977 (25 MAR). *Perf 14 (C)*

171	**146**	5p multicoloured	. . . .	10	10
172	**147**	7p multicoloured	. . . .	15	15

173	**148**	11p multicoloured	. . . .	40	3
174	**149**	13p multicoloured	. . . .	45	5
171/4		*Set of 4*	. . . .	1·00	1·0
		First Day Cover			1·2
		Presentation Pack		1·50	

Plate Nos.: 7p 1A, 1B (each ×5), 1A–2A–1A (×3), 1B–2B–1B (×3
others 1A, 1B (each ×5)
Sheets: 50 (5 ×10)
Imprint: Right-hand corner, bottom margin
Quantities sold: 5p 1,029,661; 7p 923,950; 11p 383,834; 13p 368,2
Withdrawn: 31.3.78

150 Sir William Weston and *Santa Anna*, 1530

151 Sir William Drogo and Ambulance, 1877

152 Duke of Connaught and Ambulance, 1917

153 Duke of Gloucester and Stretcher-team, 1977

St. John Ambulance Centenary

(Des A. Theobald. Litho Questa)

1977 (24 JUNE). *Perf 14×13½ (C)*

175	**150**	5p multicoloured	. . . .	10	1
176	**151**	7p multicoloured	. . . .	15	1
177	**152**	11p multicoloured	. . . .	40	3
178	**153**	13p multicoloured	. . . .	45	5
175/8		*Set of 4*	. . . .	1·00	1·
		First Day Cover			1·2
		Presentation Pack		1·50	

Plate Nos.: 5p 1A, 1B, 1C (each ×5); 7p, 11p 1A, 1B, 1C (each ×6); 13p 1A, 1B, 1C (each ×5), 1B–2B–1B–1B–1B

Sheets: 40 (8×5)

Imprint: Bottom corner, right-hand margin

Quantities sold: 5p 849,532; 7p 1,089,526; 11p 421,039; 13p 370,887

Withdrawn: 30.6.78

154 Arrival of Queen Victoria, 1846

155 Victoria College, 1852

156 Sir Galahad Statue, 1924

157 College Hall

25th Anniversary of Victoria College

(Des R. Granger Barrett. Litho Questa)

1977 (29 SEPT). *Perf* 14½ (C)

179	**154**	7p multicoloured	. . . .	20	20
180	**155**	10½p multicoloured	. . . .	25	20
		a. Black ptg double	. . . .		
181	**156**	11p multicoloured	. . . .	30	35
182	**157**	13p multicoloured	. . . .	35	35
179/82		Set of 4	. . . .	1·00	1·00
		First Day Cover	. . . .		1·25
		Presentation Pack	. . . . .	1·50	

Plate Nos.: 7p 1A, 1B (each ×6), 1A–1A–2A–1A–1A–1A, 1B–1B–2B–1B–1B–1B; 13p 1A, 1B (each ×6); others 1A, 1B (each ×5)

Sheets: 50 (5×10) 7 and 10½p, (10×5) others

Imprint: Right-hand corner, bottom margin

Quantities sold: 7p 1,496,997; 10½p 906,669; 11p 528,293; 13p 371,251

Withdrawn: 30.9.78

158 Harry Vardon Statuette and Map of Royal Jersey Course

159 Harry Vardon's Grip and Swing

160 Harry Vardon's Putt

161 Golf Trophies and Book by Harry Vardon

Centenary of Royal Jersey Golf Club

(Des Jennifer Toombs. Litho Questa)

1978 (28 FEB). *Perf* 14 (C)

183	**158**	6p multicoloured	. . . .	15	15
184	**159**	8p multicoloured	. . . .	20	20
185	**160**	11p multicoloured	. . . .	65	50
186	**161**	13p multicoloured	. . . .	65	55
183/6		Set of 4	. . . .	1·50	1·25
		First Day Cover	. . . .		1·50
		Presentation Pack	. . . .	1·75	

Plate Nos.: 6p 1A, 1B (each ×5); 8p, 11p 1A, 1B (each ×4); 13p 1A, 1B (each ×4), 2A–1A–1A–1A, 2B–1B–1B–1B

Sheets: 50 (5×10)

Imprint: Right-hand corner, bottom margin

Quantities sold: 6p 837,427; 8p 851,904; 11p 466,343; 13p 368,648

Withdrawn: 28.2.79

162 Mont Orgueil Castle

163 St. Aubin's Fort

164 Elizabeth Castle

Europa. Fortifications

(Des from paintings by Thomas Philips. Photo Courvoisier)

1978 (1 MAY). *Granite paper. Perf* 11½ (C)

187	**162**	6p multicoloured	20	20
188	**163**	8p multicoloured	40	40
189	**164**	10½p multicoloured	50	50
187/9		*Set of 3*	1·00	1·00
		First Day Cover		1·00
		Presentation Pack	1·00	

Cylinder Nos.: All values A1–1–1–1–1, B1–1–1–1–1, C1–1–1–1–1, D1–1–1–1–1

Sheets: 20 (5×4)

Imprint: Central, bottom margin

Quantities sold: 6p 2,602,412; 8p 2,592,722; 10½p 2,564,535

Withdrawn: 31.5.79

165 'Gaspé Basin'
(P. J. Ouless)

166 Map of Gaspé
Peninsula

167 *Century* (brigantine)

168 Early Map of Jersey

169 St. Aubin's Bay, Town and
Harbour

Links with Canada

(Des R. Granger Barrett. Litho Questa)

1978 (9 JUNE). *Perf* 14½ (C)

190	**165**	6p multicoloured	15	15
191	**166**	8p multicoloured	20	20
192	**167**	10½p multicoloured	25	30
193	**168**	11p multicoloured	40	35
194	**169**	13p multicoloured	45	40
190/4		*Set of 5*	1·25	1·25
		First Day Cover		1·50
		Presentation Pack	1·75	

Plate Nos.: 6p 1A, 1B, 1C, 1D (each ×5); others 1A, 1B, 1C, 1D (ea ×6)

Sheets: 50 (5 ×10)

Imprint: Right-hand corner, bottom margin

Quantities sold: 6p 1,047,825; 8p 1,095,489; 10½p 999,002; 1 443,932; 13p 367,472

Withdrawn: 30.6.79

170 Queen Elizabeth and
Prince Philip

171 Hallmarks of 1953
and 1977

25th Anniversary of Coronation

(Des and photo Courvoisier)

1978 (26 JUNE). *Granite paper. Perf* 11½ (C)

195	**170**	8p silver, black and cerise	30	3
196	**171**	25p silver, black and new blue ..	70	
195/6		*Set of 2*	1·00	1·0
		First Day Cover		1·2
		Presentation Pack	1·25	

Cylinder Nos.: Both values A1–1–1, B1–1–1

Sheets: 50 (10×5)

Quantities sold: 8p 1,060,259; 25p 459,558

Withdrawn: 30.6.79

172 Mail Cutter,
1778–1827

173 *Flamer*, 1831–37

174 *Diana*, 1877–90

175 *Ibex*, 1891–1925

176 *Caesarea*, 1960–75

centenary of England–Jersey Government Mail Packet service

(Des Jersey P.O. Litho Harrison)

978 (18 OCT). *Perf* 14½×14 (C)

7	**172**	6p black, yellow-brown and greenish yellow	15	15
8	**173**	8p black, dull yellowish green and pale yellow-green	20	20
9	**174**	10½p black, ultramarine & cobalt	40	40
0	**175**	11p blk, purple & pale rose-lilac	45	45
1	**176**	13p black, Venetian red and pink	50	50
7/201		*Set of* 5	1·50	1·50
		First Day Cover		1·60
		Presentation Pack	1·75	

Plate Nos.: All values 1A, 1B (each ×3)

Sheets: 50 (5 ×10)

Imprint: Right-hand corner, bottom margin

Quantities sold: 6p 1,157,597; 8p 1,149,500; 10½p 528,170; 11p 468,589; 13p 371,210

Withdrawn: 31.10.79

7 Jersey Calf

178 'Ansom Designette' (calf presented to the Queen, 27 June, 1978)

h World Jersey Cattle Bureau Conference

(Des Jersey P.O. and Questa. Litho Questa)

979 (1 MAR). *Perf* 13½ (C)

2	**177**	6p multicoloured	20	20
		a. Gold ptg double	£400	
3	**178**	25p multicoloured	80	80
		a. Gold ptg double	£400	
2/3		*Set of* 2	1·00	1·00
		First Day Cover.........		1·25
		Presentation Pack........	1·25	

Plate Nos.: Both values 1A, 1B, 1C, 1D, 1E, 1F (each ×8)

Sheets: 20 (4×5)

Imprint: Right-hand corner, bottom margin

Withdrawn: 29.2.80

179 Jersey Pillar Box, *c* 1860

180 Clearing a Modern Jersey Post Box

181 Telephone Switchboard, *c* 1900

182 Modern S.P.C. Telephone System

Europa. Communications

(Des Jennifer Toombs. Litho Questa)

1979 (1 MAR). *Thin paper. Perf* 14 (C)

204	**179**	8p multicoloured	25	25
		a. *Horiz pair. Nos.* 204/5	50	50
		b. *Thick paper*		
		ba. *Horiz pair. Nos.* 204b/5b ..		
		c. *Perf* 14½ (*thick paper*)	25	25
		ca. *Horiz pair. Nos.* 204c/5c ..	50	50
205	**180**	8p multicoloured	25	25
		b. *Thick paper*		
		c. *Perf* 14½ (*thick paper*)	25	25
206	**181**	10½p multicoloured	30	30
		a. *Horiz pair. Nos.* 206/7	60	65
		b. *Thick paper*	75	
		ba. *Horiz pair. Nos.* 206b/7b ..	1·60	
		c. *Perf* 14½	30	30
		ca. *Horiz pair. Nos.* 206c/7c ..	60	65
207	**182**	10½p multicoloured	30	30
		b. *Thick paper*	75	
		c. *Perf* 14½	30	30
		ca. *Greenish blue omitted*	£400	
204/7		*Set of* 4	1·00	1·00
		First Day Cover (*Nos.* 204/5, 206c/7c)		1·25
		First Day Cover (*Nos.* 204/7)		
		Presentation Pack (*either perforation*)	1·40	

Although both perforations were supplied to Jersey at the same time the 8p perforated 14½ is not known used before early April.

Plate Nos.: Both values 1A, 1B, 1C, 1D, 1E, 1F, 1G, 1H (each ×8)

Sheets: 20 (4×5) the two designs of each value were printed together, *se-tenant*, in horizontal pairs throughout

Imprint: Central, bottom margin

Quantities sold: 8p 5,149,852; 10½p 3,047,039

Withdrawn: 29.2.80

183 Percival Mew Gull *Golden City*

184 De Havilland D.H.C.1 Chipmunk

185 Druine D.31 Turbulent

186 De Havilland D.H.82A Tiger Moth

187 North American AT-6 Harvard

25th Anniversary of International Air Rally

(Des A. Theobald. Photo Courvoisier)

1979 (24 APR). *Granite paper. Perf* 11½ (C)

208	**183**	6p multicoloured	15	15
209	**184**	8p multicoloured	20	25
210	**185**	10½p multicoloured	40	25
211	**186**	11p multicoloured	45	35
212	**187**	13p multicoloured	50	40
208/12		*Set of 5*	1·50	1·25
		First Day Cover		1·60
		Presentation Pack	1·75	

Cylinder Nos.: 13p A1–1–1–1–1, B1–1–1–1–1, C1–1–1–1–1, D1–1–1–1–1; others A1–1–1–1, B1–1–1–1, C1–1–1–1, D1–1–1–1

Sheets: 20 (5×4)

Imprint: Central, bottom margin

Quantities sold: 6p 1,327,279; 8p 1,338,234; 10½p 433,127; 11p 457,566; 13p 426,528

Withdrawn: 30.4.80

188 'My First Sermon'

189 'Orphans'

190 'The Princes in the Tower'

191 'Christ in the House of His Parents'

International Year of the Child and 150th Bir Anniversary of Millais

(Des Jersey P.O. and Courvoisier. Photo Courvoisier)

1979 (13 AUG). *Granite paper. Perf* 12×12½ (25p) *or* 12×1 (*others*), *all comb*

213	**188**	8p multicoloured	25	2
214	**189**	10½p multicoloured	35	2
215	**190**	11p multicoloured	35	4
216	**191**	25p multicoloured	75	2
213/16		*Set of 4*	1·50	1·2
		First Day Cover		1·6
		Presentation Pack	1·75	

Cylinder Nos.: 25p A1–1–1–1, B1–1–1–1; others A1–1–1–1– B1–1–1–1, C1–1–1–1, D1–1–1–1

Sheets: 20 (4×5) 25p or (5×4) others

Quantities sold: 8p 1,187,969; 10½p 953,826; 11p 508,316; 2 463,234

Withdrawn: 30.8.80

192 Pink Pigeon

193 Orang-utan

194 Waldrapp Ibis

5 Lowland Gorilla

196 Rodriguez Flying Fox

ildlife Preservation Trust (Third Series)

(Des Jennifer Toombs. Photo Courvoisier)

79 (8 NOV). *Granite paper. Perf* 11½ (C)

7	**192**	6p multicoloured	15	15
8	**193**	8p multicoloured	20	30
9	**194**	11½p multicoloured	50	35
0	**195**	13p multicoloured	65	40
1	**196**	15p multicoloured	75	50
7/21		*Set of* 5	2·00	1·50
		First Day Cover		2·25
		Presentation Pack	2·25	

Cylinder Nos.: All values A1–1–1–1–1, B1–1–1–1–1, C1–1–1–1–1, D1–1–1–1–1

Sheets: 20 (11½p 4×5 others 5×4)

Imprint: Right-hand corner, bottom margin

Quantities sold: 6p 1,128,144; 8p 1,080,889; 11½p 559,534; 13p 443,140; 15p 433,115

Withdrawn: 30.11.80

97 Plan of Mont Orgueil

198 Plan of La Tour de St. Aubin

199 Plan of Elizabeth Castle

200 Map of Jersey showing Fortresses

Fortresses. Drawings by Thomas Phillips

(Litho Enschedè)

1980 (5 FEB). *Perf* 13×13½ (25p) *or* 13½×13 (*others*), *all comb*

222	**197**	8p multicoloured	30	25
223	**198**	11½p multicoloured	35	30
224	**199**	13p multicoloured	55	45
225	**200**	25p multicoloured	80	70
222/5		*Set of* 4	1·75	1·50
		First Day Cover		1·60
		Presentation Pack	2·00	

Sheets: 20 (4×5)

Imprint: Right-hand corner, bottom margin

Quantities sold: 8p 665,647; 11½p 363,246; 13p 415,790; 25p 379,743

Withdrawn: 28.2.81

201　　Sir Walter Ralegh and Paul Ivy　**202**
(engineer) discussing Elizabeth
Castle

203　Sir George Carteret receiving rights　**204**
to Smith's Island, Virginia, from
King Charles II

213

Europa. Personalities. Links with Britain

(Des Jersey Post Office and Questa. Litho Questa)

1980 (6 MAY). *Perf* 14 (C)

226	**201**	9p multicoloured	....	20	20
227	**202**	9p multicoloured	....	20	20
		a. Horiz pair. Nos. 226/7	....	50	50
228	**203**	13½p multicoloured	....	45	45
229	**204**	13½p multicoloured	....	45	45
		a. Horiz pair. Nos. 228/9	....	90	90
226/9		Set of 4	....	1·25	1·25
		First Day Cover	....		1·60
		Presentation Pack	......	1·60	

Plate Nos.: Both values 1A, 1B, 1C, 1D, 1E, 1F (each ×4)

Sheets: 20 (4×5). The two designs of each value were printed together, *se-tenant*, in horizontal pairs throughout, forming composite designs.

Imprint: Central, left-hand margin

Quantities sold: 9p 4,793,980; 13½p 2,638,136

Withdrawn: 31.5.81

205 Planting

206 Digging

207 Weighbridge

Centenary of Jersey Royal Potato

(Des R. Granger Barrett. Litho Questa)

1980 (6 MAY). *Perf* 14 (C)

230	**205**	7p multicoloured	....	15	15
231	**206**	15p multicoloured	....	35	35
232	**207**	17½p multicoloured	....	60	60
230/2		Set of 3	....	1·00	1·00
		First Day Cover	....		1·40
		Presentation Pack	......	1·60	

Plate Nos.: All values 1A, 1B, 1C, 1D, 1E, 1F (each ×6)

Sheets: 20 (4×5)

Imprint: Central, left-hand margin

Quantities sold: 7p 1,379,048; 15p 383,956; 17½p 375,082

Withdrawn: 31.5.83

208 Three Lap Event

209 Jersey International Road Race

210 Scrambling

211 Sand Racing (saloon cars)

212 National Hill Climb

60th Anniversary of Jersey Motor-cycle and Light Car Clu

(Des A. Theobald. Photo Courvoisier)

1980 (24 JULY). *Granite paper. Perf* 11½ (C)

233	**208**	7p multicoloured	....	25	2
234	**209**	9p multicoloured	....	25	2
235	**210**	13½p multicoloured	....	45	4
236	**211**	15p multicoloured	....	50	5
237	**212**	17½p multicoloured	....	55	5
233/7		Set of 5	....	1·75	1·
		First Day Cover	....		2·0
		Presentation Pack	......	2·00	

Cylinder Nos.: 7p, 15p A1–1–1–1–1, B1–1–1–1–1, C1–1–1–1– D1–1–1–1–1; others A1–1–1–1, B1–1–1–1, C1–1–1–1, D1–1–1–

Sheets: 20 (5×4)

Imprint: Left-hand corner, bottom margin

Quantities sold: 7p 1,452,280; 9p 1,426,548; 13½p 384,861; 1 350,608; 17½p 338,658

Withdrawn: 31.7.81

213 *Eye of the Wind*

214 Diving from Inflatable Dinghy

15 Exploration of Papua
New Guinea

216 Captain Scott's
Discovery

17 Using Aerial Walkways,
Conservation Project,
Sulawesi

218 *Eye of the Wind*, and
Goodyear Aerospace
Airship *Europa*

Operation Drake and 150th Anniversary of Royal Geographical Society (14p)

(Des G. Drummond. Litho Questa)

1980 (1 OCT). *Perf* 14 (C)

38	**213**	7p multicoloured	20	20
39	**214**	9p multicoloured	25	25
40	**215**	13½p multicoloured	35	35
41	**216**	14p multicoloured	45	35
42	**217**	15p multicoloured	45	35
		a. *Black (face value and inscr)* *ptg double*		
43	**218**	17½p multicoloured	55	45
		a. *Black (face value and inscr)* *ptg double*		
38/43		*Set of* 6	2·00	1·75
		First Day Cover		2·00
		Presentation Pack	2·50	

Plate Nos.: All values 1A, 1B, 1C, 1D, 1E, 1F (each ×6)

Sheets: 20 (5×4)

Imprint: Upper left-hand margin

Quantities sold: 7p 1,631,558; 9p 1,071,684; 13½p 432,201; 14p 357,109; 15p 357,922; 17½p 351,215

Withdrawn: 31.10.81

219

220

221

222

Bicentenary of Battle of Jersey. Details of painting 'The Death of Major Peirson' by J. S. Copley

(Photo Courvoisier)

1981 (6 JAN). *Granite paper. Perf* 12½×12 (C)

244	**219**	7p multicoloured	25	25
245	**220**	10p multicoloured	30	30
246	**221**	15p multicoloured	60	60
247	**222**	17½p multicoloured	80	80
244/7		*Set of* 4	1·75	1·75
		First Day Cover		1·75
		Presentation Pack	2·00	
MS248		144×97 mm. Nos. 244/7	2·00	2·00
		First Day Cover		3·50

Stamps from No. **MS**248 are without white margins.

Cylinder Nos.: All values A1–1–1–1–1, B1–1–1–1–1

Sheets: 20 (5×4)

Imprint: Right-hand corner, bottom margin

Quantities sold: 7p 997,416; 10p 1,107,456; 15p 367,971; 17½p 359,794; miniature sheet 469,953

Withdrawn: 31.1.82

223 De Bagot

224 De Carteret

225 La Cloche

226 Dumaresq

227 Payn

228 Janvrin

229 Poingdestre

230 Pipon

231 Marett

232 Le Breton

233 Le Maistre

234 Bisson

235 Robin

236 Herault

237 Messervy

238 Fiott

239 Malet

240 Mabon

241 De St. Martin

242 Hamptonne

243 Badier

244 L'Arbalestier

245 Journeaulx

246 Lempriere

247 Auvergne

248 Remon

249 Jersey Crest and
Map of Channel

250 'Queen Elizabeth II'
(Norman Hepple)

Arms of Jersey Families

(Des Courvoisier (£5). G. Drummond (ohers). Litho Questa
(½p to £1). Photo Courvoisier (£5))

1981 (24 FEB)–**88**. *Granite paper (£5). Perf 15×14 (16p, 17*
18p, 19p, 26p, 75p), 12½×12 (£5) or 14 (others), all comb

249	**223**	½p black, silver & turq-grn (a) . .	20	
250	**224**	1p multicoloured (a)	10	
		a. *Booklet pane of 6 (acf)*	40	
		b. *Perf 15×14 (o)*	25	
251	**225**	2p multicoloured (a)	10	
		a. *Booklet pane of 6 (cf)*	70	
		b. *Perf 15×14 (io)*	20	
		ba. *Booklet pane of 6 (l)*	1·00	
252	**226**	3p multicoloured (a)	20	
		a. *Booklet pane of 6 (a)*	80	
		b. *Perf 15×14 (ik)*	20	
		ba. *Booklet pane of 6 (h)*	85	
253	**227**	4p black, silver and mauve (a). .	25	
		a. *Perf 15×14 (k)*	20	
		ab. *Booklet pane of 6 (mq)*	90	
254	**228**	5p multicoloured (a)	15	
		a. *Perf 15×14 (k)*	35	
255	**229**	6p multicoloured (a)	20	
		a. *Perf 15×14 (k)*	50	
256	**230**	7p multicoloured (a)	20	
		a. *Booklet pane of 6 (ac)*	90	
257	**231**	8p multicoloured (a)	25	
		a. *Booklet pane of 6 (f)*	1·50	
258	**232**	9p multicoloured (ae)	30	
		a. *Perf 15×14 (h)*	50	
		ab. *Booklet pane of 6 (h)*	2·75	
		ac. *'Ghost impression' from No.*		
		261a*		

216

233	10p multicoloured (a)			30	30
	a. Booklet pane of 6 (ac)			1·50	
	b. Perf 15×14 (l)			35	35
	ba. Booklet pane of 6 (l)			1·60	
234	11p multicoloured (be)			35	35
	a. Booklet pane of 6 (f)			1·75	
	b. Perf 15×14 (m)			40	45
	ba. Booklet pane of 6 (m)			1·75	
235	12p multicoloured (be)			50	40
	a. Perf 15×14 (hg)			60	60
	ab. Booklet pane of 6 (hq)			3·00	
236	13p multicoloured (b)			40	40
	a. Perf 15×14 (i)			60	60
237	14p multicoloured (b)			45	45
	a. Perf 15×14 (i)			75	75
	ab. Booklet pane of 6 (l)			2·25	
238	15p multicoloured (b)			45	45
	a. Perf 15×14 (mo)			45	45
	ab. Booklet pane of 6 (m)			2·25	
239	16p multicoloured (jo)			45	45
	a. Booklet pane of 6 (q)			2·25	
240	17p multicoloured (j)			50	50
241	18p multicoloured (p)			75	75
242	19p multicoloured (p)			80	80
243	20p black, silver and lemon (b)			60	60
	a. Perf 15×14 (k)			1·00	1·00
244	25p black and dull blue (d)			60	60
223	26p black, silver and carmine (p)			60	60
245	30p multicoloured (d)			90	90
	a. Perf 15×14 (k)			1·25	1·25
246	40p multicoloured (d)			1·25	1·25
	a. Perf 15×14 (m)			1·50	1·50
247	50p multicoloured (d)			1·50	1·50
	a. Perf 15×14 (m)			2·00	2·00
248	75p multicoloured (n)			2·25	1·75
249	£1 multicoloured (d)			3·25	3·00
250	£5 multicoloured (g)			15·00	12·00
	Set of 29			28·00	25·00
	First Day Covers (7)				27·00
	Presentation Packs (4)			29·00	
	Set of 11 Gutter Pairs (½p to 10p)			5·00	

*Examples of No. 258ac show an impression of the blue
ield) plate from the 12p value. The error was caused by an
pression of the 12p plate remaining on the transfer roller.

No. 258a only occurs in the £2.16 stamp booklet issued 27
ril 1984, No. 259b from the £3.12 booklet of 1 April 1986,
. 260b from the £3.60 booklet of 6 April 1987 and No. 261a
m the £2.16 booklet of 27 April 1984 and the £3.84 booklet
17 May 1988.

Nos. 252b first occurred in the £2.16 stamp booklet of 27
ril 1984, but was subsequently issued in sheets.

rintings: (a) 24.2.81; (b) 28.7.81; (c) 1.12.81; (d) 23.2.82; (e) 11.6.82;
(f) 19.4.83; (g) 17.11.83; (h) 27.4.84; (i) 15.11.84; (j) 25.10.85;
(k) 4.3.86; (l) 1.4.86; (m) 6.4.87; (n) 23.4.87; (o) 12.1.88; (p) 26.4.88;
(q) 17.5.88

late and Cylinder Nos.: ½p, 20p 1A, 1B, 1C, 1D, 1E, 1F, 1G, 1H (each
×3); 6p, 11p, 12p, 13p, 14p, 50p, 75p 1A, 1B, 1C, 1D, 1E, 1F, 1G, 1H
(each ×5); 10p 1A, 1B, 1C, 1D, 1E, 1F, 1G, 1H (each ×5), 2A–1A
(×4), 2B–1B (×4), 2C–1C (×4), 2D–1D (×4), 2E–1E (×4), 2F–1F
(×4), 2G–1G (×4), 2H–1H (×4); 25p 1A–1A, 1B–1B, 1C–1C, 1D–1D,
1E–1E, 1F–1F, 1G–1G, 1H–1H; 26p 1A, 1B, 1C, 1D, 1F, 1G, 1H

(each ×3); £1 1A, 1B, 1C, 1D, 1E, 1F, 1G, 1H (each ×6); £5
A1–1–1–1–1, B1–1–1–1–1, C1–1–1–1–1, D1–1–1–1–1; others 1A,
1B, 1C, 1D, 1E, 1G, 1H (each ×4)

Sheets: £1 25 (5×5): £5 10 (5×2) others 50 (10×5)

Imprint: Right-hand corner, bottom margin

Withdrawn: 31.12.85 ½p; 30.4.87 £1; 31.3.90 1p to 10p; 31.1.91 11p
to 20p; 31.3.91 25p to 75p; 30.4.97 £5

251 Knight of Hambye slaying Dragon

252 Servant slaying Knight and awaiting Execution

253 St. Brelade celebrating Easter on Island

254 Island revealing itself as Huge Fish

Europa. Folklore

(Des Jennifer Toombs. Litho Questa)

1981 (7 APR). Perf 14½ (C)

275	**251**	10p multicoloured		25	25
276	**252**	10p multicoloured		25	25
		a. Horiz pair. Nos. 275/6		55	55
277	**253**	18p multicoloured		50	50
278	**254**	18p multicoloured		50	50
		a. Horiz pair. Nos. 277/8		1·10	1·10
275/8		Set of 4		1·50	1·40
		First Day Cover			1·60
		Presentation Pack		2·00	

Legends: 10p, Slaying of the Dragon of Lawrence by the
Knight of Hambye; 18p, Voyages of St. Brelade.

Plate Nos.: 10p 1A, 1B, 1C, 1D, 1E, 1F, 1G, 1H (each ×6); 18p 1A, 1B,
1C, 1D, 1E, 1F, 1G, 1H (each ×5)

Sheets: 20 (4×5). The two designs of each value were each printed
together, se-tenant, in horizontal pairs throughout

Imprint: Central, left-hand margin

Quantities sold: 10p 3,459,902; 18p 2,494,444

Withdrawn: 30.4.82

255 Harbour by Gaslight

256 Quay

257 Royal Square

258 Halkett Place

259 Central Market

150th Anniversary of Gas Lighting in Jersey

(Des R. Granger Barrett. Photo Courvoisier)

1981 (22 MAY). *Granite paper. Perf* 11½ (C)

279	**255**	7p multicoloured	. . . .	25	25
280	**256**	10p multicoloured	. . . .	30	30
281	**257**	18p multicoloured	. . . .	45	45
282	**258**	22p multicoloured	. . . .	55	55
283	**259**	25p multicoloured	. . . .	65	65
279/83		*Set of 5*	. . . .	2·00	2·00
		First Day Cover			2·00
		Presentation Pack		2·25	

Cylinder Nos.: All values A1–1–1–1–1, B1–1–1–1–1, C1–1–1–1–1, D1–1–1–1–1

Sheets: 20 (5×4)

Imprint: Left-hand corner, bottom margin

Quantities sold: 7p 1,433,090; 10p 1,416,051; 18p 384,043; 22p 417,191; 25p 333,402

Withdrawn: 31.5.82

260 Prince Charles and Lady Diana Spencer

Royal Wedding

(Des Jersey P.O. and Courvoisier. Photo Courvoisier)

1981 (28 JULY). *Granite paper. Perf* 11½ (C)

284	**260**	10p multicoloured	. . . .	75	7
285		25p multicoloured	. . . .	1·75	1·7
284/5		*Set of 2*	. . . .	2·50	2·5
		First Day Cover			4·0
		Presentation Pack		4·00	

Cylinder Nos.: Both values A1–1–1–1–1, B1–1–1–1–1

Sheets: 20 (5×4)

Imprint: Left-hand corner, bottom margin

Quantities sold: 10p 935,571; 25p 580,597

Withdrawn: 31.7.82

261 Christmas Tree in Royal Square

262 East Window, Parish Church, St. Helier

263 Boxing Da Meet of Jersey Drag Hun

Christmas

(Des A. Copp. Litho Questa)

1981 (29 SEPT). *Perf* 14½ (C)

286	**261**	7p multicoloured	. . . .	25	
287	**262**	10p multicoloured	. . . .	40	
		a. *Black (face value, inscr and choir) printed double*			
288	**263**	18p multicoloured	. . . .	50	
286/8		*Set of 3*	. . . .	1·00	1·
		First Day Cover			1·
		Presentation Pack		1·60	
		Postcards (Set of 3)		1·00	3·

Plate Nos.: All values 1A, 1B, 1C, 1D, 1E, 1F, 1G, 1H (each ×5)

Sheets: 20 (4×5)

Imprint: Central, left-hand margin

Quantities sold: 7p 1,437,626; 10p 1,386,934; 18p 422,693

Withdrawn: 30.9.82

264 Jersey, 16,000 B.C.

265 10,000 B.C.

66 7,000 B.C.   **267** 4,000 B.C.

uropa. Historic Events

(Des A. Copp. Litho Questa)

982 (20 APR). *Perf* 14 (C)

89	**264**	11p multicoloured	. . . .	30	30
90	**265**	11p multicoloured	. . . .	30	30
91	**266**	19½p multicoloured	. . . .	70	60
92	**267**	19½p multicoloured	. . . .	70	60
89/92		*Set of 4*	. . . .	1·75	1·60
		First Day Cover	. . . .		1·75
		Presentation Pack	. . . . . .	2·00	

Plate Nos.: All values 1A, 1B, 1C, 1D, 1E, 1F (each ×6)

Sheets: 20 (Nos. 289, 292, 4×5; others 5×4)

Imprint: Central, left-hand margin

Quantities sold: 11p (both designs) 3,414,424; 19½p (both designs) 2,307,769

Withdrawn: 30.4.83

68 Rollo, Duke of Normandy, William the Conqueror and 'Clameur de Haro'

269 John of England, Philippe Auguste of France and Siege of Rouen

0 Jean Martell (brandy merchant), early Still and view of Cognac

271 Victor Hugo, 'Le Rocher des Proscrits' (rock where he used to meditate) and Marine Terrace

272 Pierre Teilhard de Chardin (philosopher) and 'Maison Saint Louis' (science institute)

273 Père Charles Rey (scientist), anemo-tachymeter and The Observatory, St. Louis

Links with France

(Des R. Granger Barrett. Litho Questa)

1982 (11 JUNE–7 SEPT). *Perf* 14 (C)

293	**268**	8p multicoloured	. . . .	25	25
		a. Horiz pair. Nos. 293/4	. . . .	50	50
		b. Booklet pane. Nos. 293/4 each ×2 (7.9.82)	. . . .	1·00	
294	**269**	8p multicoloured	. . . .	25	25
295	**270**	11p multicoloured	. . . .	35	35
		a. Horiz pair. Nos. 295/6	. . . .	70	70
		b. Booklet pane. Nos. 295/6 each ×2 (7.9.82)	. . . .	1·40	
296	**271**	11p multicoloured	. . . .	35	35
297	**272**	19½p multicoloured	. . . .	60	60
		a. Horiz pair. Nos. 297/8	. . . .	1·25	1·25
		b. Booklet pane. Nos. 297/8 each ×2 (7.9.82)	. . . .	2·50	
		c. Black (face value and inscr) printed double	. . . .		
298	**273**	19½p multicoloured	. . . .	60	60
		c. Black (face value and inscr) printed double	. . . .		
293/8		*Set of 6*	. . . .	2·25	2·25
		First Day Cover	. . . .		2·25
		Presentation Pack	. . . . . .	2·50	

Each booklet pane has margins all round and text, in English or French, printed on the binding selvedge.

Nos. 297c and 298c come from an example of booklet pane No. 297b.

Plate Nos.: All values 1A, 1B, 1C, 1D (each ×4)

Sheets: 20 (4×5). The two designs of each value were printed together, *se-tenant*, in horizontal pairs throughout

Imprint: Central, left-hand margin

Quantities sold (sheet stamps): 8p (both designs) 2,019,854; 11p (both designs) 1,914,536; 19½p (both designs) 828,272

Withdrawn: 30.6.83 (sheets)

274 Sir William Smith and Proclamation of King George V, Jersey, 1910

275 Sir William Smith and Lord Baden-Powell at Boys' Brigade Display, 1903

276 Boys' Brigade Band, Jersey Liberation Parade, 1945

277 Lord and Lady Baden-Powell in St. Helier, 1924

278 Scouts in Summer Camp, Jersey

Youth Organizations

(Des A. Theobald. Photo Courvoisier)

1982 (18 NOV). *Granite paper. Perf 11½ (C)*

299	**274**	8p multicoloured		25	25
300	**275**	11p multicoloured		30	30
301	**276**	24p multicoloured		70	70
302	**277**	26p multicoloured		90	90
303	**278**	29p multicoloured		1·00	1·00
299/303		*Set of 5*		2·75	2·75
		First Day Cover			3·25
		Presentation Pack		3·50	

Nos. 299/303 were issued on the occasion of the 75th anniversary of the Boy Scout Movement, the 125th birth anniversary of Lord Baden-Powell and the centenary of the Boys Brigade (1983).

Cylinder Nos.: All values A1–1–1–1–1, B1–1–1–1–1, C1–1–1–1–1, D1–1–1–1–1

Sheets: 20 (11p, 26p 5×4; others 4×5)

Imprint: Lower left-hand margin

Quantities sold: 8p 1,006,110; 11p 1,006,206; 24p 242,482; 26p 255,359; 29p 244,746

Withdrawn: 30.11.83

279 H.M.S. *Tamar* with H.M.S. *Dolphin* at Port Egmont

280 H.M.S. *Dolphin* and H.M.S. *Swallow* off Magellan Strait

281 Discovering Pitcairn Island

282 Carteret taking possession of English Cove, New Zealand

283 H.M.S. *Swallow* sinking a Pirate, Macassar Strait

284 H.M.S. *Endymion* leading Convoy from West Indies

Jersey Adventurers (First Series). 250th Birth Anniv o Philippe de Carteret

(Des R. Granger Barrett. Litho Questa)

1983 (15 FEB). *Perf 14×14½ (C)*

304	**279**	8p multicoloured		25	2
		a. *Black (face value and inscr)* *printed double*			
305	**280**	11p multicoloured		30	3
		a. *Black (face value and inscr)* *printed double*			
306	**281**	19½p multicoloured		50	5
307	**282**	24p multicoloured		70	7
		a. *Black (face value and inscr)* *printed double*			
308	**283**	26p multicoloured		85	7
		a. *Black (face value and inscr)* *printed double*			
309	**284**	29p multicoloured		1·00	8
304/9		*Set of 6*		3·25	3·0
		First Day Cover			3·7
		Presentation Pack		4·50	

See also Nos. 417/21 and 573/8.

Plate Nos.: All values 1A, 1B, 1C, 1D, 1E, 1F (each ×6)

Sheets: 20 (4×5)

Imprint: Central, left-hand margin

Quantities sold: 8p 983,227; 11p 979,640; 19½p 377,535; 24 264,595; 26p 279,424; 29p 254,023

Withdrawn: 29.2.84

85 1969 5s. Legislative Chamber
Definitive

286 Royal Mace

87 1969 10s. Royal Court
Definitive showing Green
Border Error

288 Bailiff's Seal

Europa

(Des G. Drummond. Litho Questa)

983 (19 APR). *Perf* 14½ (C)

10	**285**	11p multicoloured	. . . .	50	50
		a. Horiz pair. Nos. 310/11	. . . .	1·00	1·00
11	**286**	11p multicoloured	. . . .	50	50
12	**287**	19½p multicoloured	. . . .	75	75
		a. Horiz pair. Nos. 312/13	. . . .	1·50	1·50
13	**288**	19½p multicoloured	. . . .	75	75
10/13		Set of 4	. . . .	2·25	2·25
		First Day Cover	. . . .		2·75
		Presentation Pack	. . . . . .	3·00	

Plate Nos.: Both values 1A, 1B, 1C, 1D, 1E, 1F (each ×6)

Sheets: 20 (4×5). The two designs of each value were printed
together, *se-tenant*, in horizontal pairs throughout

Imprint: Central, left-hand margin

Quantities sold: 11p (both designs) 2,973,691; 19½p (both designs)
1,301,579

Withdrawn: 30.4.84

89 Charles Le Geyt and
Battle of Minden

290 London to Weymouth
Mail Coach

291 P.O. Mail Packet
Chesterfield attacked
by French Privateer

292 Mary Godfray and the
Hue Street Post Office

293 Mail Steamer leaving St.
Helier Harbour

World Communications Year and 250th Birth Anniversary of Charles Le Geyt (first Jersey postmaster)

(Des A. Copp. Litho Questa)

1983 (21 JUNE). *Perf* 14 (C)

314	**289**	8p multicoloured	. . . .	25	25
315	**290**	11p multicoloured	. . . .	35	35
316	**291**	24p multicoloured	. . . .	75	75
317	**292**	26p multicoloured	. . . .	90	90
318	**293**	29p multicoloured	. . . .	1·10	1·10
314/18		Set of 5	. . . .	3·00	3·00
		First Day Cover	. . . .		3·50
		Presentation Pack	. . . .	3·25	

Plate Nos.: All values 1A, 1B, 1C, 1D (each ×5)

Sheets: 20 (4×5)

Imprint: Central, left-hand margin

Quantities sold: 8p 1,136,008; 11p 961,725; 24p 244,690; 26p
247,654; 29p 230,325

Withdrawn: 30.6.84

294 Assembly Emblem

13th General Assembly of the A.I.P.L.F. (Association Internationale des Parlementaires de Langue Francaise)

(Des A. Copp. Litho Questa)

1983 (21 JUNE). *Perf* 14½ (C)

319	**294**	19½p multicoloured	. . . .	75	75
		First Day Cover	. . . .		1·75
		Presentation Pack	. . . . . .	1·50	

Plate Nos.: 1A, 1B, 1C, 1D (each ×5)
Sheets: 20 (4×5)
Imprint: Central, left-hand margin
Quantity sold: 312,304
Withdrawn: 30.6.84

295 'Cardinal Newman'

296 'Incident in the French Revolution'

297 'Thomas Hardy'

298 'David with the Head of Goliath'

50th Death Anniversary of Walter Ouless (artist)

(Des and photo Courvoisier)

1983 (20 SEPT). *Granite paper. Perf 11½ (C)*

320	**295**	8p multicoloured	25	25
321	**296**	11p multicoloured	45	45
322	**297**	20½p multicoloured	85	85
323	**298**	31p multicoloured	1·25	1·25
320/3		*Set of* 4	2·50	2·50
		First Day Cover		3·00
		Presentation Pack	3·00	

Cylinder Nos.: All values A1, B1 (each ×5)
Sheets: 20 (4×5) 31p or (5×4) others
Imprint: Central, left-hand margin
Quantities sold: 8p 1,054,200; 11p 1,055,429; 20½p 424,049; 31p 216,128
Withdrawn: 30.9.84

299 Golden Lion Tamarin

300 Snow Leopard

301 Jamaican Boa

302 Round Island Gecko

303 Coscoroba Swan

304 St. Lucia Amazon

Wildlife Preservation Trust (Fourth Series)

(Des W. Oliver. Litho Questa)

1984 (17 JAN). *Perf 13½×14 (C)*

324	**299**	9p multicoloured	30	3
325	**300**	12p multicoloured	40	4
326	**301**	20½p multicoloured	70	7
327	**302**	26p multicoloured	1·10	1·1
328	**303**	28p multicoloured	1·25	1·2
329	**304**	31p multicoloured	1·25	1·2
324/9		*Set of* 6	4·50	4·5
		First Day Cover		5·0
		Presentation Pack	5·00	

Plate Nos.: 20½p, 28p 1B, 1C, 1E, 1F (each ×4); others 1A, 1B, 1C, 1 1E, 1F (each ×4)
Sheets: 20 (5×4)
Imprint: Central, left-hand margin
Quantities sold: 9p 1,229,713; 12p 1,365,973; 20½p 266,444; 2 239,180; 28p 255,205; 31p 221,422
Withdrawn: 31.1.85

305 C.E.P.T. 25th Anniversary Log

Europa

(Des J. Larrivière. Litho Questa)

1984 (12 MAR). *Perf* 14½×15 (C)

330	**305**	9p cobalt, ultramarine & black	30	30
331		12p light green, green and black	40	40
332		20½p rose-lilac, dp magenta & blk	70	70
330/2		*Set of 3*	1·25	1·25
		First Day Cover		1·75
		Presentation Pack	1·75	

Plate Nos.: All values 1A, 1B, 1C, 1D, 1E, 1F (each ×3)

Sheets: 20 (4×5)

Imprint: Central, left-hand margin

Quantities sold: 9p 1,352,245; 12p 1,388,802; 20½p 742,046

Withdrawn: 31.3.85

306 Map showing Commonwealth

Links with the Commonwealth

(Des A. Copp. Litho Questa)

1984 (12 MAR). *Sheet* 108×74 *mm. Perf* 15×14½ (C)

MS333	**306**	75p multicoloured	2·50	2·50
		First Day Cover		4·00
		Presentation Pack	4·00	

Quantity sold: 215,566

Withdrawn: 31.3.85

307 *Sarah Bloomshoft* at Demie de Pas Light, 1906

308 *Hearts of Oak* and *Maurice Georges*, 1949

309 *Elizabeth Rippon* and *Hanna*, 1949

310 *Elizabeth Rippon* and *Santa Maria*, 1951

311 *Elizabeth Rippon* and *Bacchus*, 1973

312 *Thomas James King* and *Cythara*, 1983

Centenary of the Jersey R.N.L.I. Lifeboat Station

(Des G. Palmer. Litho Questa)

1984 (1 JUNE). *Perf* 14½ (C)

334	**307**	9p multicoloured	40	40
335	**308**	9p multicoloured	40	40
336	**309**	12p multicoloured	50	50
337	**310**	12p multicoloured	50	50
338	**311**	20½p multicoloured	90	75
339	**312**	20½p multicoloured	90	75
334/9		*Set of 6*	3·25	3·00
		First Day Cover		4·50
		Presentation Pack	4·00	
		Postcard (as No. 339)	1·50	3·25

Plate Nos.: All values 1A, 1B, 1C, 1D, 1E, 1F (each ×5)

Sheets: 20 (4×5)

Imprint: Central, left-hand margin

Quantities sold: 9p (No. 334) 485,538; 9p (No. 335) 435, 647; 12p (No. 336) 534, 920; 12p (No. 337) 518,807; 20½p (No. 338) 298, 935; 20½p (No. 339) 290,945

Withdrawn: 30.6.85

313 Bristol Type 170 Freighter Mk 32

314 Airspeed A.S.57 Ambassador 2

315 De Havilland D.H.114 Heron 1B

316 De Havilland D.H.89A Dragon Rapide

40th Anniversary of International Civil Aviation Organization

(Des G. Drummond. Litho Questa)

1984 (24 JULY). *Perf* 14 (C)

340	**313**	9p multicoloured	30	30
341	**314**	12p multicoloured	40	40

342	**315**	26p multicoloured	....	1·10	1·10
343	**316**	31p multicoloured	....	1·40	1·40
340/3		Set of 4	....	3·00	3·00
		First Day Cover	....		4·00
		Presentation Pack	....	4·00	

Plate Nos.: All values 1A, 1B, 1C, 1D (each ×4)

Sheets: 20 (4×5)

Imprint: Central, left-hand margin

Quantities sold: 9p 563,394; 12p 751,072; 26p 262,640; 31p 193,703

Withdrawn: 31.7.85

317 'Robinson Crusoe leaves the Wreck'

318 'Edinburgh Castle'

319 'Maori Village'

320 'Australian Landscape'

321 'Waterhouse's Corner, Adelaide'

322 'Captain Cook at Botany Bay'

Links with Australia. Paintings by John Alexander Gilfillan

(Des R. Granger Barrett. Photo Courvoisier)

1984 (21 SEPT). *Granite paper. Perf* 11½×12 (C)

344	**317**	9p multicoloured	....	30	30
345	**318**	12p multicoloured	....	40	40
346	**319**	20½p multicoloured	....	75	75
347	**320**	26p multicoloured	....	95	95
348	**321**	28p multicoloured	....	1·00	1·00
349	**322**	31p multicoloured	....	1·10	1·10
344/9		Set of 6	....	4·00	4·00
		First Day Cover	....		4·25
		Presentation Pack	......	4·25	
		Postcards (Set of 3 as Nos. 347/9)	....	2·00	5·50

Cylinder Nos.: All values A1, B1 (each ×6)

Sheets: 20 (4×5)

Imprint: Central, left-hand margin

Quantities sold: 9p 541,384; 12p 635,192; 20½p 210,119; 26p 234,836; 28p 188,052; 31p 192,353

Withdrawn: 30.9.85

323 'B.L.C. St. Helier'

324 'Oda Mt Bingham'

Christmas. Jersey Orchids (First Series)

(Photo Courvoisier)

1984 (15 NOV). *Granite paper. Perf* 12×11½ (C)

350	**323**	9p multicoloured	....	50	4
351	**324**	12p multicoloured	....	75	6
350/1		Set of 2	....	1·25	1·0
		First Day Cover	....		1·7
		Presentation Pack	....	1·60	

See also Nos. 433/7, 613/17 and 892/7.

Cylinder Nos.: Both values A1, B1, C1, D1 (each ×6)
Sheets: 20 (4×5)
Imprint: Central, left-hand margin
Quantities sold: 9p 1,197,796; 12p 1,116,097
Withdrawn: 30.11.85

325 'Hebe off Corbière, 1874'

326 'The Gaspe engaging the Diomede'

327 'The Paddle-steamer London entering Naples, 1856'

328 'The Rambler entering Cape Town, 1840'

329 'St. Aubin's Bay from Mount Bingham, 1872'

Death Centenary of Philip John Ouless (artist)

(Photo Harrison)

1985 (26 FEB). *Perf* 14×15 (C)

352	**325**	9p multicoloured	....	30	30
353	**326**	12p multicoloured	....	40	40
354	**327**	22p multicoloured	....	80	80
355	**328**	31p multicoloured	....	1·40	1·40
356	**329**	34p multicoloured	....	1·50	1·50
352/6		*Set of* 5	....	4·00	4·00
		First Day Cover	....		5·00
		Presentation Pack	....	4·50	

Cylinder Nos.: 31p 1B (×5); others 1A, 1B (each ×5)
Sheets: 20 (4×5)
Imprint: Central, left-hand margin
Quantities sold: 9p 463,589; 12p 405,133; 22p 407,598; 31p 193,772; 34p 185,467
Withdrawn: 28.2.86

330 John Ireland (composer) and Faldouet Dolmen

331 Ivy St. Helier (actress) and His Majesty's Theatre, London

332 Claude Debussy (composer) and Elizabeth Castle

Europa. European Music Year

(Des Jennifer Toombs. Litho Questa)

1985 (23 APR). *Perf* 14 (C)

357	**330**	10p multicoloured	....	40	40
358	**331**	13p multicoloured	....	55	55
359	**332**	22p multicoloured	....	1·00	90
357/9		*Set of* 3	....	1·75	1·60
		First Day Cover	....		2·50
		Presentation Pack	....	2·50	

Plate Nos.: 10p 1A, 1B, 1C, 1D, 1E, 1F (each ×5); 13p 1A, 1C, 1D, 1E, 1F (each ×5); 22p 1A, 1B, 1D, 1E, 1F (each ×5)

Sheets: 20 (4×5)

Imprint: Central, left-hand margin

Quantities sold: 10p 916,040; 13p 766,179; 22p 620,375

Withdrawn: 30.4.86

Plate Nos.: All values 1A, 1B, 1C, 1D, 1E, 1F (each ×4)

Sheets: 20 (5×4)

Imprint: Central, left-hand margin

Quantities sold: 10p 943,351; 13p 944,724; 29p 175,365; 31p 183,551; 34p 175,842

Withdrawn: 30.5.86

333 Girls' Brigade

334 Girl Guides (75th anniversary)

338 *Duke of Normandy* at Cheapside

339 Saddletank at First Tower

335 Prince Charles and Jersey Youth Service Activities Base

336 Sea Cadet Corps

340 *La Moye* at Millbrook

341 *St Heliers* at St. Aubin

337 Air Training Corps

342 *St Aubyns* at Corbière

Jersey Western Railway

(Des G. Palmer. Photo Courvoisier)

1985 (16 JULY). *Granite paper. Perf* 11½ (C)

365	**338**	10p multicoloured		55	55
366	**339**	13p multicoloured		70	70
367	**340**	22p multicoloured		1·10	1·10
368	**341**	29p multicoloured		1·25	1·25
369	**342**	34p multicoloured		1·40	1·40
365/9		*Set of* 5		4·50	4·50
		First Day Cover			4·75
		Presentation Pack		5·00	

Cylinder Nos.: 10p, 13p A1, B1 (each ×5); others A1 (×5)

Sheets: 20 (4×5)

Imprint: Central, left-hand margin

Quantities sold: 10p 708,912; 13p 706,189; 22p 249,659; 29p 179,849; 34p 179,977

Withdrawn: 31.7.86

International Youth Year

(Des A. Theobald. Litho Questa)

1985 (30 MAY). *Perf* 14½×14 (C)

360	**333**	10p multicoloured		30	30
361	**334**	13p multicoloured		50	50
362	**335**	29p multicoloured		1·00	1·00
363	**336**	31p multicoloured		1·10	1·00
364	**337**	34p multicoloured		1·25	1·10
360/4		*Set of* 5		3·75	3·50
		First Day Cover			4·25
		Presentation Pack		4·00	

343 Memorial Window to Revd. James Hemery (former Dean) and St. Helier Parish Church

344 Judge Francis Jeune, Baron St. Helier, and Houses of Parliament

345 Silverware by Pierre Amiraux

346 Francis Voisin (merchant) and Russian Port

347 Robert Brohier, Schweppes Carbonation Plant and Bottles

348 George Ingouville, V.C., R.N., and Attack on Viborg

300th Anniversary of Huguenot Immigration

(Des R. Granger Barrett. Litho Questa)

1985 (10 SEPT). *Perf* 14 (C)

370	**343**	10p multicoloured	30	30
		a. Booklet pane of 4	1·10	
371	**344**	10p multicoloured	30	30
		a. Booklet pane of 4	1·10	
372	**345**	13p multicoloured	45	45
		a. Booklet pane of 4	1·75	
373	**346**	13p multicoloured	45	45
		a. Booklet pane of 4	1·75	
		ab. Black (face value and inscr) printed double		
374	**347**	22p multicoloured	75	75
		a. Booklet pane of 4	2·50	
		b. Black (inscr) printed double. .		
375	**348**	22p multicoloured	75	75
		a. Booklet pane of 4	2·50	
370/5		Set of 6	2·75	2·75
		First Day Cover.		4·00
		Presentation Pack	3·75	

Each booklet pane has margins all round and text printed on the binding selvedge.

Plate Nos.: 13p (No. 372) 1A, 1B, 1C, 1D (each ×4); 22p (No. 375) 1A, 1C, 1D (each ×5); others 1A, 1B, 1C, 1D (each ×5)

Sheets: 20 (4×5)

Imprint: Central, left-hand margin

Quantities sold (sheets): 10p (No. 370) 308,085; 10p (No. 371) 310,475; 13p (No. 372) 488,224; 13p (No. 373) 477,764; 22p (No. 374) 259,921; 22p (No. 375) 253,607

Withdrawn: 30.9.86 (sheets)

349 Howard Davis Hall, Victoria College

350 Schooner *Westward*

351 Howard Davis Park, St. Helier

352 Howard Davis Experimental Farm, Trinity

Thomas Davis (philanthropist) Commemoration

(Des A. Copp. Litho Cartor)

1985 (25 OCT). *Perf* 13½ (C)

376	**349**	10p multicoloured	40	40
377	**350**	13p multicoloured	60	60
378	**351**	31p multicoloured	1·10	1·10
379	**352**	34p multicoloured	1·25	1·25
376/9		Set of 4	3·00	3·00
		First Day Cover.		4·00
		Presentation Pack	4·00	

Plate Nos.: 10p 1A, 1B, 1C, 1D (each ×5); 13p 2A, 2B, 2C, 2D (each ×5); 31p 3A, 3B, 3C, 3D (each ×5); 34p 4A, 4B, 4C, 4D (each ×5)

Sheets: 20 (4×5)

Imprint: Central, left-hand margin

Quantities sold: 10p 939,104; 13p 831,351; 31p 170,020; 34p 156,653

Withdrawn: 31.10.86

353 'Amaryllis belladonna' (Pandora Sellars)

354 'A Jersey Lily' (Lily Langtry) (Sir John Millais)

Jersey Lilies

(Des C. Abbott. Litho Questa)

1986 (28 JAN). Perf 15×14½ (C)

380	**353**	13p multicoloured	....	75	75
381	**354**	34p multicoloured	....	1·75	1·75
380/1		Set of 2	....	2·50	2·50
		First Day Cover	....		2·75
		Presentation Pack	....	2·75	
MS382		140×96 mm. Nos. 380×4 and 381		4·25	4·25
		First Day Cover	....		5·25
		Presentation Pack	....	4·75	

Plate Nos.: 13p 1A, 1B, 1C, 1D, 1E, 1F, 1G, 1H (each ×6); 34p 1A, 1B, 1C, 1D (each ×5)

Sheets: 20 (4×5); (5×4) 34p

Imprint: Central, left-hand margin

Quantities sold: 13p 444,175; 34p 169,811; miniature sheet 157,575

Withdrawn: 31.1.87

355 King Harold, William of Normandy and Halley's Comet, 1066 (Bayeux Tapestry)

356 Lady Carteret, Edmond Halley, Map and Comet

357 Aspects of Communication in 1910 and 1986 on TV screens

Appearance of Halley's Comet

(Des Jennifer Toombs. Litho Cartor)

1986 (4 MAR). Perf 13½×13 (C)

383	**355**	10p multicoloured	....	40	4
384	**356**	22p multicoloured	....	1·00	1·0
385	**357**	31p multicoloured	....	1·40	1·4
383/5		Set of 3	....	2·50	2·5
		First Day Cover	....		2·7
		Presentation Pack	....	3·25	

Plate Nos.: All values 1A, 1B, 1C, 1D (each ×5)

Sheets: 20 (4×5)

Imprint: Central, left-hand margin

Quantities sold: 10p 552,062; 22p 245,111; 31p 182,390

Withdrawn: 31.3.87

358 Dwarf Pansy

359 Sea Stock

360 Sand Crocus

Europa. Environmental Conservation

(Des Pandora Sellars. Litho Questa)

1986 (21 APR). Perf 14½×14 (C)

386	**358**	10p multicoloured	....	40	4
387	**359**	14p multicoloured	....	75	7
388	**360**	22p multicoloured	....	1·10	1·1
386/8		Set of 3	....	2·00	2·0
		First Day Cover	....		2·5
		Presentation Pack	....	2·50	

Plate Nos.: 22p 1A, 1B, 1C, 1E, 1F (each ×5); others 1A, 1B, 1C, 1D, 1E, 1F (each ×5)

Sheets: 20 (5×4)

Imprint: Central, left-hand margin

Quantities sold: 10p 892,977; 14p 892,631; 22p 612,513

Withdrawn: 30.4.87

366 La Vallette

361 Queen Elizabeth II (from photo by Karsh)

60th Birthday of Queen Elizabeth II

(Photo Courvoisier)

1986 (21 APR). *Granite paper. Perf 14½* (C)

89	**361**	£1 multicoloured	3·25	3·25
		First Day Cover		4·00
		Presentation Pack	4·00	

No. 389 was retained in use as part of the current definitive eries until replaced by No. 500.

For a £2 value in this design see No. 491*b*.

Cylinder Nos.: A1, B1, C1, D1 (each ×6)

Sheets: 20 (4×5)

Imprint: Central, left-hand margin

Quantity sold: 431,591

Withdrawn: 31.5.90

50th Anniversary of the National Trust for Jersey

(Des A. Copp. Litho Cartor)

1986 (17 JUNE). *Perf* 13½×13 (C)

390	**362**	10p multicoloured		30	30
391	**363**	14p multicoloured		45	45
392	**364**	22p multicoloured		80	80
393	**365**	29p multicoloured		90	90
394	**366**	31p multicoloured		95	95
390/4		*Set of* 5		3·00	3·00
		First Day Cover			3·75
		Presentation Pack		4·00	

Plate Nos.: All values 1A, 1B, 1C, 1D (each ×5)

Sheets: 20 (4×5)

Imprint: Central, left-hand margin

Quantities sold: 10p 946,735; 14p 919,823; 22p 427,370; 29p 173,763; 31p 178,353

Withdrawn: 30.6.87

367 Prince Andrew and Miss Sarah Ferguson

Royal Wedding

(Des A. Copp. Litho Cartor)

1986 (23 JULY). *Perf* 13½ (C)

395	**367**	14p multicoloured		50	50
396		40p multicoloured		1·50	1·50
395/6		*Set of* 2		2·00	2·00
		First Day Cover			3·00
		Presentation Pack		3·00	

Plate Nos.: Both values 1A, 1B, 1C, 1D (each ×6)

Sheets: 20 (5×4)

Imprint: Central, left-hand margin

Quantities sold: 14p 991,943; 40p 267,312

Withdrawn: 31.7.87

362 Le Rât Cottage

363 The Elms (Trust Headquarters)

364 Morel Farm

365 Quétivel Mill

368 'Gathering Vraic'

369 'Driving Home in the Rain'

370 'The Miller'

371 'The Joy Ride'

372 'Tante Elizabeth'

Birth Centenary of Edmund Blampied (artist)

(Des A. Copp. Litho Questa)

1986 (28 AUG). *Perf* 14 (C)

397	**368**	10p multicoloured	40	40
398	**369**	14p black, brownish grey & lt bl	70	70
399	**370**	29p multicoloured	1·00	1·00
400	**371**	31p black, brownish grey and pale orange	1·25	1·25
401	**372**	34p multicoloured	1·40	1·40
397/401		*Set of 5*	4·25	4·25
		First Day Cover		5·00
		Presentation Pack	5·00	

Plate Nos.: 14p, 31p 1A, 1B, 1C, 1D (each ×3); others 1A, 1B, 1C, 1D (each ×5)

Sheets: 20 (4×5)

Imprint: Central, left-hand margin

Quantities sold: 10p 885,979; 14p 675,290; 29p 163,085; 31p 157,559; 34p 151,128

Withdrawn: 31.8.87

373 Island Map on Jersey Lily, and Dove holding Olive Branch

374 Mistletoe Wreath encircling European Robin and Dove

375 Christmas Cracker releasing Dove

Christmas. International Year of Peace

(Des G. Taylor. Litho Questa)

1986 (4 NOV). *Perf* 14½×14 (C)

402	**373**	10p multicoloured		40	40
403	**374**	14p multicoloured		60	60
404	**375**	34p multicoloured		1·25	1·25
402/4		*Set of 3*		2·00	2·00
		First Day Cover			3·25
		Presentation Pack		3·00	

Plate Nos.: All values 1A, 1B, 1C, 1D, 1E, 1F (each ×6)

Sheets: 20 (5×4)

Imprint: Central, left-hand margin

Quantities sold: 10p 947,614; 14p 940,123; 34p 169,269

Withdrawn: 30.11.87

Post Office Yearbook

1986 (4 NOV). *Comprises Nos.* 380/404

	Yearbook	30·00

Withdrawn: 31.1.88

376 *Westward* under Full Sail

377 T. B. Davis at the Helm

78 *Westward* overhauling *Britannia*

379 *Westward* fitting-out at St. Helier

Racing Schooner Westward

(Des A. Copp. Litho Cartor)

1987 (15 JAN). *Perf* 13½ (C)

05	**376**	10p multicoloured	40	40
06	**377**	14p multicoloured	60	60
07	**378**	31p multicoloured	1·25	1·10
08	**379**	34p multicoloured	1·40	1·25
05/8		Set of 4	3·25	3·00
		First Day Cover		4·50
		Presentation Pack	4·50	

Plate Nos.: All values 1A, 1B, 1C, 1D (each ×5)

Sheets: 20 (4×5)

Imprint: Central, left-hand margin

Quantities sold: 10p 519,330; 14p 370,229; 31p 173,046; 34p 158,754

Withdrawn: 31.1.88

380 De Havilland D.H.86 Dragon Express *Belcroute Bay*

381 Boeing 757 and Douglas DC-9-15

382 Britten Norman "long nose" Trislander and Islander

383 Shorts 330 and Vickers Viscount 800

384 B.A.C. One Eleven 500 and Handley Page H.P.R.7 Dart Herald

50th Anniversary of Jersey Airport

(Des G. Palmer. Litho Questa)

1987 (3 MAR). *Perf* 14 (C)

409	**380**	10p multicoloured	30	30
410	**381**	14p multicoloured	50	50
411	**382**	22p multicoloured	70	70
412	**383**	29p multicoloured	1·10	1·10
413	**384**	31p multicoloured	1·25	1·25
409/13		Set of 5	3·50	3·50
		First Day Cover		5·00
		Presentation Pack	4·50	

Plate Nos.: All values 1A, 1B, 1C, 1D (each ×4)

Sheets: 20 (4×5)

Imprint: Central, left-hand margin

Quantities sold: 10p 313,733; 14p 281,226; 22p 368,486; 29p 155,159; 31p 167,709

Withdrawn: 31.3.88

385 St. Mary and St. Peter's Roman Catholic Church

386 Villa Devereux, St. Brelade

387 Fort Regent Leisure Centre, St. Helier

Europa. Modern Architecture

(Des A. Copp. Litho Questa)

1987 (23 APR). *Perf* 15×14 (C)

414	**385**	11p multicoloured	45	45
415	**386**	15p multicoloured	65	65
416	**387**	22p multicoloured	90	90
414/16		Set of 3	1·75	1·75
		First Day Cover		3·00
		Presentation Pack	3·00	

Plate Nos.: 11p, 15p 1A, 1B, 1C, 1D, 1E, 1F, 1G, 1H, 1I, 1J (each ×6); 22p 1A, 1B, 1C, 1D, 1E, 1F, 1G, 1H (each ×6)

Sheets: 10 (2×5)

Imprint: Central, left-hand margin

Quantities sold: 11p 847,735; 15p 883,825; 22p 467,615

Withdrawn: 30.4.88

388 H.M.S. *Racehorse* and H.M.S. *Carcass* (bomb-ketches) trapped in Arctic

389 H.M.S. *Alarm* on Fire, Rhode Island

390 H.M.S. *Arethusa* wrecked off Ushant

391 H.M.S. *Rattlesnake* stranded on Isle de Trinidad

392 Mont Orgueil Castle and Fishing Boats

Jersey Adventurers (Second Series). Philippe D'Auvergne

(Des R. Granger Barrett. Litho Questa)

1987 (9 JULY). *Perf* 14 (C)

417	**388**	11p multicoloured	40	40
418	**389**	15p multicoloured	50	50
419	**390**	29p multicoloured	90	90
420	**391**	31p multicoloured	1·00	1·00
421	**392**	34p multicoloured	1·10	1·10
417/21		*Set of* 5	3·50	3·50
		First Day Cover		4·50
		Presentation Pack	4·25	

See also Nos. 501/6 and 539/44.

Plate Nos.: All values 1A, 1B, 1C, 1D (each ×4)

Sheets: 20 (4×5)

Imprint: Central, left-hand margin

Quantities sold: 11p 694,506; 15p 897,162; 29p 138,711; 31p 144,518; 34p 140,968

Withdrawn: 31.7.88

393 Grant of Lands to Normandy, 911 and 933

394 Edward the Confessor and Duke Robert I of Normandy landing on Jersey, 1030

395 King William's Coronation, 1066, and Fatal Fall, 1087

396 Death of William Rufus, 1100, and Battle of Tinchebrai, 1106

397 Civil War between Matilda and Stephen, 1135–41

398 Henry inherits Normandy, 1151: John asserts Ducal Rights in Jersey, 1213

900th Death Anniversary of William the Conqueror

(Des Jennifer Toombs. Litho Cartor)

1987 (9 SEPT–16 OCT). *Perf* 13½ (C)

422	**393**	11p multicoloured (*a*)	40	40
		a. *Booklet pane of* 4 (*b*)	1·60	
423	**394**	15p multicoloured (*a*)	45	45
		a. *Booklet pane of* 4 (*b*)	2·00	
424	**395**	22p multicoloured (*a*)	80	80
		a. *Booklet pane of* 4 (*b*)	3·25	

25	**396**	29p multicoloured (a)	95	95
		a. Booklet pane of 4 (b)	4·00	
26	**397**	31p multicoloured (a)	1·10	1·10
		a. Booklet pane of 4 (b)	4·50	
27	**398**	34p multicoloured (a)	1·25	1·25
		a. Booklet pane of 4 (b)	5·50	
22/7		Set of 6	4·50	4·50
		First Day Cover		5·50
		Presentation Pack	5·25	

Each booklet pane has margins all round and text printed on the binding selvedge.

Printings: (a) 9.9.87; (b) 16.10.87

Plate Nos.: All values 1A, 1B, 1C, 1D (each ×6)

Imprint: Central, left-hand margin

Quantities sold (sheets): 11p 869,726; 15p 968,815; 22p 217,160; 29p 139,905; 31p 147,527; 34p 143,684

Withdrawn: 30.9.88 (sheets)

399 'Grosnez Castle'

400 'St. Aubin's Bay'

401 'Mont Orgueil Castle'

402 'Town Fort and Harbour, St. Helier'

403 'The Hermitage'

Christmas. Paintings by John Le Capelain

(Photo Courvoisier)

1987 (3 NOV). Granite paper. Perf 11½ (C)

428	**399**	11p multicoloured	40	40
429	**400**	15p multicoloured	60	60
430	**401**	22p multicoloured	80	80
431	**402**	31p multicoloured	1·10	1·10
432	**403**	34p multicoloured	1·25	1·25
428/32		Set of 5	3·75	3·75
		First Day Cover		4·50
		Presentation Pack	4·75	

Cylinder Nos.: 11p, 15p, 22p A1, B1 (each ×6); 31p, 34p A1 (×6)

Sheets: 20 (5×4)

Imprint: Central, left-hand margin

Quantities sold: 11p 951,916; 15p 874,209; 22p 371,992; 31p 154,824; 34p 145,550

Withdrawn: 30.11.88

Post Office Yearbook

1987 (3 NOV). Comprises Nos. 272 and 405/32

Yearbook	25·00

Withdrawn: 28.2.89

404 Cymbidium pontac

405 Odontioda Eric Young

406 Lycaste auburn Seaford and Ditchling

407 Odontoglossum St. Brelade

408 Cymbidium mavourneen Jester

Jersey Orchids (Second Series)

(Litho Questa)

1988 (12 JAN). Perf 14 (C)

433	**404**	11p multicoloured	50	50
434	**405**	15p multicoloured	60	60
435	**406**	29p multicoloured	1·00	1·00
436	**407**	31p multicoloured	1·10	1·10
437	**408**	34p multicoloured	1·25	1·25
433/7		Set of 5	4·00	4·00
		First Day Cover		5·00
		Presentation Pack	4·50	

Plate Nos.: All values 1A, 1B, 1C, 1D (each ×5)

Sheets: 20 (4×5) 11p, 29p, 34p; (5×4) 15p, 31p

Imprint: Central, left-hand margin

Quantities sold: 11p 558,185; 15p 374,117; 29p 143,613; 31p 162,096; 34p 151,193

Withdrawn: 31.1.89

409 Labrador Retriever

410 Wire-haired Dachshund

411 Pekingese

412 Cavalier King Charles Spaniel

413 Dalmatian

Centenary of Jersey Dog Club

(Des P. Layton. Litho Questa)

1988 (2 MAR). *Perf* 14 (C)

438	**409**	11p multicoloured	50	50
439	**410**	15p multicoloured	75	75
440	**411**	22p multicoloured	1·10	1·10
441	**412**	31p multicoloured	1·10	1·10
442	**413**	34p multicoloured	1·25	1·25
438/42		Set of 5	4·25	4·25
		First Day Cover		5·00
		Presentation Pack	4·75	

Plate Nos.: All values 1A, 1B, 1C, 1D (each ×4)

Sheets: 20 (4×5)

Imprint: Central, left-hand margin

Quantities sold: 11p 371,583; 15p 374,953; 22p 178,132; 31p 154,530; 34p 146,628

Withdrawn: 31.3.89

414 De Havilland D.H.C.7 Dash Seven, London Landmarks and Jersey Control Tower

415 Weather Radar and Jersey Airport Landing System

416 Hydrofoil, St. Malo, and Elizabeth Castle, St. Helier

417 Port Control Tower and Jersey Radio Maritime Communication Centre, La Moye

Europa. Transport and Communications

(Des A. Copp. Litho Cartor)

1988 (26 APR). *Perf* 14×13½ (*horiz*) or 13½×14 (*vert*), both comb

443	**414**	16p multicoloured	50	50
444	**415**	16p multicoloured	50	50
445	**416**	22p multicoloured	90	90
446	**417**	22p multicoloured	90	90
443/6		Set of 4	2·50	2·50
		First Day Cover		3·25
		Presentation Pack	3·25	

Plate Nos.: Nos. 443/4, 446 1A, 1B, 1C, 1D (each ×5); No. 445 1A, 1B, 1C, 1D (each ×6)

Sheets: 20 (4×5) Nos. 443, 445; (5×4) Nos. 444, 446

Imprint: Central, left-hand margin

Quantities sold: 16p (No. 443) 881,324; 16p (No. 444) 865,868; 22p (No. 445) 509,086; 22p (No. 446) 510,104

Withdrawn: 30.4.89

418 Rodriguez Fody

419 Volcano Rabbit

420 White-faced Marmoset

421 Ploughshare Tortoise

422 Mauritius Kestrel

Wildlife Preservation Trust (Fifth Series)

(Des W. Oliver. Litho Cartor)

1988 (6 JULY). *Perf* 13½×14 (*vert*) *or* 14×13½ (*horiz*), *both comb*

447	**418**	12p multicoloured	55	55
448	**419**	16p multicoloured	70	70
449	**420**	29p multicoloured	1·10	1·10
450	**421**	31p multicoloured	1·25	1·25
451	**422**	34p multicoloured	1·40	1·40
447/51		Set of 5	4·50	4·50
		First Day Cover		5·25
		Presentation Pack	5·25	

Plate Nos.: All values 1A, 1B, 1C, 1D (each ×6)

Sheets: 20 (5×4) 12p, 29p, 34p; (4×5) 16p, 31p

Imprint: Central, left-hand margin

Quantities sold: 12p 875,722; 16p 969,800; 29p 146,567; 31p 155,348; 34p 151,723

Withdrawn: 31.7.89

423 Rain Forest Leaf Frog, Costa Rica

424 Archaeological Survey, Peru

425 Climbing Glacier, Chile

426 Red Cross Centre, Solomon Islands

427 Underwater Exploration, Australia

428 *Zebu* (brigantine) returning to St. Helier

Operation Raleigh

(Des V. Ambrus. Photo Courvoisier)

1988 (27 SEPT). *Granite paper. Perf* 12 (C)

452	**423**	12p multicoloured	45	45
453	**424**	16p multicoloured	55	55
454	**425**	22p multicoloured	80	80
455	**426**	29p multicoloured	1·00	1·00
456	**427**	31p multicoloured	1·10	1·10
457	**428**	34p multicoloured	1·25	1·25
452/7		Set of 6	4·50	4·50
		First Day Cover		5·00
		Presentation Pack	5·25	

No. 455 also commemorates the 40th anniversary of the World Health Organization.

Cylinder Nos.: All values A1 (×5)

Sheets: 20 (5×4)

Imprint: Central, left-hand margin

Quantities sold: 12p 706,594; 16p 507,077; 22p 226,791; 29p 127,647; 31p 127,658; 34p 128,055

Withdrawn: 30.9.89

429 St. Clement

430 St. Ouen

431 St. Brelade

432 St. Lawrence

Christmas. Jersey Parish Churches (First Series)

(Des P. Layton. Litho B.D.T.)

1988 (15 NOV). *Perf* 13½ (C)

458	**429**	12p multicoloured	. . . .	35	35
459	**430**	16p multicoloured	. . . .	60	60
460	**431**	31p multicoloured	. . . .	1·00	1·00
461	**432**	34p multicoloured	. . . .	1·10	1·10
458/61		*Set of* 4	. . . .	2·75	2·75
		First Day Cover			3·50
		Presentation Pack		4·00	
		Postcards (set of 4)	. . . . . .	2·25	6·00

See also Nos. 535/8 and 597/600.

Plate Nos.: All values 1A, 1B, 1C, 1D (each ×5)

Sheets: 20 (4×5)

Imprint: Central, left-hand margin

Quantities sold: 12p 964,161; 16p 917,883; 31p 170,477; 34p 159,688

Withdrawn: 30.11.89

Post Office Yearbook

1988 (15 NOV). *Comprises Nos.* 266a/b, 268a *and* 433/61

Yearbook . . . . 28·00

Withdrawn: 23.10.89

433 Talbot 'Type 4 CT Tourer', 1912

434 De Dion 'Bouton Type 1-D', 1920

435 Austin 7 'Chummy', 1926

436 Ford 'Model T', 1926

437 Bentley 8 Litre, 1930

438 Cadillac '452A-V16 Fleetwood Sports Phaeton', 1931

Vintage Cars (First Series)

(Des A. Copp. Litho Questa)

1989 (31 JAN). *Perf* 14 (C)

462	**433**	12p multicoloured	. . . .	40	4
463	**434**	16p multicoloured	. . . .	60	6
464	**435**	23p multicoloured	. . . .	75	7
		a. Black (*inscr etc*) *printed double*			
465	**436**	30p multicoloured	. . . .	90	9
466	**437**	32p multicoloured	. . . .	1·10	1·1
467	**438**	35p multicoloured	. . . .	1·25	1·2
462/7		*Set of* 6	. . . .	4·50	4·5
		First Day Cover			5·5
		Presentation Pack		5·00	

See also Nos. 591/6 and 905/10.

Plate Nos.: 12p, 30p 1A, 1B (each ×4); 16p, 32p 1C, 1D (each ×4 23p, 35p 1A, 1B, 1C, 1D (each ×4)

Sheets: 20 (4×5)

Imprint: Central, left-hand margin

Quantities sold: 12p 253,257; 16p 230,695; 23p 228,895; 3C 130,974; 32p 144,798; 35p 148,189

Withdrawn: 31.1.90

439 Belcroute Bay

440 High Street, St. Aubin

441 Royal Jersey Go Course

442 Portelet Bay

443 Les Charrières D'Anneport

444 St. Helier Marina

445 Sand Yacht Racing, St. Ouen's Bay

446 Rozel Harbour

447 St. Aubin's Harbour

448 Jersey Airport

449 Corbière Lighthouse

450 Val de la Mare

451 Elizabeth Castle

452 Greve de Lecq

453 Samarès Manor

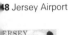

454 Bonne Nuit Harbour

455 Grosnez Castle

456 Augrès Manor

457 Central Market

458 St. Brelade's Bay

459 St. Ouen's Manor

460 La Hougue Bie

461 Mont Orgueil Castle

462 Royal Square, St. Helier

463 Queen Elizabeth II (from photo by Karsh)

464 Arms of King George VI

Jersey Scenes

(Des G. Drummond (1p to 75p). Photo Courvoisier (£2), Litho Questa (£4), B.D.T. (others))

1989 (21 MAR)–**95**. *Perf* 11½×12 (£2), 15×14 (£4) *or* 13×13½ (*others*), all comb

468	**439**	1p multicoloured (a)	....	10	10
469	**440**	2p multicoloured (a)	....	10	10
470	**441**	4p multicoloured (a)	....	10	10
		a. Booklet pane of 6 with margins all round (d)	......	60	
471	**442**	5p multicoloured (a)	....	15	15
		a. Booklet pane of 6 with margins all round (f)	......	75	
472	**443**	10p multicoloured (a)	....	30	30
473	**444**	13p multicoloured (a)	....	40	40
474	**445**	14p multicoloured (ae)	....	40	40
		a. Booklet pane of 6 with margins all round (d)	......	2·00	
		b. Booklet pane of 8 with margins all round (i)	......	2·75	
475	**446**	15p multicoloured (ae)	....	45	45
		a. Booklet pane of 6 with margins all round (f)	......	2·00	
476	**447**	16p multicoloured (ah)	....	50	50
		a. Booklet pane of 8 with margins all round (i)	......	3·50	
477	**448**	17p multicoloured (aj)	....	50	50
478	**449**	18p multicoloured (akm)	....	55	55
		a. Booklet pane of 6 with margins all round (d)	.....	2·50	
479	**450**	19p multicoloured (ano)	....	55	55
480	**451**	20p multicoloured (ae)	....	60	60
		a. Booklet pane of 6 with margins all round (f)	......	3·00	
481	**452**	21p multicoloured (b)	....	50	50
482	**453**	22p multicoloured (bh)	....	65	65
		a. Booklet pane of 8 with margins all round (i)	......	4·50	
483	**454**	23p multicoloured (bjkmo)	....	65	50
484	**455**	24p multicoloured (b)	....	65	65
485	**456**	25p multicoloured (b)	....	70	70
486	**457**	26p multicoloured (bh)	....	75	75
487	**458**	27p multicoloured (b)	....	80	80
488	**459**	30p multicoloured (c)	....	85	85
489	**460**	40p multicoloured (c)	....	90	90
490	**461**	50p multicoloured (c)	......	1·25	1·25
491	**462**	75p multicoloured (c)	....	2·25	2·25
491b	**463**	£2 multicoloured (g)	....	6·00	6·00
491c	**464**	£4 multicoloured (l)	....	8·00	8·25
468/91c		Set of 26	....	25·00	25·00
		First Day Covers (5)	......		30·00
		Presentation Packs (5)	....	26·00	

For £1 value as No. 491b see No. 389.

Printings: (a) 21.3.89; (b) 16.1.90; (c) 13.3.90; (d) 3.5.90; (e) 13.11.90; (f) 12.2.91; (g) 19.3.91; (h) 7.1.92; (i) 22.5.92; (j) 11.1.93; (k) 18.2.94; (l) 24.1.95; (m) 21.3.95; (n) 1.9.95; (o) 12.11.96

Cylinder or Plate Nos.: £2 A1, B1, C1, D1 (each ×6); £4 1A (×5); others 1A, 1B, 1C, 1D, 1E, 1F (each ×4)

Sheets: £2 20 (4×5); £4 10 (5×2); others 50 (5×10)

Imprint: Left-hand corner, bottom margin (£4) or central, left-hand margin (others)

Withdrawn: 31.3.99 1p to £2

465 Agile Frog

466 *Heteropterus morpheus* (butterfly)

467 Barn Owl

468 Green Lizard

Endangered Jersey Fauna

(Des W. Oliver. Litho Cartor)

1989 (25 APR). *Perf* 13½×13 (*Nos. 492 and 495*), 13×13½ (*No. 493*) *or* 13½×14 (*No. 494*), *all comb*

492	**465**	13p multicoloured	....	1·00	1·00
493	**466**	13p multicoloured	....	1·00	1·00
494	**467**	17p multicoloured	....	1·10	1·10
495	**468**	17p multicoloured	....	1·10	1·10
492/5		*Set of* 4	....	3·75	3·75
		First Day Cover	....		4·75
		Presentation Pack	....	4·25	

Plate Nos.: All designs 1A, 1B, 1C, 1D (each ×5)

Sheets: 20 (4×5) Nos. 492 and 495; (5×4) Nos. 493/4

Imprint: Central, left-hand margin

Quantities sold: 13p (No. 492) 650,061; 13p (No. 493) 589,329; 17p (No. 494) 552,582; 17p (No. 495) 515,262

Withdrawn: 30.4.90

469 Toddlers' Toys

470 Playground Games

471 Party Games

472 Teenage Sports

Europa. Children's Toys and Games

(Des from clay plaques by Clare Luke. Litho Questa)

1989 (25 APR). *Perf* 14 (C)

496	**469**	17p multicoloured	....	50	50
497	**470**	17p multicoloured	....	50	50
498	**471**	23p multicoloured	....	90	90
499	**472**	23p multicoloured	....	90	90
496/9		*Set of* 4	....	2·50	2·50
		First Day Cover	....		3·00
		Presentation Pack	....	3·25	

Plate Nos.: All designs 1A, 1B, 1C, 1D, 1E, 1F (each ×4)

Sheets: 20 (4×5)

Imprint: Central, left-hand margin

Quantities sold: 17p (No. 496) 473,930; 17p (No. 497) 471,124; 23p (No. 498) 424,212; 23p (No. 499) 424,340

Withdrawn: 30.4.90

473 Queen Elizabeth II and Royal Yacht *Britannia* in Elizabeth Harbour

Royal Visit

(Des A. Copp. Litho Questa)

1989 (24 MAY). *Perf* 14½ (C)

500	**473**	£1 multicoloured	....	3·00	3·2
		First Day Cover	....		4·0
		Presentation Pack	....	4·00	

No. 500 was retained in use as part of the current definitiv series until replaced by No. 634.

Sheets: 20 (4×5)

Imprint: Central, left-hand margin

Withdrawn: 30.6.94

474 Philippe D'Auvergne presented to Louis XVI, 1786

475 Storming the Bastille, 1789

238

JERSEY 23

FRENCH REVOLUTION

6 Marie de Bouillon and
Revolutionaries, 1790

JERSEY 30

FRENCH REVOLUTION

477 Auvergne's
Headquarters at Mont
Orgueil, 1795

JERSEY 32

FRENCH REVOLUTION

'8 Landing Arms for
Chouan Rebels, 1796

JERSEY 35

FRENCH REVOLUTION

479 The Last Chouan
Revolt, 1799

**:entenary of the French Revolution. Philippe
Auvergne**

(Des V. Ambrus. Litho Cartor)

:89 (7 JULY). *Perf* 13½ (C)

1	**474**	13p multicoloured	. . . .	45	45
		a. *Booklet pane of 4*		1·25	
2	**475**	17p multicoloured	. . . .	60	60
		a. *Booklet pane of 4*		2·00	
3	**476**	23p multicoloured	. . . .	80	80
		a. *Booklet pane of 4*		2·50	
4	**477**	30p multicoloured	. . . .	1·10	1·10
		a. *Booklet pane of 4*		4·25	
5	**478**	32p multicoloured	. . . .	1·25	1·25
		a. *Booklet pane of 4*		4·25	
6	**479**	35p multicoloured	. . . .	1·40	1·40
		a. *Booklet pane of 4*		4·75	
1/6		*Set of 6*		5·00	5·00
		First Day Cover			5·50
		Presentation Pack		5·50	

:Each booklet pane has margins all round and text printed on
e binding selvedge.
See also Nos. 539/44.

²late Nos.: All values 1A, 1B, 1C, 1D (each ×4)

:heets: 20 (5×4)

mprint: Central, left-hand margin

Quantities sold: 13p 637,422; 17p 840,904; 23p 408,967; 30p
  133,642; 32p 148,474; 35p 151,639

Withdrawn: 31.7.90

ERSEY 13

480 *St. Helier* off Elizabeth
Castle

JERSEY 17

481 *Caesarea II* off Corbière
Lighthouse

JERSEY 27

482 *Reindeer* in St. Helier
Harbour

JERSEY 32

483 *Ibex* racing *Frederica* off
Portelet

JERSEY 35

484 *Lynx* off Noirmont

***Centenary of Great Western Railway Steamer Service to
Channel Islands***

(Des G. Palmer. Litho Questa)

1989 (5 SEPT). *Perf* 13½×14 (C)

507	**480**	13p multicoloured	. . . .	40	40
508	**481**	17p multicoloured	. . . .	50	50
509	**482**	27p multicoloured	. . . .	1·00	1·00
510	**483**	32p multicoloured	. . . .	1·25	1·25
511	**484**	35p multicoloured	. . . .	1·40	1·40
507/11		*Set of 5*		4·00	4·00
		First Day Cover			4·75
		Presentation Pack		4·50	

Plate Nos.: 13p, 27p 1A, 1B (each ×4); 17p, 32p 1C, 1D (each ×4);
  35p 1A, 1B, 1C, 1D (each ×4)

Sheets: 20 (4×5)

Imprint: Central, left-hand margin

Quantities sold: 13p 265,382; 17p 294,992; 27p 135,226; 32p
  128,966; 35p 134,800

Withdrawn: 28.9.90

485 Gorey Harbour

486 La Corbière

487 Grève de Lecq

488 Bouley Bay

489 Mont Orgueil

150th Birth Anniversary of Sarah Louisa Kilpack (artist)

(Litho Enschedé)

1989 (24 OCT). *Perf* 13×12½ (C)

512	**485**	13p multicoloured	. . . .	40	40
513	**486**	17p multicoloured	. . . .	50	50
514	**487**	23p multicoloured	. . . .	1·00	1·00
515	**488**	32p multicoloured	. . . .	1·25	1·25
516	**489**	35p multicoloured	. . . .	1·40	1·40
512/16		*Set of* 5	. . . .	4·00	4·00
		First Day Cover			4·75
		Presentation Pack		4·50	

Plate Nos.: 13p, 17p 1A, 1B, 1C (each ×5); 23p, 32p, 35p 1A, 1B (each ×5)

Sheets: 20 (4×5)

Imprint: Central, left-hand margin

Quantities sold: 13p 649,308; 17p 571,503; 23p 159,487; 32p 138,562; 35p 137,950

Withdrawn: 31.10.90

Post Office Yearbook

1989 (24 OCT). *Comprises Nos.* 462/80 and 492/516

Yearbook . . . . 32·00

Sold out: 12.11.90

490 Head Post Office, Broad Street, 1969

491 Postal Headquarters, Mont Millais, 1990

492 Hue Street Post Office, 1815

493 Head Post Office, Halkett Place, 1890

Europa. Post Office Buildings

(Des P. Layton. Litho Cartor)

1990 (13 MAR). *Perf* 13½×14 (*vert*) or 14×13½ (*horiz*), bo︎
comb

517	**490**	18p multicoloured	. . . .	50	5︎
518	**491**	18p multicoloured	. . . .	50	5︎
519	**492**	24p multicoloured	. . . .	90	9︎
520	**493**	24p multicoloured	. . . .	90	9︎
517/20		*Set of 4*	. . . .	2·50	2·5︎
		First Day Cover			3·5︎
		Presentation Pack		4·25	

Plate Nos.: All designs 1A, 1B, 1C, 1D (each ×5)

Sheets: 20 (5×4) 18p; (4×5) 24p

Imprint: Central, left-hand margin

Quantities sold: 18p (No. 517) 596,221; 18p (No. 518) 595,918; 24︎ (No. 519) 400,441; 24p (No. 520) 406,656

Withdrawn: 31.3.91

494 'Battle of Flowers' Parade

495 Sports

6 Mont Orgueil
Castle and
German Under-
ground Hospital
Museum

497 Salon Culinaire

500 Radio Jersey
Broadcaster

501 Channel Television
Studio Cameraman

estival of Tourism

(Des A. Copp. Litho Enschedé)

90 (3 MAY). *Perf* 14×13½ (C)

?1	**494**	18p multicoloured	60	60
?2	**495**	24p multicoloured	75	75
?3	**496**	29p multicoloured	95	95
?4	**497**	32p multicoloured	1·00	1·00
?1/4		*Set of 4*	3·00	3·00
		First Day Cover		4·00
		Presentation Pack	4·00	
S525	151×100 mm. Nos. 521/4		3·00	3·00
		First Day Cover		4·75
		Presentation Pack	4·00	

Plate Nos.: 18p 1A, 1B, 1C, 1D, 1E (each ×5); 24p 1A, 1B, 1C, 1D
(each ×5); 29p 1A (×5); 32p 1A, 1B (each ×5)

Sheets: 20 (5×4)

Imprint: Central, left-hand margin

Quantities sold: 18p 630,610; 24p 252,670; 29p 168,528; 32p
127,334; miniature sheet 110,177

Withdrawn: 31.5.91

498 Early Printing Press and
Jersey Newspaper
Mastheads

499 Modern Press, and
Offices of *Jersey
Evening Post* in 1890
and 1990

International Literacy Year. Jersey News Media

(Des A. Copp. Litho Cartor)

1990 (26 JUNE). *Perf* 13½ (C)

526	**498**	14p multicoloured	55	55
527	**499**	18p multicoloured	60	60
528	**500**	34p multicoloured	1·10	1·10
529	**501**	37p multicoloured	1·10	1·10
526/9		*Set of 4*	3·00	3·00
		First Day Cover		3·50
		Presentation Pack	3·75	

Plate Nos.: All values 1A, 1B, 1C, 1D (each ×4)

Sheets: 20 (4×5)

Imprint: Central, left-hand margin

Quantities sold: 14p 926,906; 18p 795,733; 34p 121,842; 37p
129,468

Withdrawn: 30.6.91

502 British Aerospace
Hawk T.1

503 Supermarine Spitfire

504 Hawker Hurricane Mk I

505 Vickers-Armstrong
Wellington

506 Avro Type 683 Lancaster

50th Anniversary of Battle of Britain

(Des G. Palmer. Litho Questa)

1990 (4 SEPT). *Perf* 14 (C)

530	**502**	14p multicoloured	....	45	45
531	**503**	18p multicoloured	....	60	60
532	**504**	24p multicoloured	....	90	90
533	**505**	34p multicoloured	....	1·60	1·60
534	**506**	37p multicoloured	....	1·75	1·75
530/4		Set of 5	....	4·75	4·75
		First Day Cover	....		5·50
		Presentation Pack	....	5·50	

Plate Nos.: 14p, 34p 1A, 1B (each ×5); 18p, 37p 1C, 1D (each ×5); 24p 1A, 1B, 1C, 1D (each ×5)

Sheets: 20 (4×5)

Imprint: Central, left-hand margin

Quantities sold: 14p 495,815; 18p 519,684; 24p 206,541; 34p 136,330; 37p 134,747

Withdrawn: 30.9.91

507 St. Helier

508 Grouville

509 St. Saviour

510 St. John

Christmas. Jersey Parish Churches (Second Series)

(Des P. Layton. Litho B.D.T.)

1990 (13 NOV). *Perf* 13½ (C)

535	**507**	14p multicoloured	....	40	40
536	**508**	18p multicoloured	....	60	60

537	**509**	34p multicoloured	....	1·25	1·2
538	**510**	37p multicoloured	....	1·40	1·4
535/8		Set of 4	....	3·25	3·2
		First Day Cover	....		3·7
		Presentation Pack	....	4·00	
		Postcards (set of 4)	......	2·00	6·0

Plate Nos.: All values 1A, 1B, 1C, 1D (each ×5)

Sheets: 20 (4×5)

Imprint: Central, left-hand margin

Quantities sold: 14p 948,076; 18p 690,282; 34p 141,514; 37 147,468

Withdrawn: 30.11.91

Post Office Yearbook

1990 (13 NOV). *Comprises Nos.* 481/91 *and* 517/38

	Yearbook	....	32·00

Withdrawn: 30.11.91

511 Prince's Tower, La Hougue Bie

512 Auvergne's Arrest in Paris

513 Auvergne plotting against Napoleon

514 Execution of George Cadoudal

515 H.M.S. *Surly* (cutter) attacking French Convoy

516 Auvergne's Last Days in London

175th Death Anniversary of Philippe d'Auvergne

(Des V. Ambrus. Litho Cartor)

1991 (22 JAN). *Perf* 13½ (C)

539	**511**	15p multicoloured	....	50	
540	**512**	20p multicoloured	....	60	
541	**513**	26p multicoloured	....	80	

2	**514**	31p multicoloured	....	1·00	1·00
3	**515**	37p multicoloured	....	1·25	1·25
4	**516**	44p multicoloured	....	1·40	1·40
9/44		*Set of 6*	....	5·00	5·00
		First Day Cover	....		5·75
		Presentation Pack	....		5·75

Plate Nos.: All values 1A, 1B, 1C, 1D (each ×4)

Sheets: 20 (4×5)

Imprint: Central, left-hand margin

Quantities sold: 15p 709,403; 20p 454,921; 26p 159,902; 31p 140,379; 37p 341,103; 44p 153,157

Withdrawn: 31.1.92

17 'Landsat 5' and Thematic Mapper Image over Jersey

518 'ERS-1' Earth Resources Remote Sensing Satellite

9 'Meteosat' Weather Satellite

520 'Olympus' Direct Broadcasting Satellite

ropa. Europe in Space

(Des A. Copp. Litho Enschedé)

91 (19 MAR). *Perf* 14½×13 (C)

5	**517**	20p multicoloured	....	55	55
6	**518**	20p multicoloured	....	55	55
7	**519**	26p multicoloured	....	85	85
8	**520**	26p multicoloured	....	85	85
5/8		*Set of 4*	....	2·50	2·50
		First Day Cover	....		3·50
		Presentation Pack	....	3·50	

Plate Nos.: All designs 1A, 1B, 1C (each ×5)

Sheets: 20 (5×4)

Imprint: Central, left-hand margin

Quantities sold: 20p (No. 545) 682,799; 20p (No. 546) 690,871; 26p (No. 547) 442,476; 26p (No. 548) 439,415

Withdrawn: 31.3.92

521 1941 1d. Stamp (50th anniv of first Jersey postage stamp)

522 Steam Train (centenary of Jersey Eastern Railway extension to Gorey Pier)

523 Jersey Cow and Herd Book (125th anniv of Jersey Herd Book)

524 Stone-laying Ceremony (painting by P. Ouless) (150th anniv of Victoria Harbour)

525 Marie Bartlett and Hospital (250th anniversary of Marie Bartlett's hospital bequest)

Anniversaries

(Des A. Copp. Litho Cartor)

1991 (16 MAY). *Perf* 13½ (C)

549	**521**	15p multicoloured	....	40	40
550	**522**	20p multicoloured	....	60	60
551	**523**	26p multicoloured	....	80	80
552	**524**	31p multicoloured	....	90	90
553	**525**	53p multicoloured	....	1·75	1·75
549/53		*Set of 5*	....	4·00	4·00
		First Day Cover	....		5·00
		Presentation Pack	....	5·00	

Plate Nos.: All values 1A, 1B, 1C, 1D (each ×4)

Sheets: 20 (5×4)

Imprint: Central, left-hand margin

Quantities sold: 15p 618,479; 20p 608,585; 26p 245,772; 31p 133,604; 53p 135,394

Withdrawn: 30.5.92

526 *Melitaea cinxia*

527 *Euplagia quadripunctaria*

528 *Deilephilia porcellus*

529 *Inachis io*

Butterflies and Moths

(Des W. Oliver. Litho Enschedé)

1991 (9 JULY). *Perf* 13×12½ (C)

554	**526**	15p multicoloured	40	40
555	**527**	20p multicoloured	50	50
556	**528**	37p multicoloured	1·60	1·60
557	**529**	57p multicoloured	2·00	2·00
554/7		Set of 4	4·00	4·00
		First Day Cover		4·75
		Presentation Pack	4·50	

Plate Nos.: All values 1A, 1B, 1C (each ×4)

Sheets: 20 (4×5)

Imprint: Central, left-hand margin

Quantities sold: 15p 489,632; 20p 646,607; 37p 130,494; 57p 142,646

Withdrawn: 31.7.92

530 Drilling for Water, Ethiopia

531 Building Construction, Rwanda

532 Village Polytechnic, Kenya

533 Treating Leprosy, Tanzania

534 Ploughing, Zambia

535 Immunisation Clinic, Lesotho

Overseas Aid

(Des A. Theobald. Litho B.D.T.)

1991 (3 SEPT). *Perf* 13½×14 (C)

558	**530**	15p multicoloured	50	4
559	**531**	20p multicoloured	60	6
560	**532**	26p multicoloured	80	8
561	**533**	31p multicoloured	1·00	1·0
562	**534**	37p multicoloured	1·25	1·2
563	**535**	44p multicoloured	1·40	1·4
558/63		Set of 6	5·00	5·0
		First Day Cover		5·7
		Presentation Pack	5·75	

Plate Nos.: All values 1A, 1B (each ×4)

Sheets: 20 (4×5)

Imprint: Central, left-hand margin

Quantities sold: 15p 517,917; 20p 644,721; 26p 177,179; 3 115,769; 37p 111,112; 44p 142,024

Withdrawn: 30.9.92

536 'This is the Place for Me'

537 'The Island Come True'

244

8 'The Never
Bird'

539 'The Great
White Father'

543 Lapwing

544 Fieldfare

Winter Birds

(Des W. Oliver. Litho Cartor)

1992 (7 JAN). Perf 13½×14 (C)

568	**540**	16p multicoloured	55	55
569	**541**	22p multicoloured	80	80
570	**542**	28p multicoloured	90	90
571	**543**	39p multicoloured	1·40	1·40
572	**544**	57p multicoloured	1·90	1·90
568/72		Set of 5	5·00	5·00
		First Day Cover..........		5·50
		Presentation Pack........	5·75	

See also Nos. 635/9.

Plate Nos.: All values 1A, 1B, 1C, 1D (each ×4)
Sheets: 20 (5×4)
Imprint: Central, left-hand margin
Quantities sold: 16p 481,678; 22p 462,647; 28p 268,973; 39p
151,671; 57p 132,065
Withdrawn: 30.1.93

hristmas. Illustrations by Edmund Blampied for J. M.
arrie's 'Peter Pan'

(Litho Questa)

991 (5 NOV). Perf 14 (C)

54	**536**	15p multicoloured	40	40
5	**537**	20p multicoloured	65	65
6	**538**	37p multicoloured	1·25	1·25
7	**539**	53p multicoloured	1·60	1·60
4/7		Set of 4	3·50	3·50
		First Day Cover..........		4·25
		Presentation Pack........	4·50	

Sheets: 20 (5×4)
Imprint: Central, left-hand margin
Quantities sold: 15p 917,860; 20p 693,203; 37p 128,585; 53p
117,877
Withdrawn: 30.11.92

st Office Yearbook

991 (5 NOV). Comprises Nos. 491b and 539/67
Yearbook .... 32·00

Sold out: By 9.93

545 Shipping at Shanghai,
1860

546 Mesny's Junk running
Taiping Blockade,
1862

40 Pied Wagtail

541 Firecrest

542 Common
Snipe

547 General Mesny
outside River Gate,
1874

548 Mesny in Burma,
1877

549 Mesny and Governor Chang, 1882

550 Mesny in Mandarin's Sedan Chair, 1886

Jersey Adventurers (Third Series). 150th Birth Anniversary of William Mesny

(Des V. Ambrus. Litho Cartor)

1992 (25 FEB). *Perf* 13½ (C)

573	**545**	16p multicoloured	....	50	50
		a. Black printed double	......		
		b. Booklet pane of 4	....	1·50	
574	**546**	16p multicoloured	....	50	50
		a. Booklet pane of 4	....	1·50	
575	**547**	22p multicoloured	....	75	75
		a. Booklet pane of 4	....	2·00	
576	**548**	22p multicoloured	....	75	75
		a. Booklet pane of 4	....	2·00	
577	**549**	33p multicoloured	....	1·00	1·00
		a. Booklet pane of 4	....	3·00	
578	**550**	33p multicoloured	....	1·00	1·00
		a. Booklet pane of 4	....	3·00	
573/8		Set of 6	....	4·00	4·00
		First Day Cover	....		4·75
		Presentation Pack	....	4·75	

Each booklet pane has margins all round and text printed on the binding selvedge.

Plate Nos.: All values 1A, 1B, 1C, 1D (each ×4)

Sheets: 20 (4×5)

Imprint: Central, left-hand margin

Quantities sold: 16p (No. 573) 346,732; 16p (No. 574) 336,655; 22p (No. 575) 377,299; 22p (No. 576) 360,220; 33p (No. 577) 129,904; 33p (No. 578) 130,637

Withdrawn: 27.2.93 (sheets)

551 *Tickler* (brigantine)

552 *Hebe* (brig)

553 *Gemini* (barque)

554 *Percy Douglas* (full-rigged ship)

Jersey Shipbuilding

(Des A. Copp. Litho Questa)

1992 (14 APR). *Perf* 14 (C)

579	**551**	16p multicoloured	....	50	5
580	**552**	22p multicoloured	....	80	8
581	**553**	50p multicoloured	....	1·60	1·6
582	**554**	57p multicoloured	....	1·90	1·9
579/82		Set of 4	....	4·25	4·2
		First Day Cover	....		4·7
		Presentation Pack	....	4·75	
MS583		148×98 mm. Nos. 579/82	....	4·25	4·2
		First Day Cover	....		4·7
		Presentation Pack	....	4·75	

Plate Nos.: 16p 1A, 1B, 1C, 1D, 1E, 1F (each ×4); 22p, 57p 1A, 1B, 1 1D (each ×4); 50p 1A, 1B (each ×4)

Sheets: 20 (5×4)

Imprint: Central, left-hand margin

Quantities sold: 16p 673,830; 22p 462,972; 50p 138,158; 57 111,044; miniature sheet 126,594

Withdrawn: 30.4.93

555 John Bertram (ship owner) and Columbus

556 Sir George Carteret (founder of New Jersey)

557 Sir Walter Ralegh (founde of Virginia)

Europa. 500th Anniversary of Discovery of America Columbus

(Des V. Ambrus. Litho Questa)

1992 (14 APR). *Perf* 14×14½ (C)

584	**555**	22p multicoloured	....	70	
585	**556**	28p multicoloured	....	85	8
586	**557**	39p multicoloured	....	1·25	1·
584/6		Set of 3	....	2·50	2·
		First Day Cover	....		3·
		Presentation Pack	....	3·50	

Plate Nos.: 22p 1A, 1B (each ×5); 28p 1A, 1B, 1C, 1D (each ×5); 39p 1C, 1D (each ×5)

Sheets: 20 (4×5)

Imprint: Central, left-hand margin

Quantities sold: 22p 459,817; 28p 664,537; 39p 298,597

Withdrawn: 30.4.93

558 'Snow Leopards' (Allison Griffiths)

559 'Three Elements' (Nataly Miorin)

560 'Three Men in a Tub' (Amanda Crocker)

561 'Cockatoos' (Michelle Millard)

atik Designs

(Litho Questa)

992 (23 JUNE). *Perf* 14½ (C)

57	**558**	16p multicoloured	. . . .	50	50
58	**559**	22p multicoloured	. . . .	70	70
59	**560**	39p multicoloured	. . . .	1·25	1·25
60	**561**	57p multicoloured	. . . .	1·75	1·75
57/90		*Set of 4*	. . . .	3·75	3·75
		First Day Cover	. . . .		5·00
		Presentation Pack	. . . .	4·75	

Plate Nos.: 16p, 39p 1A, 1B (each ×4); 22p, 57p 1C, 1D (each ×4)

Sheets: 20 (5×4)

Imprint: Central, left-hand margin

Quantities sold: 16p 427,970; 22p 472,443; 39p 112,188; 57p 113,465

Withdrawn: 30.6.93

562 Morris Cowley 'Bullnose', 1925

563 Rolls Royce 20/25, 1932

564 Chenard and Walcker T5, 1924

565 Packard 900 series Light Eight, 1932

566 Lanchester 21, 1927

567 Buick 30 Roadster, 1913

Vintage Cars (Second Series)

(Des A. Copp. Litho Enschedé)

1992 (8 SEPT). *Perf* 13×12½ (C)

591	**562**	16p multicoloured	. . . .	35	35
592	**563**	22p multicoloured	. . . .	50	50
593	**564**	28p multicoloured	. . . .	80	80
594	**565**	33p multicoloured	. . . .	1·00	1·00
595	**566**	39p multicoloured	. . . .	1·25	1·25
596	**567**	50p multicoloured	. . . .	1·75	1·75
591/6		*Set of 6*	. . . .	5·00	5·00
		First Day Cover	. . . .		5·75
		Presentation Pack	. . . .	5·75	

Plate Nos.: All values 1A, 1B (each ×4)

Sheets: 20 (4×5)

Imprint: Central, left-hand margin

Quantities sold: 16p 434,984; 22p 426,734; 28p 290,202; 33p 134,477; 39p 124,759; 50p 127,917

Withdrawn: 30.9.93

568 Trinity

569 St. Mary

JERSEY Christmas 1992   JERSEY Christmas 1992

570 St. Martin   **571** St. Peter

Christmas. Jersey Parish Churches (Third Series)

(Des P. Layton. Litho B.D.T.)

1992 (3 NOV). *Perf* 13½ (C)

597	**568**	16p multicoloured	40	35
598	**569**	22p multicoloured	65	70
599	**570**	39p multicoloured	1·25	1·25
600	**571**	57p multicoloured	1·60	1·60
597/600		Set of 4	3·50	3·50
		First Day Cover		4·50
		Presentation Pack	4·50	
		Postcards (set of 4)	2·00	5·50

Plate Nos.: All values 1A, 1B, 1C, 1D (each ×5)

Sheets: 20 (4×5)

Imprint: Central, left-hand margin

Quantities sold: 16p 894,098; 22p 729,413; 39p 93,764; 57p 95,936

Withdrawn: 30.11.93

Post Office Yearbook

1992 (3 NOV). *Comprises Nos.* 568/600

Yearbook .... 35·00

Sold out: By 10.95

572 Farmhouse   **573** Trinity Church   **574** Daffodils and Cows

575 Jersey Cows   **576** Sunbathing   **577** Windsurfing

578 Crab (Queen's head at left)   **579** Crab (Queen's head at right)   **580** 'Singin' in the Rain' Float

581 'Dragon Dance' Float   **582** 'Bali, Morning of the World' Float   **583** 'Zulu Fantasy' Float

Booklet Stamps

(Des A. Copp. Litho B.D.T.)

1993 (11 JAN). *Perf* 13 (C)

601	**572**	(–) multicoloured	50	
		a. Booklet pane. Nos. 601/4, each ×2, with margins all round ..	4·50	
602	**573**	(–) multicoloured	50	
603	**574**	(–) multicoloured	50	
604	**575**	(–) multicoloured	50	
605	**576**	(–) multicoloured	60	
		a. Booklet pane. Nos. 605/8, each ×2, with margins all round ..	5·00	
606	**577**	(–) multicoloured	60	
607	**578**	(–) multicoloured	60	
608	**579**	(–) multicoloured	60	
609	**580**	(–) multicoloured	75	
		a. Booklet pane. Nos. 609/12, each ×2, with margins all round ...	6·50	
610	**581**	(–) multicoloured	75	
611	**582**	(–) multicoloured	75	
612	**583**	(–) multicoloured	75	
601/12		Set of 12	6·50	6
		First Day Cover		17
		Presentation Pack	9·00	

The above do not show face values, but are inscrib 'BAILIWICK POSTAGE PAID' (Nos. 601/4), 'U.K. MINIMU POSTAGE PAID' (Nos. 605/8) or 'EUROPE POSTAGE PA (Nos. 609/12). They were initially sold at 17p, 23p or 28p, Nos. 601/4 and 609/12 were increased to 18p and 30p on January 1994 and Nos. 601/4 to 19p on 4 July 1995. On March 1997 Nos. 601/4 were increased to 20p, Nos. 605/8 24p and Nos. 609/12 to 31p.

Withdrawn: 30.9.99

584 *Phragmipedium* Eric Young 'Jersey'   **585** *Odontoglossum* Augres 'Trinity'

248

86 *Miltonia* St. Helier 'Colomberie'

587 *Phragmipedium pearcei*

588 *Calanthe* Grouville 'Gorey'

ersey Orchids (Third Series)

(Litho Enschedé)

993 (26 JAN). *Perf* 14×13 (C)

3	**584**	17p multicoloured	. . . .	50	50
		a. *Black printed double*	. . . . .		
4	**585**	23p multicoloured	. . . .	75	75
		a. *Black printed double*	. . . . .		
5	**586**	28p multicoloured	. . . .	90	90
		a. *Black printed double*	. . . . .		
6	**587**	39p multicoloured	. . . .	1·50	1·50
7	**588**	57p multicoloured	. . . .	2·00	2·00
		a. *Black printed double*	. . . . .		
3/17		*Set of 5*	. . . .	5·00	5·00
		First Day Cover	. . . .		5·50
		Presentation Pack	. . . .	5·75	

Plate Nos.: 17p, 23p 1A, 1B, 1C (each ×5); 28p, 39p, 57p 1A, 1B (each ×5)

Sheets: 20 (5×4)

Imprint: Central, left-hand margin

Quantities sold: 17p 391,802; 23p 391,444; 28p 188,149; 39p 141,610; 57p 141,463

Withdrawn: 31.1.94

89 Douglas DC-3 Dakota

590 Wight Seaplane

591 Avro Shackleton A.E.W.2

592 Gloster Meteor Mk III and De Havilland D.H.100 Vampire FB.5

593 Hawker Siddeley Harrier GR.1A

594 Panavia Tornado F Mk 3

75th Anniversary of Royal Air Force

(Des A. Theobald. Litho Questa)

1993 (1 APR). *Perf* 14 (C)

618	**589**	17p multicoloured	. . . .	50	50
619	**590**	23p multicoloured	. . . .	70	70
620	**591**	28p multicoloured	. . . .	80	80
621	**592**	33p multicoloured	. . . .	90	90
622	**593**	39p multicoloured	. . . .	1·10	1·10
623	**594**	57p multicoloured	. . . .	1·60	1·60
618/23		*Set of 6*	. . . .	5·00	5·00
		First Day Cover	. . . .		5·75
		Presentation Pack	. . . .	5·75	
MS624		147×98 mm. Nos. 619 and 623	. . . .	5·00	5·25
		First Day Cover	. . . .		6·00
		Presentation Pack	. . . .	5·50	

Nos. 618/24 also commemorate the 50th anniversary of the Royal Air Force Association and the 40th anniversary of the first air display on Jersey.

Plate Nos.: 17p, 23p 1A, 1B, 1C, 1D (each ×4); 28p, 33p, 39p, 57p 1A, 1B (each ×4)

Sheets: 20 (5×4)

Imprint: Central, left-hand margin

Quantities sold: 17p 578,871; 23p 581,661; 28p 184,066; 33p 140,430; 39p 144,522; 57p 159,447; miniature sheet 113,236

Withdrawn: 30.4.94

JERSEY

EUROPA 23ᵖ

595 'Jersey's Opera
House' (Ian
Rolls)

JERSEY

EUROPA 28ᵖ

596 'The Ham and
Tomato Bap'
(Jonathan
Hubbard)

JERSEY

EUROPA 39ᵖ

597 'Vase of Flowers' (Neil MacKenzie)

Europa. Contemporary Art

(Litho Cartor)

1993 (1 APR). *Perf* 13½×14 (C)

625	**595**	23p multicoloured	70	70
626	**596**	28p multicoloured	85	85
627	**597**	39p multicoloured	1·25	1·25
625/7		Set of 3	2·50	2·50
		First Day Cover		3·00
		Presentation Pack	3·25	

Plate Nos.: All values 1A, 1B, 1C, 1D (each ×4)

Sheets: 20 (5×4)

Imprint: Central, left-hand margin

Quantities sold: 23p 422,536; 28p 340,206; 39p 230,510

Withdrawn: 30.4.94

598 1943 Occupation ½d
Stamp

599 1943 1d Stamp

600 1943 1½d Stamp

601 1943 2d Stamp

602 1943 2½d Stamp

603 1943 3d Stamp

50th Anniversary of Edmund Blampied's Occupatio Stamps

(Des G. Drummond. Litho Cartor)

1993 (2 JUNE). *Perf* 13½ (C)

628	**598**	17p myrtle-green, pale grn & blk	40	4
629	**599**	23p vermilion, salmon-pink & blk	55	5
630	**600**	28p chocolate, cinnamon & black	75	7
631	**601**	33p reddish orge, salmon & blk	1·00	1·0
632	**602**	39p royal blue, cobalt and black	1·40	1·4
633	**603**	50p bright magenta, pale mauve and black	1·50	1·5
628/33		Set of 6	5·00	5·0
		First Day Cover		5·5
		Presentation Pack	5·50	

Plate Nos.: All values 1A, 1B, 1C, 1D (each ×3)

Sheets: 20 (4×5)

Imprint: Central, left-hand margin

Quantities sold: 17p 549,708; 23p 565,711; 28p 174,159; 3
120,570; 39p 93,502; 50p 99,135

Withdrawn: 30.6.94

604 Queen Elizabeth II (from painting
by Marca McGregor)

40th Anniversary of Coronation

(Litho Questa)

1993 (2 JUNE). *Perf* 14½ (C)

634	**604**	£1 multicoloured (*ab*)	2·50	2·50
		First Day Cover		3·50
		Presentation Pack	3·75	

No. 634 was retained in use as part of the current definitive series until replaced by No. 796.

Printings: (*a*) 2.6.93; (*b*) 1.9.95

Plate Nos.: 1A, 1B, 1C, 1D (each ×4)

Sheets: 20 (5×4)

Imprint: Central, left-hand margin

Withdrawn: 31.3.99

605 Short-toed Treecreeper

606 Dartford Warbler

607 Common Wheatear

608 Cirl Bunting

609 Jay

Summer Birds

(Des W. Oliver. Litho Cartor)

1993 (7 SEPT). *Perf* 13½×14 (C)

635	**605**	17p multicoloured	50	50
636	**606**	23p multicoloured	75	75
637	**607**	28p multicoloured	85	85
638	**608**	39p multicoloured	1·25	1·25
639	**609**	57p multicoloured	1·75	1·75
635/9		Set of 5	4·50	4·50
		First Day Cover		5·50
		Presentation Pack	5·50	

Plate Nos.: All values 1A, 1B, 1C, 1D (each ×4)

Sheets: 20 (5×4)

Imprint: Central, left-hand margin

Quantities sold: 17p 495,975; 23p 496,942; 28p 170,135; 39p 139,630; 57p 138,994

Withdrawn: 30.9.94

610 Two Angels holding 'Hark the Herald Angels Sing' Banner

611 Two Angels playing Harps

612 Two Angels playing Violins

613 Two Angels holding 'Once in Royal David's City' Banner

Christmas. Stained Glass Windows by Henry Bosdet from St. Aubin on the Hill Church

(Des N. MacKenzie. Litho Enschedé)

1993 (2 NOV). *Perf* 14×13 (C)

640	**610**	17p multicoloured	45	45
641	**611**	23p multicoloured	65	65
642	**612**	39p multicoloured	1·25	1·25
643	**613**	57p multicoloured	1·90	1·90
640/3		Set of 4	3·75	3·75
		First Day Cover		4·50
		Presentation Pack	4·50	

Plate Nos.: All values 1A, 1B, 1C (each ×4)

Sheets: 20 (5×4)

Imprint: Central, left-hand margin

Quantities sold: 17p 877,806; 23p 744,661; 39p 110,131; 57p 108,703

Withdrawn: 30.11.94

Post Office Yearbook

1993 (2 NOV). *Comprises Nos.* 601/43

	Yearbook	40·00

Sold out: By 9.97

614 *Coprinus comatus*

615 *Amanita muscaria*

616 *Cantharellus cibarius*

617 *Macrolepiota procera*

618 *Clathrus ruber*

Fungi

(Des W. Oliver. Litho Questa)

1994 (11 JAN). *Perf* 14½ (C)

644	**614**	18p multicoloured	....	45	45
645	**615**	23p multicoloured	....	70	70
646	**616**	30p multicoloured	....	90	90
647	**617**	41p multicoloured	....	1·25	1·25
648	**618**	60p multicoloured	....	1·75	1·75
644/8		Set of 5	....	4·50	4·50
		First Day Cover..........			4·75
		Presentation Pack........		5·00	

Plate Nos.: 18p 1A (×4); 23p 1B (×4); 30p 1C (×4); 41p 1D (×4); 60p 1E (×4)

Sheets: 20 (5×4)

Imprint: Central, left-hand margin

Quantities sold: 18p 735,158; 23p 482,461; 30p 188,095; 41p 184,418; 60p 137,309

Withdrawn: 30.1.95

619*a* Pekingese (*illustration reduced. Actual size* 110×75 mm

'Hong Kong '94' International Stamp Exhibition. 'Chinese Year of the Dog'

(Des P. Layton, adapted A. Copp. Litho Questa)

1994 (18 FEB). *Sheet* 110×75 mm. *Perf* 15×14½ (C)

MS649	**619***a*	£1 multicoloured	....	3·00	3·00
		First Day Cover..........			3·75
		Presentation Pack........		3·75	

Quantity sold: 120,029
Withdrawn: 28.2.95

620 Maine Coon

621 British Shorthair

622 Persian

623 Siamese

624 Non-pedigree

21st Anniversary of Jersey Cat Club

(Des P. Layton. Litho B.D.T)

1994 (5 APR). *Perf* 14 (C)

650	**620**	18p multicoloured	45	45
651	**621**	23p multicoloured	70	70
652	**622**	35p multicoloured	90	90
653	**623**	41p multicoloured	1·25	1·25
654	**624**	60p multicoloured	1·75	1·75
650/4		*Set of 5*	4·50	4·50
		First Day Cover..........		5·25
		Presentation Pack	5·50	

Plate Nos.: 35p 1A, 1B, 1C, 1D (each ×4); others 1A, 1B (each ×4)

Sheets: 20 (5×4) 18p, 35p, 60p; (4×5) 23p, 41p

Imprint: Central, left-hand margin

Quantities sold: 18p 491,500; 23p 490,820; 35p 221,769; 41p 185,206; 60p 132,276

Withdrawn: 29.4.95

625 Mammoth Hunt, La Cotte de St. Brelade

626 Stone Age Hunters pulling Mammoth into Cave

627 Chambered Passage, La Hougue Bie

628 Transporting Stones

Europa. Archaeological Discoveries

(Des A. Copp. Litho Enschedé)

1994 (5 APR). *Perf* 13½×14 (C)

655	**625**	23p multicoloured	55	55
		a. Horiz pair. Nos. 655/6	1·10	1·10
656	**626**	23p multicoloured	55	55
657	**627**	30p multicoloured	85	85
		a. Horiz. pair. Nos. 657/8	1·75	1·75
658	**628**	30p multicoloured	85	85
655/8		*Set of 4*	2·50	2·50
		First Day Cover..........		3·25
		Presenation Pack	3·25	

Plate Nos.: Both values 1A, 1B (each ×4)

Sheets: 20 (4×5) the two horizontal designs for each value printed together, *se-tenant*, in horizontal pairs throughout the sheets

Imprint: Central, left-hand margin

Quantities sold: No. 655 371,149; No. 656 373,190; No. 657 273,889; No. 658 275,833

Withdrawn: 29.4.95

629 Gliders and Towing Aircraft approaching France

630 Landing Craft approaching Beaches

631 Disembarking from Landing Craft on Gold Beach

632 British Troops on Sword Beach

633 Spitfires over Beaches

634 Invasion Map

50th Anniversary of D-Day

(Des A. Theobald. Litho B.D.T.)

1994 (6 JUNE). *Perf* 13½×14 (C)

659	**629**	18p multicoloured	60	60
		a. Booklet pane. Nos. 659/60, each ×3, with margins all round	2·75	
		b. Booklet pane. Nos. 659/64, with margins all round	6·00	
660	**630**	18p multicoloured	60	60
661	**631**	23p multicoloured	80	80
		a. Booklet pane. Nos. 661/2, each ×3, with margins all round	5·50	
662	**632**	23p multicoloured	80	80

663	**633**	30p multicoloured	90	90
		a. Booklet pane. Nos. 663/4, each ×3, with margins all round	6·00	
664	**634**	30p multicoloured	90	90
659/64		Set of 6	4·00	4·00
		First Day Cover..........		4·50
		Presentation Pack	4·50	

No. 659*b* was also available as a loose pane from the Philatelic Bureau.

Plate Nos.: All values 1A, 1B (each ×4)

Sheets: 20 (4×5)

Imprint: Central, left-hand margin

Quantities sold: No. 659, 361,667; No. 660, 365,169; No. 661, 377,546; No. 662, 367,033; No. 663, 229,455; No. 664, 226,520

Withdrawn: 30.6.95

635 Sailing

636 Rifle Shooting

637 Hurdling

638 Swimming

639 Hockey

Centenary of International Olympic Committee

(Des A. Theobald. Litho Questa)

1994 (6 JUNE). *Perf* 14 (C)

665	**635**	18p multicoloured	45	45
666	**636**	23p multicoloured	60	60
667	**637**	30p multicoloured	85	85
668	**638**	41p multicoloured	1·25	1·25
669	**639**	60p multicoloured	1·60	1·60
665/9		Set of 5	4·25	4·25
		First Day Cover..........		4·75
		Presentation Pack	4·75	

Plate Nos.: All values 1A (×4)

Sheets: 20 (5×4)

Imprint: Central, left-hand margin

Quantities sold: 18p 279,163; 23p 276,438; 30p 178,234; 41p 183,875; 60p 133,357

Withdrawn: 30.6.95

640 Strawberry Anemone

641 Hermit Crab and Parasitic Anemone

642 Velvet Swimming Crab

643 Common Jellyfish

Marine Life

(Des W. Oliver. Litho Cartor)

1994 (2 AUG). *Perf* 13½ (C)

670	**640**	18p multicoloured	50	50
671	**641**	23p multicoloured	75	75
672	**642**	41p multicoloured	1·40	1·40
673	**643**	60p multicoloured	1·75	1·75
670/3		Set of 4	4·00	4·00
		First Day Cover..........		4·75
		Presentation Pack	4·75	

Plate Nos.: All values 1A, 1B, 1C, 1D (each ×4)

Sheets: 20 (4×5)

Imprint: Central, left-hand margin

Quantities sold: 18p 465,890; 23p 453,750; 41p 171,459; 60p 175,656

Withdrawn: 31.8.95

644 Condor 10 Wavepiercer Catamaran

645 Map of Jersey and Pillar Box

6 Vicker's Type 953
Vanguard of B.E.A.

647 Shorts 360 of Aurigny
Air Services

648 *Caesarea* (Sealink ferry)

5th Anniversary of Jersey Postal Administration

(Des A. Copp. Litho Questa)

994 (1 OCT). *Perf* 14 (C)

74	**644**	18p multicoloured	45	45
75	**645**	23p multicoloured	60	60
76	**646**	35p multicoloured	85	85
77	**647**	41p multicoloured	1·10	1·10
78	**648**	60p multicoloured	1·50	1·50
74/8		Set of 5	4·00	4·00
		First Day Cover		5·25
		Presentation Pack	5·50	
S679		150×100 mm. Nos. 674/8	4·50	4·50
		First Day Cover		5·50
		Presentation Pack	5·50	

Plate Nos.: All values 1A (×5)

Sheets: 20 (5×4)

mprint: Central, left-hand margin

Quantities sold: 18p 473,837; 23p 472,468; 35p 184,871; 41p
186,653; 60p 182,108; miniature sheet 76,623

Withdrawn: 31.10.95

49 'Away in a Manger'

650 'Hark! the Herald
Angels Sing'

651 'While Shepherds
watched'

652 'We Three Kings of
Orient Are'

Christmas. Carols

(Des A. Copp. Litho Questa)

1994 (8 NOV). *Perf* 14 (C)

680	**649**	18p multicoloured	45	45
681	**650**	23p multicoloured	60	60
682	**651**	41p multicoloured	1·25	1·25
683	**652**	60p multicoloured	1·60	1·60
680/3		Set of 4	3·50	3·50
		First Day Cover		5·00
		Presentation Pack	5·00	

Plate Nos.: All values 1A, 1B (each ×4)

Sheets: 20 (5×4)

Imprint: Central, left-hand margin

Quantities sold: 18p 981,010; 23p 883,715; 41p 174,413; 60p
179,888

Withdrawn: 30.11.95

Post Office Yearbook

1994 (8 NOV). *Comprises Nos.* **MS**248 *and* 644/83

Yearbook . . . . 37·00

653 Dog and
'GOOD
LUCK'

654 Rose and
'WITH LOVE'

655 Chick and
'CONGRAT-
ULATIONS'

656 Bouquet of
Flowers and
'THANK
YOU'

657 Dove with
Letter and
'WITH LOVE'

658 Cat and
'GOOD
LUCK'

659 Carnations and 'THANK YOU'

660 Parrot and 'CONGRATU-LATIONS'

661 Pig and 'HAPPY NEW YEAR'

664 'Elsie Jury'

665 'Augusto L'Gouveia Pinto'

666 'Bella Romana'

Greetings Stamps

(Des A. Copp. Litho B.D.T.)

1995 (24 JAN). *Perf* 13 (C)

684	**653**	18p multicoloured	45	45
		a. *Horiz strip of 4. Nos. 684/7*	1·75	
		b. *Booklet pane of 9. Nos. 684/92*	5·50	
685	**654**	18p multicoloured	45	45
686	**655**	18p multicoloured	45	45
687	**656**	18p multicoloured	45	45
688	**657**	23p multicoloured	55	55
		a. *Horiz strip of 4. Nos. 688/91*	2·25	
689	**658**	23p multicoloured	55	55
690	**659**	23p multicoloured	55	55
691	**660**	23p multicoloured	55	55
692	**661**	60p multicoloured	1·40	1·40
684/92		*Set of 9*	5·00	5·00
		First Day Cover (Nos. 684/91)		5·25
		First Day Cover (No. 692) . .		2·00
		Presentation Pack	5·25	

No. 692 commemorates the Chinese New Year of the Pig.

Plate Nos.: All values 1A, 1B, 1C, 1D (each ×4)

Sheets: 60p 10 (5×2); others 20 (4×5) the four designs for each value printed together, *se-tenant*, in horizontal strips of 4 throughout the sheets

Imprint: Central, left-hand margin

Quantities sold: 18p 369,217; 23p 338,047; 60p 101,753

Withdrawn: 31.1.96 (sheets)

662 'Captain Rawes'

663 'Brigadoon'

Camellias

(Des and litho Questa)

1995 (21 MAR). *Perf* 14½ (C)

693	**662**	18p multicoloured	60	
694	**663**	23p multicoloured	80	
695	**664**	30p multicoloured	95	
696	**665**	35p multicoloured	1·00	1·
697	**666**	41p multicoloured	1·10	1·
693/7		*Set of 5*	4·00	4·
		First Day Cover		4·
		Presentation Pack	4·75	

Plate Nos.: All values 1A (×5)

Sheets: 20 (5×4)

Imprint: Central, left-hand margin

Quantities sold: 18p 398,810; 23p 480,040; 30p 187,651; 3 160,765; 41p 133,208

Withdrawn: 31.3.96

667 'Liberation' (sculpture, Philip Jackson)

Europa. Peace and Freedom

(Des A. Theobald. Litho Cartor)

1995 (9 MAY). *Perf* 13½ (C)

698	**667**	23p black and dull violet-blue . .	55	
699		30p black and rose-pink	70	
698/9		*Set of 2*	1·25	1·
		First Day Cover		2·
		Presentation Pack	2·25	

Plate Nos.: Both values 1A, 1B, 1C (each ×4)

Sheets: 10 (5×2)

Imprint: Bottom margin

Quantities sold: 19p 251,352; 30p 278,162

Withdrawn: 31.5.96

668 Bailiff and Crown Officers in Launch

669 *Vega* (Red Cross supply ship)

670 H.M.S. *Beagle* (destroyer)

671 British Troops in Ordnance Yard, St. Helier

672 King George VI and Queen Elizabeth in Jersey

673 Unloading Supplies from Landing Craft, St. Aubin's

674a Royal Family with Winston Churchill on Buckingham Palace Balcony, V.E. Day (*illustration reduced. Actual size* 110×75 *mm*)

50th Anniversary of Liberation

(Des A. Theobald. Litho B.D.T.)

1995 (9 MAY). *Perf* 15×14 (C)

700	**668**	18p multicoloured	40	40
		a. Booklet pane. Nos. 700/1, each ×3, with margins all round	2·00	
701	**669**	18p multicoloured	40	40
702	**670**	23p multicoloured	60	60
		a. Booklet pane. Nos. 702/3, each ×3, with margins all round	2·75	
703	**671**	23p multicoloured	60	60
704	**672**	60p multicoloured	1·50	1·50
		a. Booklet pane. Nos. 704/5, each ×3, with margins all round	7·50	
705	**673**	60p multicoloured	1·50	1·50
700/5		Set of 6	4·50	4·50
		First Day Cover		5·50
		Presentation Pack	5·50	
MS706	110×75 mm.	**674**a £1 multicoloured	2·75	2·75
		a. Booklet pane. As No. **MS**706 with additional margins all round showing arms, mace and inscriptions	2·50	
		First Day Cover		3·50
		Presentation Pack	3·50	

Plate Nos.: All values 1A, 1B (each ×4)

Sheets: 20 (4×5)

Imprint: Central, left-hand margin

Quantities sold: 18p (No. 700) 207,666; 18p (No. 701) 214,869; 23p (No. 702) 279,930; 23p (No. 703) 274,379; 60p (No. 704) 131,342; 60p (No. 705) 136,508; £1 122,855

Withdrawn: 31.5.96 (sheets)

675 Bell Heather

676 Sea Campion

677 Spotted Rock-rose

678 Thrift

679 Sheep's-bit
Scabious

680 Field Bind-weed

681 Common Bird's-
foot Trefoil

682 Sea-holly

683 Common
Centaury

684 Dwarf Pansy

European Nature Conservation Year. Wild Flowers

(Des N. Parlett. Litho B.D.T.)

1995 (4 JULY). *Perf* 13 (C)

707	**675**	19p multicoloured	. . . .	55	55
		a. Horiz strip of 5. Nos. 707/11		2·75	
708	**676**	19p multicoloured	. . . .	55	55
709	**677**	19p multicoloured	. . . .	55	55
710	**678**	19p multicoloured	. . . .	55	55
711	**679**	19p multicoloured	. . . .	55	55
712	**680**	23p multicoloured	. . . .	65	65
		a. Horiz strip of 5. Nos. 712/16		3·25	
713	**681**	23p multicoloured	. . . .	65	65
714	**682**	23p multicoloured	. . . .	65	65
715	**683**	23p multicoloured	. . . .	65	65
716	**684**	23p multicoloured	. . . .	65	65
707/16		Set of 10	. . . .	5·50	5·50
		First Day Cover	. . . .		6·00
		Presentation Pack	. . . .	6·00	

Plate Nos.: Both values 1A, 1B (each ×4)

Sheets: 20 (5×4) the five designs for each value printed togeth
se-tenant, in horizontal strips of 5 throughout the sheets,
backgrounds forming composite designs

Imprint: Central, left-hand margin

Quantities sold: 19p 454,143; 23p 554,070

Withdrawn: 31.7.96

685 *Precis almana*

686 *Papilio palinurus*

687 *Catopsilia scylla*

688 *Papilio rumanzovia*

689 *Troides helena*

Butterflies

(Des W. Oliver. Litho Questa)

1995 (1 SEPT). *Perf* 14 (C)

717	**685**	19p multicoloured	. . . .	55	
718	**686**	23p multicoloured	. . . .	70	
719	**687**	30p multicoloured	. . . .	90	
720	**688**	41p multicoloured	. . . .	1·10	1·
721	**689**	60p multicoloured	. . . .	1·75	1·
717/21		Set of 5	. . . .	4·50	4·
		First Day Cover	. . . .		5·
		Presentation Pack	. . . .	5·50	
MS722		150×100 mm. Nos. 720/1	. . . .	3·00	3·
		a. 41p value imperforate	. . . .		
		First Day Cover	. . . .		3·
		Presentation Pack	. . . .	3·50	

No. **MS**722 includes the "Singapore '95" Internatio
Stamp Exhibition logo on the sheet margin and shows the tv
stamp designs without frames.

Plate Nos.: All values 1A (×4)

Sheets: 20 (5×4)

Imprint: Central, left-hand margin

Quantities sold: 19p 475,496; 23p 466,880; 30p 246,270;
117,354; 60p 133,026; miniature sheet 76,062

Withdrawn: 30.9.96

JERSEY 19

JERSEY 23

690 Peace Doves and
United Nations
Anniversary Emblem

691 Symbolic Wheat and
Anniversary Emblem

50th Anniversary of United Nations

(Des A. Copp. Litho Enschedé)

1995 (24 OCT). *Perf* 13×14½ (C)

723	**690**	19p cobalt and royal blue	55	55
724	**691**	23p turq-green & dp blue-green	65	65
725		41p dp blue-green & turq-green	1·10	1·10
726	**690**	60p royal blue and cobalt	1·60	1·60
723/6		Set of 4	3·50	3·50
		First Day Cover		4·50
		Presentation Pack	4·50	

Plate Nos.: 19p, 23p 1A, 1B (each ×2); others 1A (×2)

Sheets: 20 (5×4)

Imprint: Central, left-hand margin

Withdrawn: 31.10 96

JERSEY CHRISTMAS 1995 19p

JERSEY CHRISTMAS 1995 23p

692 'Puss in Boots'

693 'Cinderella'

JERSEY CHRISTMAS 1995 41p

JERSEY CHRISTMAS 1995 60p

694 'Sleeping Beauty'

695 'Aladdin'

Christmas. Pantomimes

(Des V. Ambrus. Litho Cartor)

1995 (24 OCT). *Perf* 13½ (C)

727	**692**	19p multicoloured	55	55
728	**693**	23p multicoloured	70	70
729	**694**	41p multicoloured	1·00	1·00
730	**695**	60p multicoloured	1·60	1·60
727/30		Set of 4	3·50	3·50
		First Day Cover		4·00
		Presentation Pack	4·00	

Plate Nos.: All values 1A, 1B, 1C, 1D (each ×4)

Sheets: 20 (5×4)

Imprint: Central, left-hand margin

Withdrawn: 31.10.96

Post Office Yearbook

1995 (24 OCT). *Comprises Nos. 491c and 684/730*
Yearbook . . . . 40·00

696a Rat with Top Hat
(*illustration reduced. Actual size* 110×75 *mm*)

Chinese New Year ('Year of the Rat')

(Des V. Ambrus. Litho Questa)

1996 (19 FEB). *Sheet* 110×75 *mm. Perf* 13½×14 (C)

MS731	**696a**	£1 multicoloured	3·00	3·00
		First Day Cover		3·75
		Presentation Pack	3·75	

Withdrawn: 28.2.97

JERSEY 19 unicef 50th Anniversary United Nations Children's Fund

JERSEY 23 unicef 50th Anniversary United Nations Children's Fund

697 African Child and Map

698 Children and Globe

JERSEY 30 unicef 50th Anniversary United Nations Children's Fund

JERSEY 35 unicef 50th Anniversary United Nations Children's Fund

699 European Child and
Map

700 South American Child
and Map

701 Asian Child and Map

702 South Pacific Child and Map

704 Elizabeth Garrett (first British woman doctor)

705 Emmeline Pankhurst (suffragette)

50th Anniversary of U.N.I.C.E.F.

(Des A. Copp. Litho Questa)

1996 (19 FEB). *Perf* 14½ (C)

732	**697**	19p multicoloured	. . . .	50	50
733	**698**	23p multicoloured	. . . .	60	60
734	**699**	30p multicoloured	. . . .	80	80
735	**700**	35p multicoloured	. . . .	95	95
736	**701**	41p multicoloured	. . . .	1·10	1·10
737	**702**	60p multicoloured	. . . .	1·60	1·60
732/7		*Set of* 6	. . . .	5·00	5·00
		First Day Cover	. . . .		5·50
		Presentation Pack	. . . .	5·50	

Plate Nos.: All values 1A (×4)

Sheets: 20 (4×5)

Imprint: Central, left-hand margin

Withdrawn: 28.2.97

703 Queen Elizabeth II (from photo by T. O'Neill)

70th Birthday of Queen Elizabeth II

(Litho Questa)

1996 (21 APR). *Perf* 14×15 (C)

738	**703**	£5 multicoloured	. . . .	10·00	10·50
		First Day Cover	. . . .		12·00
		Presentation Pack	. . . .	11·00	

No. 738 will be retained as part of the current definitive series.

Plate Nos.: 1A (×5)

Sheets: 10 (2×5)

Imprint: Central, left-hand margin

Europa. Famous Women

(Des Jennifer Toombs. Litho B.D.T.)

1996 (25 APR). *Perf* 13½×14 (C)

739	**704**	23p multicoloured	. . . .	60	60
740	**705**	30p multicoloured	. . . .	80	80
739/40		*Set of* 2	. . . .	1·40	1·40
		First Day Cover	. . . .		2·00
		Presentation Pack	. . . .	2·00	

Plate Nos.: 23p 1A, 1B, 1C (each ×4); 30p 1A, 1B, 1C, 1D, 1E (each ×4)

Sheets: 10 (5×2)

Imprint: Bottom margin

Withdrawn: 30.4.97

706 Player shooting at Goal

707 Two Players chasing Ball

708 Player avoiding Tackle

709 Two Players competing for Ball

710 Players heading Ball

uropean Football Championship, England

(Des A. Theobald. Litho B.D.T.)

996 (25 APR). *Perf* 13½×14 (C)

41	**706**	19p multicoloured	50	50
42	**707**	23p multicoloured	70	70
43	**708**	35p multicoloured	95	95
44	**709**	41p multicoloured	1·10	1·10
45	**710**	60p multicoloured	1·75	1·75
41/5		*Set of 5*	4·50	4·50
		First Day Cover		5·25
		Presentation Pack	5·25	

Plate Nos.: 19p, 23p 1A, 1B (each ×4); others 1A (×4)

Sheets: 20 (5×4)

Imprint: Central, left-hand margin

Withdrawn: 30.4.97

11 Rowing

712 Judo

13 Fencing

714 Boxing

715 Basketball

16a Olympic Torch and Stadium
(*illustration reduced. Actual size 150×100 mm*)

Sporting Anniversaries

(Des A. Theobald. Litho Questa)

1996 (8 JUNE). *Perf* 13½ (*No.* **MS751**) *or* 14 (*others*), *both comb*

746	**711**	19p multicoloured	50	50
747	**712**	23p multicoloured	70	70
748	**713**	35p multicoloured	95	95
749	**714**	41p multicoloured	1·10	1·10
750	**715**	60p multicoloured	1·75	1·75
746/50		*Set of 5*	4·50	4·50
		First Day Cover		5·25
		Presentation Pack	5·25	
MS751	150×100 mm.	**716a** £1 mult. . . .	2·75	2·75
		First Day Cover		3·50
		Presentation Pack	3·50	

Anniversaries:—Nos. 746/8, 750/1, Centenary of Modern Olympic Games; No. 749, 50th anniversary of International Amateur Boxing Association.

No. **MS751** also includes the 'CAPEX '96' International Stamp Exhibition logo.

Plate Nos.: All values 1A (×4)

Sheets: 20 (5×4)

Imprint: Central, left-hand margin

Withdrawn: 30.6.97

717 Bay on North Coast

718 Portelet Bay

719 Greve de Lecq Bay

720 Beauport Beach

721 Plemont Bay

722 St. Brelade's Bay

261

Tourism. Beaches

(Des A. Copp. Litho B.D.T.)

1996 (8 JUNE). *Perf* 14 (C)

752	**717**	19p multicoloured		50	50
		a. *Booklet pane. Nos. 752/3,*			
		each ×3, with margins all			
		round	2·50		
		b. *Booklet pane. Nos. 752/7,*			
		with margins all round	4·25		
753	**718**	23p multicoloured		60	60
754	**719**	30p multicoloured		80	80
		a. *Booklet pane. Nos. 754/5,*			
		each ×3, with margins all			
		round	4·00		
755	**720**	35p multicoloured		95	95
756	**721**	41p multicoloured		1·10	1·10
		a. *Booklet pane. Nos. 756/7,*			
		each ×3, with margins all			
		round	6·00		
757	**722**	60p multicoloured		1·60	1·60
752/7		*Set of* 6		5·00	5·00
		First Day Cover			5·50
		Presentation Pack		5·50	
		Postcards (set of 6)		2·75	8·00

Plate Nos.: 19p, 23p 1A, 1B (each ×4); others 1A (×4)

Sheets: 20 (5×4)

Imprint: Central, left-hand margin

Withdrawn: 30.6.97 (sheets)

723 Drag Hunt

724 Pony and Trap

725 Training Racehorses on Beach

726 Show-jumping

727 Pony Club Event

728 Shire Mare and Foal

Horses

(Des P. Layton. Litho Enschedé)

1996 (13 SEPT). *Perf* 13½×14 (C)

758	**723**	19p multicoloured		50	5
759	**724**	23p multicoloured		60	6
760	**725**	30p multicoloured		80	8
761	**726**	35p multicoloured		95	9
762	**727**	41p multicoloured		1·10	1·1
763	**728**	60p multicoloured		1·60	1·6
758/63		*Set of* 6		5·00	5·0
		First Day Cover			5·5
		Presentation Pack		5·50	
		Postcards (set of 6)		2·75	8·0

Plate Nos.: All values 1A, 1B (each ×4)

Sheets: 20 (4×5)

Imprint: Central, left-hand margin

Withdrawn: 30.9.97

729 The Journey to Bethlehem

730 The Shepherds

731 The Nativity

732 The Three Kings

Christmas

(Des V. Ambrus. Litho Cartor)

1996 (12 NOV). *Perf* 13×13½ (C)

764	**729**	19p multicoloured		60
765	**730**	23p multicoloured		70
766	**731**	30p multicoloured		1·00	1·
767	**732**	60p multicoloured		1·60	1·
764/7		*Set of* 4		3·50	3·
		First Day Cover			4·
		Presentation Pack		4·50	

Plate Nos.: All values 1A, 1B, 1C (each ×4)

Sheets: 20 (4×5)

Imprint: Central, left-hand margin

Withdrawn: 28.11.97

96 (12 NOV). *Comprises Nos.* **MS**731/63
        Yearbook . . . . 35·00

33*a* Jersey Cow wearing Scarf
   (*illustration reduced. Actual size* 110×75 *mm*)

Chinese New Year (*'Year of the Ox'*)

(Des V. Ambrus. Litho Questa)

997 (7 FEB). *Sheet* 110×74 *mm. Perf* 14×13½ (C)
MS768 **733***a* £1 multicoloured . . . . 3·00   3·00
        First Day Cover . . . .   3·50
        Presentation Pack . . . . 3·75

Withdrawn: 28.2.98

HONG KONG '97' International Stamp Exhibition

997 (7 FEB). *No.* **MS**768 *optd with exhibition emblem in black and 'JERSEY AT HONG KONG '97' in red, both on sheet margin*
MS769 **733***a* £1 multicoloured . . . . 3·00   3·00
        First Day Cover . . . .   3·75
        Presentation Pack . . . . 3·75

Withdrawn: 28.2.98

34 Lillie the Cow on the
   Beach

735 Lillie taking
      Photograph

36 Carrying Bucket and
   Spade

737 Eating Meal at Mont
      Orgueil

Tourism. 'Lillie the Cow'

(Des A. Copp. Litho B.D.T.)

1997 (12 FEB)–**99**. *Self-adhesive. Perf* 9½ (C)
770	**734**	(23p) multicoloured (*a*)	70	70
		a. With copyright symbol after date (*b*)	50	55
771	**735**	(23p) multicoloured (*a*)	70	70
		a. With copyright symbol after date (*b*)	50	55
772	**736**	(23p) multicoloured (*a*)	70	70
		a. With copyright symbol after date (*b*)	50	55
773	**737**	(23p) multicoloured (*a*)	70	70
		a. With copyright symbol after date (*b*)	50	55
770/3		Set of 4	2·50	2·50
770*a*/3*a*		Set of 4	2·00	2·10
		First Day Cover		3·50
		Presentation Pack	3·50	

Nos. 770/3, which are inscribed 'UK MINIMUM POSTAGE PAID', come, *se-tenant*, in strips of 4 or rolls of 100 with the surplus self-adhesive paper around each stamp removed. Nos. 770/3 were initially sold at 23p each; this was increased to 24p on 10 March 1997.

Printings: (*a*) 12.2.97. Inscr '1997'; (*b*) 2.7.99. Inscr '1999'

738 Red-breasted
   Merganser

739 Sanderling

740 Northern Gannet

741 Great Crested
      Grebe

742 Common Tern

743 Black-headed Gull

744 Dunlin

745 Sandwich Tern

746 Ringed Plover

747 Bar-tailed Godwit

758 Common
Cormorant

759 Curlew

748 Puffin

749 Brent Goose

760 Oystercatcher

761 Turnstone

750 Grey Plover

751 Common Scoter

762 Herring Gull

763 Rock Pipit

752 Lesser Black-
backed Gull

753 Little Egret

764 Great Black-
backed Gull

765 Avocet

754 Fulmar

755 Golden Plover

766 Grey Heron

767 Redshank

756 Greenshank

757 Little Grebe

768 Razorbill

769 Shag

264

eabirds and Waders

(Des N. Parlett. Litho Questa)

997 (12 Feb)–**99**. *Perf* 14½ (C)

74	**738**	1p multicoloured (*a*)	10	10
75	**739**	2p multicoloured (*b*)	10	10
76	**740**	4p multicoloured (*d*)	10	10
77	**741**	5p multicoloured (*b*)	10	15
78	**742**	10p multicoloured (*a*)	20	25
79	**743**	15p multicoloured (*a*)	30	35
80	**744**	20p multicoloured (*a*)	40	45
		a. With copyright symbol after date (*c*)	40	45
81	**745**	21p multicoloured (*b*)	40	45
82	**746**	22p multicoloured (*d*)	45	50
83	**747**	23p multicoloured (*e*)	45	50
84	**748**	24p multicoloured (*a*)	45	50
		a. With copyright symbol after date (*c*)	45	50
85	**749**	25p multicoloured (*b*)	50	55
86	**750**	26p multicoloured (*d*)	50	55
87	**751**	27p multicoloured (*e*)	55	60
88	**752**	28p multicoloured (*e*)	60	65
89	**753**	29p multicoloured (*e*)	60	65
90	**754**	30p multicoloured (*b*)	60	65
91	**755**	31p multicoloured (*d*)	60	65
92	**756**	32p multicoloured (*d*)	65	70
93	**757**	33p multicoloured (*e*)	65	70
94	**758**	34p multicoloured (*e*)	70	75
95	**759**	35p multicoloured (*d*)	70	75
96	**760**	37p multicoloured (*a*)	75	80
97	**761**	40p multicoloured (*b*)	80	85
98	**762**	44p multicoloured (*d*)	90	95
99	**763**	45p multicoloured (*e*)	90	95
800	**764**	50p multicoloured (*d*)	1·00	1·10
801	**765**	60p multicoloured (*b*)	1·25	1·40
802	**766**	65p multicoloured (*e*)	1·25	1·40
803	**767**	75p multicoloured (*a*)	1·50	1·60
804	**768**	£1 multicoloured (*b*)	2·00	2·10
805	**769**	£2 multicoloured (*a*)	4·00	4·25
774/805		Set of 32	24·00	26·00
		First Day Covers (4)		27·00
		Presentation Packs (4)	26·00	
		Postcards (set of 32)	13·00	40·00

MS806 Four sheets, each 136×130 mm. (*a*)
Nos. 774, 778/80, 784, 796, 803 and 805 (*a*).
(*b*) Nos. 775, 777, 781, 785, 790, 797, 801
and 804 (*b*). (*c*) Nos. 776, 782, 786, 791/2,
795, 798 and 800 (*d*). (*d*) Nos. 783, 787/9,
793/4, 799 and 802 (*e*)

	Set of 4 sheets	24·00	26·00
	First Day Covers (4)		27·00
	Souvenir Folders (4)	30·00	
	Complete series Souvenir Folder	28·00	

Printings: (*a*) 12.2.97. Inscr '1997' without copyright symbol; (*b*) 28.1.98. Inscr '1998' with copyright symbol; (*c*) 2.4.98. Inscr '1998' with copyright symbol; (*d*) 11.8.98. Inscr '1998' with copyright symbol; (*e*) 21.8.99. Inscr '1999' with copyright symbol

Plate Nos.: 1p, 2p, 20p, 22p, 24p, 25p, 26p, £2 1A, 1B, 1C, 1D (each ×4); 4p, 21p, 50p, 60p 1A, 1B, 1C, 1D, 1E, 1F, 1G, 1H (each ×4); **MS**806 1A (×4); others 1A, 1B (each ×4)

Sheets: 20 (4×5)
Imprint: Central, left-hand margin

770 De Havilland D.H.95 Flamingo

771 Handley Page H.P.R. Marathon

772 De Havilland D.H.114 Heron

773 Boeing 737-236

774 Britten Norman Trislander

775 BAe 146-200

60th Anniversary of Jersey Airport

(Des A. Theobald. Litho Enschedé)

1997 (10 MAR). *Perf* 13½×14 (C)

807	**770**	20p multicoloured	55	55
808	**771**	24p multicoloured	65	65
809	**772**	31p multicoloured	80	80
810	**773**	37p multicoloured	1·00	1·00
811	**774**	43p multicoloured	1·10	1·10
812	**775**	63p multicoloured	1·75	1·75
807/12		Set of 6	5·25	5·25
		First Day Cover		6·00
		Presentation Pack	6·00	

Plate Nos.: All values 1A, 1B, 1C (each ×4)
Sheets: 20 (4×5)
Imprint: Central, left-hand margin
Withdrawn: 31.3.98

776 The Bull of St. Clement

777 The Black Horse of St. Ouen

778 The Black Dog of Bouley Bay

779 Les Fontaines des Mittes

Europa. Tales and Legends

(Des Jennifer Toombs. Litho B.D.T.)

1997 (15 APR). *Perf* 15×14 (C)

813	**776**	20p multicoloured	60	60
814	**777**	24p multicoloured	70	70
815	**778**	31p multicoloured	1·00	1·00
816	**779**	63p multicoloured	1·60	1·60
813/16		Set of 4	3·50	3·50
		First Day Cover		4·50
		Presentation Pack	4·50	

Nos. 814/15 include the 'EUROPA' emblem.

Plate Nos.: All values 1A, 1B (each ×5)

Sheets: 10 (5×2)

Imprint: Bottom margin

Withdrawn: 30.4.98

'Pacific 97' International Stamp Exhibition, San Francisco

1997 (29 May). *No.* **MS**806a *optd with exhibition emblem on sheet margin*

MS817	136×130 mm. Nos. 774, 778/80, 784, 796, 803 and 805	7·50	8·00
	Souvenir Folder	9·50	

780 Cycling

781 Archery

782 Windsurfing

783 Gymnastics

784 Volleyball

785 Running

7th Island Games, Jersey

(Des A. Theobald. Litho B.D.T.)

1997 (28 JUNE). *Perf* 13½ (C)

818	**780**	20p multicoloured	55	55
		a. Booklet pane. Nos. 818/19, each ×3, with margins all round	2·50	
		b. Booklet pane. Nos. 818/23, with margins all round	5·25	
819	**781**	24p multicoloured	65	65
820	**782**	31p multicoloured	80	80
		a. Booklet pane. Nos. 820/1, each ×3, with margins all round	4·00	
821	**783**	37p multicoloured	1·00	1·00
822	**784**	43p multicoloured	1·10	1·10
		a. Booklet pane. Nos. 822/3, each ×3, with margins all round	6·25	
823	**785**	63p multicoloured	1·75	1·75
818/23		Set of 6	5·25	5·25
		First Day Cover		6·00
		Presentation Pack	6·00	

Plate Nos.: 20p, 24p 1A, 1B (each ×4); others 1A (×4)

Sheets: 20 (5×4)

Imprint: Central, left-hand margin

Withdrawn; 30.6.98 (sheets)

786 Mallorcan Midwife Toad

787 Aye-Aye

88 Echo Parakeet

789 Pigmy Hog

90 St. Lucia Whip-tail

791 Madagascar Teal

794 Beech

795 Sweet Chestnut

796 Hawthorn

797 Common Oak

Wildlife Preservation Trust (Sixth Series)

(Des W. Oliver. Litho Cartor)

997 (2 SEPT). *Perf* 13 (C)

24	**786**	20p multicoloured	. . . .	55	50
25	**787**	24p multicoloured	. . . .	65	65
26	**788**	31p multicoloured	. . . .	80	80
27	**789**	37p multicoloured	. . . .	1·00	1·00
28	**790**	43p multicoloured	. . . .	1·10	1·10
29	**791**	63p multicoloured	. . . .	1·75	1·75
24/9		*Set of* 6	. . . .	5·25	5·25
		First Day Cover	. . . .		6·00
		Presentation Pack	. . . .	6·00	

Plate Nos.: All values 1A, 1B (each ×4)

Sheets: 20 (5×4)

Imprint: Central, left-hand margin

Withdrawn: 30.9.98

Trees

(Des Norah Bryan. Litho Questa)

1997 (2 SEPT). *Perf* 14½ (C)

830	**792**	20p multicoloured	. . . .	55	55
831	**793**	24p multicoloured	. . . .	65	65
832	**794**	31p multicoloured	. . . .	80	80
833	**795**	37p multicoloured	. . . .	1·00	1·00
834	**796**	43p multicoloured	. . . .	1·10	1·10
835	**797**	63p multicoloured	. . . .	1·75	1·75
830/5		*Set of* 6	. . . .	5·25	5·25
		First Day Cover	. . . .		6·00
		Presentation Pack	. . . .	6·00	

Plate Nos.: 20p, 24p 1A, 1B (each ×4); others 1A (×4)

Sheets: 20 (5×4)

Imprint: Central, left-hand margin

Withdrawn: 30.9.98

92 Ash

793 Elder

798 Father Christmas and Reindeer outside Jersey Airport

799 Father Christmas with Presents, St. Aubin's Harbour

800 Father Christmas in
Sleigh, Mont Orgueil
Castle

801 Father Christmas with
Children, Royal Square,
St. Helier

Christmas

(Des Colleen Corlett. Litho B.D.T.)

1997 (11 NOV). *Perf* 14 (C)

836	**798**	20p multicoloured	. . . .	55	55
837	**799**	24p multicoloured	. . . .	65	65
838	**800**	31p multicoloured	. . . .	90	90
839	**801**	63p multicoloured	. . . .	1·75	1·75
836/9		*Set of* 4	. . . .	3·50	3·50
		First Day Cover.			5·00
		Presentation Pack.		5·00	

Plate Nos.: 20p, 31p 1A, 1B (each ×5); others 1A, 1B (each ×4)

Sheets: 20 (4×5)

Imprint: Central, left-hand margin

Withdrawn: 30.11.98

802 Wedding Photograph,
1947

803 Queen Elizabeth and
Prince Philip, 1997

804*a* Full-length Wedding Photograph, 1947
(*illustration reduced. Actual size* 150×100 *mm*)

Golden Wedding of Queen Elizabeth and Prince Philip

(Des G. Drummond. Litho Questa)

1997 (20 NOV). *Perf* 13½ (**MS**842) *or* 14½ (*others*), *both comb*

840	**802**	50p multicoloured	. . . .	1·50	1·5(
		a. Horiz pair. Nos. 840/1	. . . .	3·00	3·0(
841	**803**	50p multicoloured	. . . .	1·50	1·5(
840/1		*Set of* 2	. . . .	3·00	3·0(
		First Day Cover.			3·7
		Presentation Pack.		3·75	
MS842		150×100 mm. **804***a* £1.50, mult . .		4·50	4·5(
		First Day Cover.			5·0(

Plate Nos.: 1A, 1B, 1C, 1D (each ×5)

Sheets: 20 (4×5). The two designs were printed together,
se-tenant, in horizontal pairs throughout the sheets

Imprint: Central, left-hand margin

Withdrawn: 30.11.98

Year Pack 1997

1997 (20 NOV). *Comprises Nos.* **MS**768, 770/4, 778/80, 784
796, 803, 805, 807/16 *and* 818/42

Year Pack. . . . . 45·00

Post Office Yearbook

1997 (20 NOV). *Comprises Nos.* **MS**768, 770/4, 778/80, 784
796, 803, 805, 807/16 *and* 818/42

Yearbook . . . . 50·00

805*a* Tiger wearing Scarf
(*illustration reduced. Actual size* 110×75 *mm*)

Chinese New Year ('Year of the Tiger')

(Des V. Ambrus. Litho Questa)

1998 (28 JAN). *Sheet* 110×75 mm. *Perf* 14×13½ (C)

MS843	**805***a*	£1 multicoloured	. . . .	2·50	2·5(
		First Day Cover.			3·75
		Presentation Pack.		3·75	

Withdrawn: 30.1.99

806 J.M.T. Bristol 4 Tonner, 1923

807 Safety Coach Service Regent Double Decker, 1934

808 Slade's Dennis Lancet, *circa* 1934

809 Tantivy Leyland PLSC, Lion, 1947

812 Creative Arts Festival

813 Jazz Festival

814 Good Food Festival

815 Floral Festival

Europa. National Festivals

(Des A. Copp. Litho Enschedé)

1998 (2 APR). *Perf* 14×13½ (C)

850	**812**	20p multicoloured	60	60
851	**813**	24p multicoloured	65	65
852	**814**	31p multicoloured	85	85
853	**815**	63p multicoloured	1·50	1·50
850/3		Set of 4	3·25	3·25
		First Day Cover..........		4·00
		Presentation Pack........	4·00	

Nos. 851/2 include the 'EUROPA' emblem.

Plate Nos.: All values 1A, 1B (each ×4)

Sheets: 10 (5×2)

Imprint: Bottom, left-hand corner margin

Withdrawn: 30.4.99

816 Hobie Cat and *Duke of Normandy* (launch)

817 Hobie Cat with White, Yellow, Red and Green Sails

---

810 J.B.S. Morris, *circa* 1958

811 J.M.T. Titan TD4 Double Decker, *circa* 1961

75th Anniversary of Jersey Motor Transport Company. Buses

(Des A. Copp. Litho B.D.T.)

1998 (2 APR). *Perf* 14 (C)

844	**806**	20p multicoloured	55	55
		a. Booklet pane. Nos. 844/5, each ×3, with margins all round	2·75	
		b. Booklet pane. Nos. 844/9 with margins all round	4·50	
845	**807**	24p multicoloured	65	65
846	**808**	31p multicoloured	75	75
		a. Booklet pane. Nos. 846/7, each ×3, with margins all round	4·00	
847	**809**	37p multicoloured	1·00	1·00
848	**810**	43p multicoloured	1·10	1·10
		a. Booklet pane. Nos. 848/9, each ×3, with margins all round	6·25	
849	**811**	63p multicoloured	1·50	1·50
844/9		Set of 6	5·00	5·00
		First Day Cover...........		6·00
		Presentation Pack........	6·00	

Plate Nos.: 20p, 24p 1A, 1B (each ×4); others 1A (×4)

Sheets: 20 (4×5)

Imprint: Central, left-hand margin

Withdrawn: 30.4.99 (sheets)

818 Hobie Cats with Pink, Purple and Orange Sails

819 Bow of Hobie Cat with Yellow, Blue and Purple Sail

820 Hobie Cat Heeling

821 Yacht with Red, White and Blue Spinnaker

822 Yacht with Pink Spinnaker

823 Yacht with Two White Sails

824 Trimaran

825 Yacht with Blue, White and Yellow Spinnaker in Foreground

Opening of Elizabeth Marina, St. Helier

(Des A. Theobald. Litho Cartor)

1998 (15 MAY). *Perf* 13 (C)

854	**816**	20p multicoloured	....	50	5C
		a. Horiz strip of 5. Nos. 854/8		2·50	
855	**817**	20p multicoloured	....	50	5C
856	**818**	20p multicoloured	....	50	5C
857	**819**	20p multicoloured	....	50	5C
858	**820**	20p multicoloured	....	50	5C
859	**821**	24p multicoloured	....	60	6C
		a. Horiz strip of 5. Nos. 859/63		3·00	
860	**822**	24p multicoloured	....	60	6C
861	**823**	24p multicoloured	....	60	6C
862	**824**	24p multicoloured	....	60	6C
863	**825**	24p multicoloured	....	60	6C
854/63		Set of 10	....	5·00	5·0C
		First Day Cover	....		6·0C
		Presentation Pack	....	6·00	

Plate Nos.: Both values 1A (×4)

Sheets: 20 (5×4), the designs were each printed together, *se-tenant* in horizontal strips of five throughout the sheets, each strip forming a composite design.

Imprint: Central, left-hand margin

Withdrawn: 31.5.99

826 Bass

827 Red Gurnard

828 Skate

829 Mackerel

830 Tope

831 Cuckoo Wrasse

(Des W. Oliver. Litho B.D.T.)

998 (11 AUG). *Perf* 15×14 (C)

64	**826**	20p multicoloured	. . . .	50	50
65	**827**	24p multicoloured	. . . .	65	65
66	**828**	31p multicoloured	. . . .	80	80
67	**829**	37p multicoloured	. . . .	1·00	1·00
68	**830**	43p multicoloured	. . . .	1·10	1·10
69	**831**	63p multicoloured	. . . .	1·50	1·50
64/9		Set of 6	. . . .	5·00	5·00
		First Day Cover.			6·00
		Presentation Pack.		6·00	

Plate Nos.: 20p, 24p 1A, 1B (each ×4); others 1A (×4)

Sheets: 20 (4×5)

Imprint: Central, left-hand margin

Withdrawn: 31.8.99

32 Cider-making

833 Potato Barrels on Cart

34 Collecting Seaweed for Fertiliser

835 Milking Jersey Cows

Days Gone By

(Des A. Copp. Litho SNP Cambec, Melbourne)

998 (11 AUG)–**99.** *Self-adhesive. Perf* 11 (*Die-cut*)

70	**832**	(20p) multicoloured (a)	45	50
		a. With copyright symbol after date (b)	40	45
71	**833**	(20p) multicoloured (a)	45	50
		a. With copyright symbol after date (b)	40	45
72	**834**	(20p) multicoloured (a)	45	50
		a. With copyright symbol after date (b)	40	45
73	**835**	(20p) multicoloured (a)	45	50
		a. With copyright symbol after date (b)	40	45
370/3		Set of 4	1·75	2·00
370a/3a		Set of 4	1·60	1·75
		First Day Cover		3·00
		Presentation Pack	2·50	

Nos. 870/3, which are inscribed 'BAILIWICK MINIMUM POSTAGE PAID' and were initially sold at 20p each; come, *se-tenant*, in strips of 4 or rolls of 100 with the surplus self-adhesive paper around each stamp removed.

Printings: (a) 11.8.98. Inscr '1998'; (b) 16.7.99. Inscr '1999'

836 Irises

837 Carnations

838 Chrysanthemums

839 Pinks

840 Roses

841 Lilies

842a Lilium 'Star Gazer'
(*illustration reduced. Actual size* 150×100 *mm*)

271

Flowers

(Des Wendy Tait. Litho Questa)

1998 (23 OCT). *Perf* 14×13½ (*No.* **MS**880) *or* 14½ (*others*), *both comb*

874	**836**	20p multicoloured	50	50
875	**837**	24p multicoloured	65	65
876	**838**	31p multicoloured	80	80
877	**839**	37p multicoloured	1·00	1·00
878	**840**	43p multicoloured	1·10	1·10
879	**841**	63p multicoloured	1·50	1·50
874/9		*Set of 6*	5·00	5·00
		First Day Cover		6·00
		Presentation Pack	6·00	
MS880	150×100 mm.	**842**a £1.50, mult . .	3·50	3·50
		First Day Cover		5·00
		Presentation Pack	5·00	

No. **MS**880 includes the 'ITALIA '98' stamp exhibition emblem on the margin.

Plate Nos.: 20p, 24p 1A, 1B (each ×4); 31p, 37p 1A (×4); 43p, 63p 1A, 1B, 1C (each ×4)

Sheets: 20 (4×5)

Imprint: Central, left-hand margin

Withdrawn: 30.10.99

843 Central Market Crib

844 St. Thomas's Church Crib

845 Trinity Parish Church Crib

846 Royal Square Crib

Christmas. Cribs

(Des Colleen Corlett. Litho Cartor)

1998 (10 NOV). *Perf* 13 (C)

881	**843**	20p multicoloured	45	45
882	**844**	24p multicoloured	55	55
883	**845**	31p multicoloured	65	65
884	**846**	63p multicoloured	1·40	1·40
881/4		*Set of 4*	3·00	3·00
		First Day Cover		4·00
		Presentation Pack	4·00	

Plate Nos.: All values 1A (×4)

Sheets: 20 (4×5)

Imprint: Central, left-hand margin

Withdrawn: 31.11.99

Year Pack 1998

1998 (10 NOV). *Comprises Nos.* 775/7, 781/2, 785/6, 790/2, 795, 797/8, 800/1, 804 *and* **MS**843/84

Year Pack . . . . 45·00

Post Office Yearbook

1998 (10 NOV). *Comprises Nos.* 775/7, 781/2, 785/6, 790/2, 795, 797/8, 800/1, 804 *and* **MS**843/84

Yearbook . . . . 52·00

847a Rabbit
(*illustration reduced. Actual size* 110×75 *mm*)

Chinese New Year ('Year of the Rabbit')

(Des V. Ambrus. Litho Questa)

1999 (16 FEB). *Sheet* 110×75 mm. *Perf* 14×13½ (C)

MS885	**847**a £1 multicoloured	2·00	2·10
	First Day Cover.		2·50
	Presentation Pack.	2·50	

848 Jersey Eastern Railway Mail Train

849 *Brighton* (paddle-steamer)

850 De Havilland D.H.86 Dragon Express at Jersey Airport

851 Jersey Postal Service Morris Minor Van

125th Anniversary of Universal Postal Union

(Des A. Theobald. Litho B.D.T.)

1999 (16 FEB). *Perf* 14 (C)

886	**848**	20p multicoloured	. . . .	40	45
887	**849**	24p multicoloured	. . . .	50	55
888	**850**	43p multicoloured	. . . .	85	90
889	**851**	63p multicoloured	. . . .	1·25	1·40
886/9		*Set of 4*	. . . .	3·00	3·25
		First Day Cover.			3·75
		Presentation Pack.	3·75	

Plate Nos.: All values 1A (×4)

Sheets: 20 (4×5)

Imprint: Central, left-hand margin

852 *Jessie Eliza*, St. Catherine

853 *Alexander Coutanche*, St. Helier

175th Anniversary of Royal National Lifeboat Institution

(Litho Questa)

1999 (16 FEB). *Perf* 14½ (C)

890	**852**	75p multicoloured	. . . .	1·50	1·60
		a. Horiz pair. Nos. 890/1	. . . .	3·50	
891	**853**	£1 multicoloured	. . . .	2·00	2·25
890/1		*Set of 2*	. . . .	3·50	3·75
		First Day Cover.			4·25
		Presentation Pack.	4·25	

Plate Nos.: 1A, 1B (each ×7)

Sheets: 20 (4×5), the two values printed together, *se-tenant*, in horizontal pairs throughout the sheet

Imprint: Central, left-hand margin

856 *Paphiopedilum* Transvaal

857 *Paphiopedilum* Elizabeth Castle

858 *Calanthe* Five Oaks

859 *Cymbidium* Icho Tower 'Trinity'

860*a Miltonia* Portelet
(*illustration reduced. Actual size* 150×100 *mm*)

Jersey Orchids (4th series)

(Litho Enschedé)

1999 (19 MAR). *Perf* 13½ (*No.* **MS**898) *or* 14×13, *both comb*

892	**854**	21p multicoloured	. . . .	45	50
893	**855**	25p multicoloured	. . . .	50	55
894	**856**	31p multicoloured	. . . .	65	70
895	**857**	37p multicoloured	. . . .	75	80
896	**858**	43p multicoloured	. . . .	85	90
897	**859**	63p multicoloured	. . . .	1·25	1·40
892/7		*Set of 6*	. . . .	4·25	4·75
		First Day Cover.			5·25
		Presentation Pack.	5·25	

854 *Cymbidium* Maufant 'Jersey'

855 *Miltonia* Millbrook 'Jersey'

MS898 150×100 mm. **860**a £1.50, mult . .   3·00   3·25
First Day Cover. . . . .   3·75
Presentation Pack. . . . . . .   3·75

No. **MS**898 also includes the 'Australia '99' World Stamp
Exhibition, Melbourne, emblem on the margin at top left.

Plate Nos.: 21p, 25p 1A, 1B (each ×5); others 1A (×5)

Sheets: 20 (5×4)

Imprint: Central, left-hand margin

861 Howard Davis Park

862 Sir Winston Churchill
Memorial Park

863 Coronation Park

864 La Collette Gardens

Europa. Parks and Gardens

(Des Ariel Luke. Litho Cartor)

1999 (27 APR). Perf 13×13½ (C)

899	**861**	21p multicoloured	. . . .	45	50
900	**862**	25p multicoloured	. . . .	50	55
901	**863**	31p multicoloured	. . . .	65	70
902	**864**	63p multicoloured	. . . .	1·25	1·40
899/902		Set of 4	. . . .	2·75	3·00
		First Day Cover.			3·50
		Presentation Pack.		3·50	

Nos. 900/1 include the 'EUROPA' logo at top left and all four
values show the 'iBRA '99' International Stamp Exhibition,
Nuremberg, emblem at top right.

Plate Nos.: All values 1A (×4)

Sheets: 10 (2×5)

Imprint: Central, left-hand margin

865 Prince Edward and Miss
Sophie Rhys-Jones

Royal Wedding

(Des A. Copp. Litho Questa)

1999 (19 JUNE). Perf 14½ (C)

903	**865**	35p mult (yellow background) . .		70	75
		a. Pair. Nos. 903/4		1·40	
904		35p mult (blue background)		70	75
903/4		Set of 2		1·40	1·50
		First Day Cover.			2·25
		Presentation Pack.		2·25	

Plate Nos.: 1A, 1B, 1C, 1D (each ×4)

Sheets: 20 (4×5) with the two designs printed together, se-tenant, in
horizontal or vertical pairs throughout the sheet

Imprint: Central, left-hand margin

866 Jersey-built Benz, 1899

867 Star Tourer, 1910

868 Citroen 'Traction Avant',
1938

869 Talbot BG110 Tourer,
1937

870 Morris Cowley Six
Special Coupé, 1934

871 Ford Anglia Saloon,
1946

Vintage Cars (3rd series). Centenary of Motoring in Jersey

(Des A. Copp. Litho B.D.T.)

1999 (2 JULY). Perf 14 (C)

905	**866**	21p multicoloured	. . . .	40	45
		a. Booklet pane. Nos. 905/6,
each ×3, with margins all
round		2·75	
		b. Booklet pane. Nos. 905/10,
with margins all round		4·25	

06	**867**	25p multicoloured	50	55
07	**868**	31p multicoloured	60	65
		a. Booklet pane. Nos. 907/8, each ×3, with margins all round	4·00	
08	**869**	37p multicoloured	75	80
09	**870**	43p multicoloured	85	90
		a. Booklet pane. Nos. 909/10, each ×3, with margins all round	6·25	
10	**871**	63p multicoloured	1·25	1·40
05/10		Set of 6	4·25	4·75
		First Day Cover..........		5·50
		Presentation Pack.......	5·50	

Nos. 905a/b, 906a and 909a also include the 'PhilexFrance 9' International Stamp Exhibition emblem on the margins at op right.

Plate Nos.: 21p, 25p 1A, 1B (each ×4); others 1A (×4)

Sheets: 20 (4×5)

Imprint: Central, left-hand margin

21p

872 West European Hedgehog

25p

873 Eurasian Red Squirrel

31p

874 Nathusius Pipistrelle

37p

875 Jersey Bank Vole

43p

876 Lesser White-toothed Shrew

63p

877 Common Vole

Small Mammals

(Des W. Oliver. Litho Cartor)

1999 (21 AUG). Perf 13½×13 (C)

911	**872**	21p multicoloured	40	45
912	**873**	25p multicoloured	50	55
913	**874**	31p multicoloured	60	65
914	**875**	37p multicoloured	75	80
915	**876**	43p multicoloured	85	90
916	**877**	63p multicoloured	1·25	1·40
911/16		Set of 6	4·25	4·75
		First Day Cover..........		5·50
		Presentation Pack........	5·50	

Plate Nos.: All values 1A (×4)

Sheets: 20 (4×5)

Imprint: Central, left-hand margin

21

GOREY PIERHEAD LIGHT

878 Gorey Pierhead Light

25

LA CORBIERE LIGHTHOUSE

879 La Corbiere

34

NOIRMONT POINT LIGHT TOWER

880 Noirmont Point

38

DEMIE DE PAS LIGHTHOUSE

881 Demie de Pas

44

GREVE D'AZETTE LIGHTHOUSE

882 Greve d'Azette

64

SOREL POINT LIGHT

883 Sorel Point

150th Anniversary of First Lighthouse on Jersey

(Des A. Copp. Litho Walsall)

1999 (5 OCT). *Perf* 14 (C)

917	**878**	21p multicoloured	....	40	45
918	**879**	25p multicoloured	....	50	55
919	**880**	34p multicoloured	....	70	75
920	**881**	38p multicoloured	....	75	80
921	**882**	44p multicoloured	....	90	95
922	**883**	64p multicoloured	....	1·25	1·40
917/22		*Set of 6*	....	4·50	5·00
		First Day Cover.	....		5·50
		Presentation Pack.	....	5·50	

Plate Nos.: All values 1A, 1B (each ×4)

Sheets: 20 (5×4)

Imprint: Central, left-hand margin

884 Mistletoe

885 Holly

886 Ivy

887 Christmas Rose

Christmas. Festive Foliage

(Des Colleen Corlett. Litho B.D.T)

1999 (9 NOV). *Perf* 14 (C)

923	**884**	21p multicoloured	....	40	45
924	**885**	25p multicoloured	....	50	55
925	**886**	34p multicoloured	....	70	75
926	**887**	64p multicoloured	....	1·25	1·40
923/6		*Set of 4*	....	2·75	3·00
		First Day Cover.	....		3·75
		Presentation Pack.	....	3·75	

Plate Nos.: All values 1A, 1B (each ×4)

Sheets: 20 (5×4)

Imprint: Central, left-hand margin

Year Pack 1999

1999 (1 DEC). *Comprises Nos.* 783, 787/9, 793/4, 799, 802 *an* **MS**885/926

Year Pack. . . . . 47·00

Post Office Yearbook

1999 (1 DEC). *Comprises Nos.* 783, 787/9, 793/4, 799, 802 *an* **MS**885/926

Yearbook . . . . 54·00

COMMEMORATIVE POSTAL STATIONERY ENVELOPE

0th Anniversary of Liberation

985 (7 MAY). *Cover showing imprinted stamp design as No. 36. Sold at 25p*

S1	13p multicoloured	. . . .	1·00	1·50

Quantity sold: 79,744
Sold out: 6.85

POSTAGE DUE STAMPS

1   D **2** Map   D **3** Map

(Des F. Guenier. Litho Bradbury, Wilkinson)

969 (1 OCT). *Perf* 14×13½ (C)

1	D **1**	1d bluish violet (ab)	. . . .	1·50	1·50
2		2d sepia (ad)	. . . .	2·25	2·00
3		3d magenta (ad)	. . . .	3·00	2·75
4	D **2**	1s bright emerald (acd)	. . . . . .	9·00	7·50
5		2s 6d olive-grey (acd)	. . . .	21·00	16·00
6		5s vermilion (ad)	. . . .	30·00	27·00
1/6		*Set of* 6	. . . .	60·00	50·00
		Set of 6 *Gutter Pairs*	. . . .	£175	

Sheets: 120 (2 panes 6×10)
Imprint: Central, bottom margin
Printings: (a) 1.10.69; (b) 16.12.69; (c) 18.2.70; (d) 6.6.70
Quantities sold: 1d 98,535; 2d 181,601; 3d 155,832; 1s 174,599; 2s 6d 205,962; 5s 200,698
Withdrawn and Invalidated: 14.2.72

Decimal Currency

(Des F. Guenier. Litho Bradbury, Wilkinson)

971 (15 FEB)–**75**. *Perf* 14×13½ (C)

7	D **3**	½p black (a)	. . . .	10	10
8		1p violet-blue (a)	. . . .	10	10
9		2p olive-grey (a)	. . . .	10	10
10		3p reddish purple (a)	. . . .	10	10
11		4p pale red (a)	. . . .	10	10
12		5p bright emerald (a)	. . . .	15	15
13		6p yellow-orange (b)	. . . .	20	15
14		7p bistre-yellow (b)	. . . .	20	15
15		8p light greenish blue (c)	. . . .	30	25
16		10p pale olive-grey (a)	. . . . . .	40	35
17		11p ochre (c)	. . . .	40	40
18		14p violet (a)	. . . .	45	45
19		25p myrtle-green (b)	. . . .	90	90
20		50p dull purple (c)	. . . .	1·50	1·50
7/20		*Set of* 14	. . . .	4·50	4·25
		Presentation Pack	. . . .	5·00	

Printings: (a) 15.2.71; (b) 12.8.74; (c) 1.5.75
Plate Nos.: 3p 1a, 1d; 8, 25p 1b, 1c, 1d; 11p 1a, 1b, 1d; others 1a, 1b, 1c, 1d
Sheets: 50 (5×10)
Quantities sold: ½p 313,604; 1p 281,598; 2p 205,263; 3p 183,353; 4p 180,948; 5p 199,771; 6p 161,580; 7p 156,534; 8p 154,904; 10p 198,530; 11p 151,638; 14p 147,075; 25p 158,663; 50p 146,602
Imprint: Central, bottom margin
Withdrawn: 31.1.79

D **4** Arms of St. Clement and Dovecote at Samares

D **5** Arms of St. Lawrence and Handois Reservoir

D **6** Arms of St. John and Sorel Point

D **7** Arms of St. Ouen and Pinnacle Rock

D **8** Arms of St. Peter and Quetivel Mill

D **9** Arms of St. Martin and St. Catherine's Breakwater

D **10** Arms and Harbour of St. Helier

D **11** Arms of St. Saviour and Highlands College

D **12** Arms of St. Brelade and Beauport Bay

D **13** Arms of Grouville and La Hougue Bie

D **14** Arms of St. Mary and Perry Farm

D **15** Arms of Trinity and Bouley Bay

277

(Des G. Drummond. Litho Questa)

1978 (17 JAN). *Perf* 14 (C)

D21	D **4**	1p blue-green and black	10	10
D22	D **5**	2p orange-yellow and black . .	10	10
D23	D **6**	3p lake-brown and black.	10	10
D24	D **7**	4p orange-vermilion and black. .	10	10
D25	D **8**	5p ultramarine and black	10	10
D26	D **9**	10p brown-olive and black	30	20
D27	D **10**	12p greenish blue and black. . . .	35	25
D28	D **11**	14p red-orange and black	35	30
D29	D **12**	15p bright magenta and black . .	35	30
D30	D **13**	20p yellow-green and black	50	40
D31	D **14**	50p deep brown and black	1·10	1·10
D32	D **15**	£1 chalky blue and black	2·25	2·25
D21/32		*Set of 12*	5·00	4·75
		Presentation Pack	5·00	

Plate Nos.: All values 1A–1A, 1B–1B, 1C–1C, 1D–1D, 1E–1E, 1F–1F

Sheets: 50 (10×5)

Imprint: Right-hand corner, bottom margin

Withdrawn: 30.9.83

D **16** St. Brelade

D **17** St. Aubin

D **18** Rozel

D **19** Greve de Lecq

D **20** Bouley Bay

D **21** St. Catherine

D **22** Gorey

D **23** Bonne Nuit

D **24** La Rocque

D **25** St. Helier

D **26** Ronez

D **27** La Collette

D **28** Elizabeth Castle

D **29** Upper Harbour Marina

(Des G. Drummond. Litho Questa)

1982 (7 SEPT). *Perf* 14 (C)

D33	D **16**	1p brt turquoise-green & black	10	10
D34	D **17**	2p chrome yellow and black . .	10	10
D35	D **18**	3p lake-brown and black.	10	10
D36	D **19**	4p red and black	10	10
D37	D **20**	5p bright blue and black	10	10
D38	D **21**	6p yellow-olive and black	10	15
D39	D **22**	7p reddish mauve and black . .	15	20
D40	D **23**	8p bright orange-red and black	15	20
D41	D **24**	9p bright green and black	20	25
D42	D **25**	10p turquoise-blue and black . .	20	25
D43	D **26**	20p apple-green and black	40	45
D44	D **27**	30p bright purple and black	60	65
D45	D **28**	40p dull orange and black.	80	85
D46	D **29**	£1 bright reddish violet & black	2·00	2·10
D33/46		*Set of 14*	4·50	5·00
		Presentation Pack	4·75	

Plate Nos.: All values 1A, 1B, 1C, 1D, 1E, 1F, 1G, 1H (each ×2)

Sheets: 50 (10×5)

Imprint: Right-hand corner, bottom margin

278

STAMP BOOKLETS

PRICES given are for complete booklets. All booklets are stitched unless otherwise stated.

B **1** Map

1969 (1 OCT)–**70**.

2s Booklet. Blue cover as Type B **1**
SB1   Containing 5×4d (No. 19a), 4×1d (No. 16a), all in panes of one with wide margins . . . .   2·50

B **2** Arms and Royal Mace

7s Booklet. Yellow cover as Type B **2**
SB2   Containing 12×4d (No. 19), 6×5d (No. 20), 6×1d (No. 16b), all in vertical pairs . . . .   14·00
SB2a   Containing 12×4d (No. 19b), 6×5d (No. 20a), 6×1d (No. 16), all in vertical pairs (5.5.70) . .   £110

10s Booklet. Pink cover as Type B **2** showing Mont Orgueil Castle
SB3   Containing 14×4d (No. 19), 12×5d (No. 20), 4×1d (No. 16b), all in vertical pairs . . . .   12·00
SB3a   Containing 14×4d (No. 19b), 12×5d (No. 20a), 4×1d (No. 16), all in vertical pairs (5.5.70) . .   42·00

Special printings in sheets of 48 were made for manufacturing the 2s. booklets, but the 7s. and 10s. booklets were made up from ordinary sheets, using vertical pairs with stitching through the side margins. Stamps from both sides of the sheet were utilised so that the panes come inverted.

Decimal Currency

1971 (15 FEB).

10p Booklet. Blue cover as Type B **1** showing Martello Tower
SB4   Containing 2×½p (No. 42a), 2×2p (No. 45a) and 2×2½p (No. 46a). Each stamp with wide margin at bottom . . . .   1·00
SB4a   Containing 2×½p (No. 42a), 2×2p (No. 45a) and 2×2½p (No. 46a). Each stamp with wide margin at top . . . .   3·25

35p Booklet. Yellow cover as Type B **2** showing The Royal Court
SB5   Containing 10×2p (No. 45) and 6×2½p (No. 46)   1·25

50p Booklet. Pink cover as Type B **2** showing Elizabeth Castle
SB6   Containing 10×2p (No. 45) and 12×2½p (No. 46) . . . .   2·50

The panes for Nos. SB4/a were produced in sheets of 48, of which half were tête-bêche. In consequence, half the booklets have the blank margin at the bottom (SB4), and the other half at the top (SB4a).

Owing to the postal information printed in the booklets being out of date, supplies of Nos. SB4/a dispensed from machines between 10 July and early September 1972 bore an adhesive label on the front with the words 'RATE TO UNITED KINGDOM LETTERS up to 4 ozs. and postcards 3p' in two lines. They were primarily to warn holiday-makers of the new rate and were issued only through the machines. Of these about 52,000 were sold.

Quantities sold: SB4/a 244,544; SB5 20,875; SB6 17,638

1972 (15 MAY).

20p Booklet. Green cover as Type B **2** showing Jersey Cow
SB7   Containing 8×2½p (No. 46), all in vertical pairs. .   3·25

30p Booklet. Yellow cover as Type B **2** showing Portelet Bay
SB8   Containing 10×3p (No. 47), all in vertical pairs. .   28·00

50p Booklet. Pink cover as Type B **2** showing La Corbière Lighthouse
SB9   Containing 8×2½p (No. 46) and 10×3p (No. 47), all in vertical pairs . . . .   1·50

1972 (1 DEC).

10p Booklet. Orange cover as Type B **1** showing Legislative Chamber
SB10   Containing 3×½p (No. 42a), 1×2½p (No. 45a) and 2×3p (No. 47a). Each stamp with wide margin at bottom   75
SB10a   As SB10 but with margin at top   75

Quantity sold: 126,877

1973 (1 JUNE).

10p Booklet. Green cover as Type B **1** showing Mont Orgueil by night

| SB11 | Contents as No. SB10. Each stamp with wide margin *at bottom* . . . . | 75 |
| SB11a | As SB11 but with margin *at top* . . . . | 75 |

Quantity sold: 109,129

1973 (10 SEPT).

20p Booklet. Green cover as Type B **2** showing Jersey Wildlife Preservation Trust species

| SB12 | Containing 8×2½p (No. 46) . . . . | 3·50 |

30p Booklet. Buff cover as Type B **2** showing Jersey Wild Flowers

| SB13 | Containing 10×3p (No. 47) . . . . | 2·50 |

50p Booklet. Blue cover as Type B **2** showing 'English Fleet in the Channel' by Peter Monamy

| SB14 | Containing 8×2½p (No. 46) and 10×3p (No. 47) | 1·75 |

Quantities sold: SB12 8,790; SB13 11,450; SB14 14,145

1974 (7 JAN). *Jersey Wildlife Preservation Trust*

20p Booklet. Green cover as Type B **2** showing Spectacled Bear

| SB15 | Containing 8×2½p (No. 46) . . . . | 1·75 |

30p Booklet. Yellow cover as Type B **2** showing White-eared Pheasant

| SB16 | Containing 10×3p (No. 47) . . . . | 1·75 |

50p Booklet. Red cover as Type B **2** showing Thick-billed Parrot

| SB17 | Containing 8×2½p (No. 46) and 10×3p (No. 47) | 1·75 |

Quantities sold: SB15 14,283; SB16 14,049; SB17 15,976

1974 (1 JULY).

10p Booklet. Orange cover as Type B **1** showing Jersey Airport

| SB18 | Containing 1×3p (No. 47a) and 2×3½p (No. 48a). Each stamp with wide margin *at bottom* . . . . | 75 |
| SB18a | As SB18 but with margin *at top* . . . . | 75 |

Quantity sold: 129,235

1974 (1 JULY). *Jersey Wildlife Preservation Trust*

60p Booklet. Pink cover as Type B **2** showing Ring-tailed Lemur

| SB19 | Containing 6×3p (No. 47) and 12×3½p (No. 48) | 2·00 |

Quantity sold: 22,274

1974 (1 OCT). *Jersey Wildlife Preservation Trust*

60p Booklet. Green cover as Type B **2** showing Tuatara Lizard

| SB20 | Contents as No. SB19 . . . . | 2·00 |

Quantity sold: 20,984

B **3** Artillery Shako

1975 (25 FEB). *Military Headgear*

10p Booklet. Grey cover as Type B **3**

| SB21 | Containing 1×½p (No. 42a), 2×3p (No. 47a) and 1×3½p (No. 48a). Each stamp with wide margin *at bottom* . . . . | 7 |
| SB21a | As SB21 but with margin *at top* . . . . | 7 |

20p Booklet. Rose cover as Type B **3** showing Shako, 2n North Regt

| SB22 | Containing 2×3p (No. 47a) and 4×3½p (No. 48a). Each stamp with wide margin *at bottom* . . . . | 1·0 |
| SB22a | As SB22 but with margin *at top* . . . . | 1·0 |

Quantities sold: SB21/a 37,849; SB22/a 38,854

STAMP SACHETS These are booklet covers with the stamp loose inside and contained in clear plastic sachets. They ar noted but not priced as such items are outside the scope this checklist.

B **4** Post Office Crest

1975 (1 APR). 20p Stamp Sachet. Red cover as Type B **4** Containing 2×1p (No. 43), 2×4p (No. 49) and 2×5p (No. 50)

JERSEY POSTAGE STAMPS
AVIATION HISTORY

£1 Contents 8 at 1p 8 at 4p 12 at 5p

5 Astra Biplane
(*Illustration reduced. Actual size* 94×56 mm)

975 (21 APR). *Aviation History. Pale blue cover* (SB23) *or yellow cover* (SB24)

0p Booklet as Type B **2** *showing Supermarine Sea Eagle*
B23   Containing 6×1p (No. 43), 6×4p (No. 49) and
     4×5p (No. 50) . . . .   1·50

1 *Booklet as Type* B **5**
B24   Containing 8×1p (No. 43), 8×4p (No. 49) and
     12×5p (No. 50) . . . .   2·75

Quantities sold: SB23 29,872; SB24 29,608

976 (29 JAN). 20*p Stamp Sachet. Blue cover as Type* B **4**
ontaining 3×1p (No. 138), 2×5p (No. 139) and 1×7p (No.
41)

TRINITY PARISH CREST

JERSEY POSTAGE STAMPS
50p

CONTENTS   2 at 1p   4 at 5p   4 at 7p

6 Trinity Parish Crest

976 (5 APR). *Green cover* (SB25) *or magenta cover* (SB26) *as Type* B **6**

0p Booklet. Trinity Parish Crest
B25   Containing booklet panes Nos. 138*a*, 139*a* and
     141*a* . . . .   2·00

£1 *Booklet. St. Ouen's Parish Crest*
SB26   Containing booklet panes Nos. 138*b*, 139*a*×2
     and 141*a*×2 . . . .   3·00

Quantities sold: SB25 85,210; SB26 64,609

1976 (2 NOV). 20*p Stamp Sachet. Green cover as Type* B **4**
Containing 3×1p, 2×5p and 1×7p (Nos. 138/9 and 141)

1977 (29 SEPT). 20*p Stamp Sachet. Brown cover as Type* B **4**
Containing 3×1p, 2×5p and 1×7p (Nos. 138/9 and 141)

1978 (28 FEB). *Orange-red cover* (SB27) *or pale blue cover* (SB28) *as Type* B **6**

£1 *Booklet. Grouville Parish Arms*
SB27   Containing booklet panes Nos. 138*b* and 140*a*
     ×4 . . . .   3·00

£1 *Booklet. St. Saviour Parish Arms*
SB28   Containing booklet panes Nos. 138*b* and 142*a*
     ×3 . . . .   3·00

Quantities sold: SB27 43,446; SB28 45,015

1978 (1 MAY). 30*p Stamp Sachet. Violet cover as Type* B **4**
Containing 2×1p, 2×6p and 2×8p (Nos. 138, 140 and 142)

1979 (13 AUG). 30*p Stamp Sachet. Purple cover as Type* B **4**
Containing 2×1p, 2×6p and 2×8p (Nos. 138, 140 and 142)

B **7** Jersey Post Office Headquarters, Mont Millais, St. Helier
(*illustration reduced. Actual size* 90×65 mm)

1979 (1 OCT). *Bistre-brown on buff cover as Type* B **7**. *Stapled*
SB29   £1.20 booklet containing Nos. 138*b*, 140*a* and
     142*a* each ×2 . . . .   3·50

Quantity sold: 82,738

1980 (6 MAY). *Black on red cover as Type* B **6** *showing St. Helier Parish Arms. Stapled*
SB30 £1.40 booklet containing Nos. 138b×3, 141a
×2 and 143a×2 . . . .   4·00

Quantity sold: 29,900

1980 (6 MAY). *20p Stamp Sachet. Black on red cover as Type* B **4**
Containing 4×1p, 1×7p and 1×9p (Nos. 138, 141 and 143)

1981 (24 FEB). *Black on blue cover as Type* B **6**, *but* 82×65 *mm, showing De Bagot crest. Stapled*
SB31 £1.32 booklet containing Nos. 250a×2, 252a,
256a and 259a . . . .   4·25

Quantity sold: 49,486

1981 (24 FEB). *20p Stamp Sachet. Black on blue cover as Type* B **4**
Containing 2×3p and 2×7p (Nos. 252 and 256)

1981 (1 DEC). *Black on green cover as Type* B **6**, *but* 82×65 *mm, showing Poingdestre Arms. Stapled*
SB32 £1.20 booklet containing Nos. 250a, 251a,
256a and 259a . . . .   3·50

Quantity sold: 43,434

B **8** Jean Martell
(*illustration reduced. Actual size* 155×80 *mm*)

Martell Cognac

1982 (7 SEPT). *Multicoloured cover as Type* B **8**. *Booklet contains text and illustrations on labels attached to panes and on interleaving pages*
SB33 £3.08 booklet containing Nos. 293b, 295b and
297b each ×2 . . . .   7·00

Quantity sold: 54,654

1983 (19 APR). *Black on orange-red cover as Type* B **6**, *but* 82×65 *mm, showing Bisson crest. Stapled*
SB34 £1.32 booklet containing Nos. 250a, 251a,
257a and 260a . . . .   4·00

Quantity sold: 29,393

1983 (19 APR). *20p Stamp Sachet. Black on turquoise-gree* *as Type* B **4**
Containing 2×½p, 1×8p and 1×11p (Nos. 249, 257 and 260)

1984 (3 JAN). *30p Stamp Sachet. Black on pink cover as Typ* B **4**
Containing 2×9p and 1×12p (Nos. 258 and 261)

1984 (27 APR). *Black on rose-lilac cover as Type* B **6**, *b* 80×65 *mm, showing Robin crest. Stapled*
SB35 £2.16 booklet containing Nos. 252ba×2,
258ab ×2 and 261ab . . . .   7·2

Quantity sold: 38,782

1985 (15 APR). *50p Stamp Sachet. Black on light green cov* *as Type* B **4**
Containing 1×1p, 3×3p and 4×10p (Nos. 250, 252b and 25*

B **9** Cross of Lorraine
(*illustration reduced. Actual size* 155×80 *mm*)

300th Anniversary of Huguenot Immigration

1985 (10 SEPT). *Multicoloured cover as Type* B **9**
SB36 £3.60 booklet containing Nos. 370a/5a . . . . . .   9·0

Quantity sold: 31,042

1986 (1 APR). *Black on carmine cover as Type* B **6**, *but* 81× *mm, showing Messervy crest. Stapled*
SB37 £3.12 booklet containing Nos. 251ba, 259ba
and 263ab, each ×2 . . . .   7·

Quantity sold: 23,729
Withdrawn: 31.3.91

B **10** Post Office Emble

86 (1 APR). *50p Stamp Sachet. Black and orange-vermilion cover as Type B* **10**
ntaining 1×2p, 2×4p and 4×10p (Nos. 251*b*, 253*a* and 259)

87 (6 APR). *Black on blue cover as Type B* **6***, but 81×65 mm, showing Fiott crest. Stapled*
38   £3.60 booklet containing Nos. 253*ab*, 260*ba* and 264*ab*, each ×2 . . . .   8·25

Quantity sold: 23,647
Withdrawn: 31.3.91

87 (6 APR). *50p Stamp Sachet. Black and orange-vermilion cover as Type B* **10**
ntaining 1×2p, 1×3p, 3×4p and 3×11p (Nos. 251*b*, 252*b*, 3*a* and 260)

11 Vikings
ustration reduced. Actual size 168×80 mm)

0th Death Anniversary of William the Conqueror

87 (16 OCT). *Multicoloured cover as Type B* **11**. *Booklet contains text and illustrations on labels attached to panes and on interleaving pages*
39   £5.50 booklet containing Nos. 422*a*/7*a* . . . . . .   18·00

uantity sold: 30,107
old out: 4.88

88 (17 MAY). *Black on bright green cover as Type B* **6***, but 31×65 mm, showing Malet crest. Stapled*
40   £3.84 booklet containing Nos. 253*ab*, 261*ab* and 265*a*, each ×2 . . . .   9·00

Quantity sold: 16,566
Withdrawn: 31.3.91

88 (17 MAY). *50p Stamp Sachet. Black and orange-vermilion cover as Type B* **10**
ntaining 1×2p, 3×4p and 3×12p (Nos. 251*b*, 253*a* and 261)

B **12** Chouan Rebels
(illustration reduced. Actual size 155×80 mm)

Bicentenary of the French Revolution. Philippe D'Auvergne

1989 (7 JULY). *Multicoloured cover as Type B* **12**. *Booklet contains text on labels attached to panes and on interleaving pages*
SB41   £6 booklet containing Nos. 501*a*/6*a* . . . .   16·00

Quantity sold: 31,052
Sold out: 7.8.89

B **13** Flags of Jersey and Great Britain
(illustration reduced. Actual size 108×63 mm)

'Stamp World London 90' International Stamp Exhibition

1990 (3 MAY). *Multicoloured cover as Type B* **13**
SB42   £4.20 booklet containing Nos. 470*a*, 474*a* and 478*a*, each ×2 . . . .   9·00

Withdrawn: 30.6.96

POSTAGE STAMPS 50p   B **14**

1990 (3 MAY). *50p Stamp Sachet. Multicoloured cover as Type B* **14** *showing 18p stamp (No. 478)*
Containing 2×4p and 3×14p (Nos. 470 and 474)

B **15** Elizabeth Castle
(*illustration reduced. Actual size 108×63 mm*)

1991 (12 FEB). *Jersey Scenes. Multicoloured cover as Type B* **15**
SB43 £4.80 booklet containing Nos. 471*a*, 475*a* and
480*a*, each ×2 . . . . 11·00

Withdrawn: 30.6.96

1992 (25 FEB). *£1 Stamp Sachet. Multicoloured cover as Type B* **14** *showing design of 22p stamp (No. 480)*
Containing 1×2p, 2×16p, 3×22p (Nos. 467, 474 and 480)

B **16** William Mesny on Horseback
(*illustration reduced. Actual size 155×80 mm*)

Jersey Adventurers (3rd series). 150th Birth Anniversary of William Mesny

1992 (25 FEB). *Multicoloured cover as Type B* **16**. *Booklet contains text on labels attached to panes and on interleaving pages*
SB44 £5.50 booklet containing Nos. 573*b*/8*a* . . . . 12·00

Withdrawn: 30.6.96

B **17** Jersey Post Logo

1992 (25 MAY). *Covers as Type B* **17**. *Panes attached b selvedge*
SB45 £1.12 booklet (scarlet on white cover)
containing No. 474*b* . . . . 2·7
SB46 £1.28 booklet (bright yellow on scarlet cover)
containing No. 476*a* . . . . 3·5
SB47 £1.76 booklet (scarlet on bright yellow cover)
containing No. 482*a* . . . . 4·5

Withdrawn: 30.6.96

1993 (26 JAN). *Covers as Type B* **17**. *Panes attached t selvedge*
SB48 (£1.36) booklet (bright yellow on green cover)
containing pane No. 601*a* . . . . 4·
SB49 (£1.84) booklet (scarlet on flesh cover)
containing pane No. 605*a* . . . . 5·
SB50 (£2.24) booklet (white on bright new blue
cover) containing pane No. 609*a* . . . . 6·

Face values quoted for each booklet are those at which th were initially sold. The price of No. SB48 was increased £1.44 and that of No. SB50 to £2.40 on 10 January 1994. SB48 was sold at £1.52 from 4 July 1995. On 10 March 19 No. SB48 was increased to £1.60, No. SB49 to £1.92 and SB50 to £2.48.

Withdrawn: 30.9.99

B **18** Invasion Map
(*illustration reduced. Actual size 162×98 mm*)

0th Anniversary of D-Day

994 (6 JUNE). *Multicoloured cover as Type* B **18**. *Booklet contains text and illustrations on panes and interleaving pages*

B51 £5.68 booklet containing Nos. 659a/b, 661a and 663a............................. 20·00

Sold out: 12.94

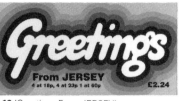

19 'Greetings From JERSEY'
(Illustration reduced. Actual size 152×75 mm)

reetings Stamps

95 (24 JAN). *Multicoloured cover as Type* B **19**. *Pane attached by selvedge*

B52 £2.24 booklet containing pane No. 684b .... 5·50

Quantity sold: 65,810

Withdrawn: 30.9.99

20 Crowd Celebrating
(Illustration reduced. Actual size 162×97 mm)

0th Anniversary of Liberation

95 (9 MAY). *Multicoloured cover as Type* B **20**. *Booklet contains text and illustrations on panes and interleaving pages*

B53 £7.06 booklet containing Nos. 700a, 702a, 704a and **MS**706a .... 14·00

21 Mont Orgueil Castle, Gorey
(Illustration reduced. Actual size 164×97 mm)

Tourism

1996 (8 JUNE). *Multicoloured cover as Type* B **21**. *Booklet contains text and illustrations on panes and interleaving pages*

SB54 £8.32 booklet containing Nos. 752a/b, 754a and 756a............................. 16·00

B **22** Island Sports
(illustration reduced. Actual size 163×98 mm)

7th Island Games, Jersey

1997 (28 JUNE). *Multicoloured cover as Type* B **22**. *Booklet contains text and illustrations on panes and interleaving pages*

SB55 £8.72 booklet containing Nos. 818a/b, 820a and 822a............................. 17·00

B **23** Buses in Royal Square, St. Helier
(illustration reduced. Actual size 164×98 mm)

75th Anniversary of Jersey Motor Transport Company. Buses

1998 (2 APR). *Multicoloured cover as Type* B **23**. *Booklet contains text and illustrations on panes and interleaving pages*

SB56 £8.72 booklet containing Nos. 844a/b, 846a and 848a............................. 17·00

B **24** Four Vintage Humbers at the Weighbridge, 1905
(*illustration reduced. Actual size* 164×98 *mm*)

Centenary of Motoring in Jersey

1999 (2 JULY). *Multicoloured cover as Type* B **24**. *Booklet contains text and illustrations on panes and interleaving pages*
SB57 £8.80 booklet containing Nos. 905*a*/*b*, 907*a*
   and 909*a*. . . . . 17·00

Special Collections Available From Stanley Gibbons Mail Order

The Stanley Gibbons London Mail Order Department are pleased to offer the following special collections. They would make an ideal gift to a friend or relative who may be interested in stamp collecting, or just starting, or you could expand your current field of interest

Collection	Recommended Retail Price	Special Offer Price
Guernsey	£350	£280
Alderney (complete to 1998)	£230	£185
Jersey	£350	£280
Isle of Man	£550	£440

To take advantage of these special offers, please contact Mark Leonard on 0800 731 8052 (UK Only) or +44(0)207 836 8444 during office hours

The World's oldest and most famous name in stamps

Stanley Gibbons Limited
399 Strand, London WC2R 0LX
Tel: +44 (0)207 836 8444 Fax: +44 (0)207 836 7342
e-mail: mailorder@stangiblondon.demon.co.uk
http://www.stanleygibbons.com/

ALL THE BRITISH ISLANDS IN JUST TWO VOLUMES

For Collectors who want value for their Money

Standard Albums

These binders are covered with finely woven navy canvas and like the Luxury Hingeless albums are clearly branded with the nation's crest on the cover and spine.

High Capacity at a Low Price

This album range manages to condense the British Islands into just two binders. Furthermore, these superb quality binders are handmade to the highest specifications, containing professionally laid out album pages that feature selected stamp illustrations. An optional luxury matching slipcase is also available, for what many collectors consider the best album money can buy.

Standard Albums

5287	Alderney, Guernsey, Jersey & Isle of Man Volume 1	1969 - 1990
5294	Alderney, Guernsey, Jersey & Isle of Man Volume 2	1991 - to date

To find out about special offers, to order, or for your complimentary mail order brochure phone free on 0800 611 622 (UK only). Alternatively contact us at the address below, quoting reference CHA2/00.

Stanley Gibbons
5 Parkside, Christchurch Rd
Hants, BH24 3SH, England
Tel: +44 (0)1425 472363   Fax: +44 (0)1425 470247
email: sales@stanleygibbons.co.uk